GW00579348

Barbara Bird

269 — Modifications at each stage

p. 275 — Sullivan
absence of feedback

p 289 — design candeasts
∆ mant.
(Danny Thai)

p 21   W/YRS — property appraisal
modules
– functional
– physical
– etc

Building Maintenance
Economics and management

Building Maintenance Economics and management

Edited by

Alan Spedding

Transactions of the Research and Development Conference
on the management and economics of
maintenance of built assets

Supported by
Royal Institution of Chartered Surveyors
Association of Heads of Departments of Surveying in Polytechnics
Science and Engineering Research Council

Held at
Bristol Polytechnic (Department of Surveying)
13-15 May, 1987

LONDON
E & F.N. SPON

First published in 1987 by
E. & F.N. Spon Ltd
11 New Fetter Lane, London EC4P 4EE

© 1987 A.H. Spedding

Printed in Great Britain at the
University Press, Cambridge

ISBN 0 419 14290 8

All rights reserved. No part of this book may be
reprinted, or reproduced or utilized in any form or
by an electronic, mechanical or other means, now
known or hereafter invented, including
photocopying and recording, or in any information
storage and retrieval system, without permission in
writing from the publisher.

British Library Cataloguing in Publication Data

Building maintenance economics and
management.
1. Buildings—Maintenance—Management
I. Spedding, Alan
658.2'02   TH3351
ISBN 0-419-14290-8

Contents

v

Preface

The management and economics of maintenance of built assets is the theme for a conference at Bristol Polytechnic in May 1987. It is one of a series organized by members of the Association of Heads of Departments of Surveying in Polytechnics. We are happy to record that the conference also enjoys the support of the Royal Institution of Chartered Surveyors and the Science and Engineering Research Council.

Whilst there have been other conferences on the topic of maintenance this one sets out to achieve as wide a spread as possible of good quality contributions from practitioners and researchers, and to put these together in a publication which will provide a source of reference on the state of the art.

The concern which, in some quarters, is being evidenced for the conservation of good buildings is only one indication of a growing consciousness of the finite nature of much of the world's resources. Many of the post-1946 buildings which we now have to maintain were designed at a time when it was believed that demolition and replacement of outmoded or unsatisfactory buildings were going to be economic in the future. However, economic conditions are currently such that a wholesale replacement policy cannot be afforded, and thus the aim in most cases in the United Kingdom and in many other countries is to obtain the maximum benefit from the existing stock.

Nowhere is this more so than in the public sector and it is pleasing to see a wide range of contributions from professionals of long experience in the management of public sector property. A large number of people were apprised of the call for papers and therefore it is a matter of some regret that, whilst much interest was shown by the private sector in the topic, there was reluctance to submit papers from this field.

It is, however, pleasing that the bulk of contributions, not only from researchers, but from practitioners, refer to research or development work of fairly recent provenance. This is encouraging for those working in this field of interest because it indicates that a systematized body of knowledge is being built up. The codification and recording of new knowledge is of very great significance for progress in any discipline. The exchange of information across national boundaries at a conference such as this one should help to speed up the development of appropriate databases and information systems for maintenance management.

Alan Spedding

Part I
Management information
and computing

COMPUTERISING INFORMATION SYSTEMS: A CASE STUDY

B. L. ATKIN
Department of Construction Management, University of Reading

Abstract
The task of computerising information systems within a local authority for property and maintenance management is reflected through a detailed case study. The investigation that formed the basis of this study related to several objectives laid down by the authority. These objectives included specifying an overall structure for the information systems and identifying feasible solutions for their integration within the existing information systems of the authority. Targets for computerisation were established and a structured analysis and design undertaken. The findings of the analysis phase confirmed that most activities were simply reporting functions and that there was a need to maintain an integrated information-base of properties and work undertaken on them. The subsequent design phase revealed the need for a management information system and two decision support systems: appropriate computer solutions were then investigated. Details of these investigations are presented, with the implementation plan for the management information system.
Key words: Property management, Maintenance management, Computers, Systems analysis, Management information systems, Relational databases, Decision support systems.

1. Introduction

Increasing financial accountability in the public sector has led to many property services departments experiencing reviews of their methods of operation, resourcing and value for money. O & M studies are not unknown and are often followed by detailed investigations of opportunities for employing computer technology. This paper records one such investigation as it affected a large local authority and attempts to draw conclusions that might benefit similar property services departments contemplating large scale computerisation projects.

2. The organisation

2.1 Background
The property services department had been established for five years and provided services for all properties in the ownership of the authority. The level of funding at the time of the investigation was in the region of £10m per annum and spread over a diverse range of projects. Thirty professional, technical, clerical and secretarial staff were employed within the department, with occasional appointments of consultants

[architect, engineer, quantity surveyor] for large capital works projects. Additionally, the department supervised approximately one hundred and fifty direct works operatives employed mainly on maintenance and repair works.

2.2 Scope of work
The relevant 'standing orders' regulating the department's activities stipulated that it should:

(a) Provide properties and improvements to them as and when required by client departments.
(b) Continuously monitor the performance of all properties to ensure economic levels of utilisation of the authority's built assets.

Within this framework, the department had defined procedures for responding to requests for day-to-day repairs [emergencies in most cases], planned preventive maintenance management and works of improvement, modification and extension. Capital works projects were similarly regulated. Two contrasting features of the activities within the department were that:

(a) A few very large projects [over £1M] were commissioned in each year, sometimes lasting over twelve months.
(b) A large number of jobbing works [approximately 1000 orders per month] were undertaken, often lasting less than one day.

3. Objectives and benefits

3.1 Objectives of the investigation
The authority identified five objectives for the investigation:

(a) To specify an overall structure for the property services department's information systems.
(b) To take account of the need to integrate the systems within the authority's existing information systems.
(c) To identify the alternative solutions available.
(d) To recommend the most cost effective solution.
(e) To produce a plan for implementing the recommendation.

These were translated into corresponding stages of work, with some overlap between stages so as to compress the timescale into a three month period.

3.2 Expected benefits
It was expected that the introduction of computers would improve the prospects for completing building projects on time and within budget. At no point was it considered by the department that computers would result in the reduction of staff. However, it was believed that the demand for further staff might be eliminated and that some vacant posts might not need to be filled.

Other expected benefits included increasing the rate at which financial and related information on properties could be provided. An overall improvement in the monitoring, control and reporting of contracts was, therefore, expected to occur as a result of introducing computers.

3.3 Existing computer systems
Fig. 1 illustrates the authority's existing computer systems:

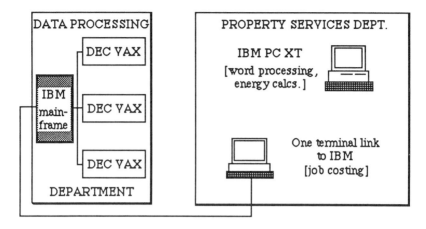

Fig. 1. Scheme of existing computer systems

The terminal to the IBM mainframe and the stand alone IBM PC XT microcomputer were housed in a room segregated from the main office environment. The reasons given for this were the need to have noisy equipment isolated, and the belief that the computers should be accessible to all staff and not seen as the preserve of one individual or group.

The net effect of this segregation was to reinforce the view that computer technology was not considered as part of a normal office routine. Computers were seen by the staff as having been provided for the benefit of computer-minded people. The stand alone microcomputer was used for word processing specification documents and energy calculation routines. In addition, the isolation often felt by the user working in the room disuaded most from spending time at the computers.

3.4 Targets for computerisation
Prior to the investigation, the department had identified a number of discrete applications for possible computerisation. These were based either on a perception of where computers were known to be used successfully elsewhere or on areas of work that were considered as a high priority for computerisation. These targets included:

(a) Job/project costing.
(b) Financial control, monitoring and reporting.
(c) Fees calculation and monitoring.
(d) Buildings, plant and equipment registers.
(e) Building contract management.
(f) Energy management.
(g) Cost estimating.
(h) Planned preventive maintenance management.

Planned preventive maintenance is normally regarded as a high priority, but the department had largely decided that such a target for computerisation was unlikely to be achieved. They had preconceived ideas which, as the remainder of this paper will

5

bear out, might have unnecessarily constrained the investigation.

Job/project costing represented the largest proportion of the paperwork generated within the department and was closely followed by financial control, monitoring and reporting. The remaining targets, whilst important, were not considered to consume as many resources and were accordingly down-graded in priority.

3.5 Method of investigation

The analysis phase was conducted in accordance with the principles of a 'structured systems analysis and design' as prescribed by De Marco (1978), Dickinson (1981) and McMenamin and Palmer (1984). Extensive use was made of data flow diagrams [DFD's] and supporting data dictionaries to model information flows and processes. Both tools helped identify deficiencies and hint at possible remedies.

A top-down approach to the analyses was undertaken for all areas of the department's work. These produced a levelled set of DFD's to provide sufficient detail of the information flows and processes within the department. The analyses were complemented by data gathering at the bottom [operational] level. These data represented the various standard forms, notes and reports that formed an integral part of the paper-based manual information systems.

The models of these information systems [representing by DFD's and data dictionaries] were improved and developed in line with the authority's stated objectives for the department. From these modified DFD's and data dictionaries, it was possible to progress towards the design and specification of appropriate solution(s).

4. Findings

4.1 Scope of the problem

The findings of the analysis phase were discussed with the department's management team prior to the commencement of the design and specification phase. This provided an important opportunity to reflect on the state of the existing systems and, thereby, highlight areas where improvements could be effected almost immediately. The more significant findings and their suggested remedies were recorded:

(a) Information was fragmented, duplicated and inconsistent - a centralised filing and accounting facility was essential.

(b) Many activities were simply reporting functions from information gathered in the course of the department's day-to-day work.

(c) There was a plethora of standard forms - these needed to be streamlined before any computerisation could take place.

Other findings included the need to enforce a strict job/project referencing system, and the provision of a system for planned preventive maintenance work [ie. programming and monitoring progress, resources, time and costs]. A functional specification was produced for the equivalent [ideal] computer solutions.

It is suggested that specifications should always reflect the ideal computer solution, although in practice it might prove difficult to find an exact match. However, it is better to compromise at the selection stage of individual solutions, than at the point of defining the specification. Setting aspiration levels too low might result in under-achievement.

4.2 System requirements

Further analysis of these findings confirmed the need for two distinct types of computer solutions. First, a system was needed to support most of the routine activities [initiating, monitoring, controlling and reporting on jobs/projects]. This system was characterised by an integrated information-base of properties with details of the work carried out or required to be carried out. The system specification was found to conform, more or less, to the definition of a management information system [MIS].

Second, systems were required to handle a small number of specialist activities supporting the decision-making of management and supervisory functions. The term decision support systems [DSS's] was, therefore, considered appropriate in these circumstances.

5. Review of computer solutions

5.1 Complete [turnkey] systems

At the time of the investigation there were in excess of thirty computer [software] systems described by vendors as property management systems. On closer examination, none was found to offer the features specified for the MIS. Many were geared to commercial property letting and residential estate agency. Of those that were similar to the specification requirements, none was sufficiently flexible to accommodate the necessary modifications.

5.2 Individual systems

The alternative to a single system solution is to integrate a number of individual software packages. An inspection of over fifty such packages revealed that there were, indeed, a number that could deal adequately with discrete applications. Unfortunately, most of these packages were incompatible with one another, such that they could not be linked together to form a single system solution. Basic differences in hardware, operating systems and file structures would have meant that the department would have had to accept unreasonable restrictions on their activities. Such a situation would have been little better than the existing paper-based information systems, except that some processes might have been 'speeded up'.

5.3 Applications generation systems

The investigation focused on an examination of fourth generation programming languages/environments [4GL's] as a means for developing a tailor-made solution to the MIS. [It is becoming increasingly the practice to 'craft' dedicated applications from 4GL's that are based upon relational databases.] This approach avoids writing file handling routines that in commercial applications account for a large proportion of the total computer code. The main advantage of relational structures over the traditional hierarchical type is the flexibility of the database (Date, 1981). The 4GL approach can represent a time [and usually a cost] effective alternative to writing applications software from scratch. Naturally, there are disadvantages in this approach, such as the time and effort needed to develop a working solution. The situation represents a clear choice between the cost of a purpose-written solution and the time and cost needed to develop the application(s) from a 4GL.

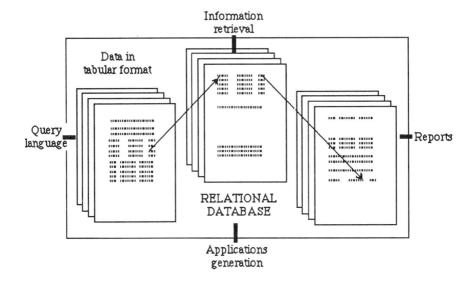

Fig. 2. Features of a 4GL/relational database

A further advantage of the 4GL approach, apart from maintaining and reporting from the database, is the ability to generate computer code for specific applications. In the case of the DSS's, it was decided that the resources required for developing these applications could not be made available in the short term. It was decided, therefore, to use low cost, off-the-shelf software packages for the planning and control, and cost estimating applications. This meant that progress on these applications would not be impaired by the time and effort needed to implement the MIS. The arrangement of the proposed installation [hardware only] is shown schematically in Fig. 3.

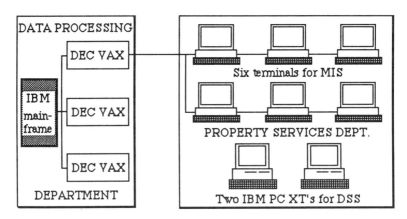

Fig. 3. Scheme of proposed computer systems

8

The cost of the total installation was approximately £50,000 including application development costs, terminals and printers [but assuming no up-grade requirements for the existing DEC VAX minicomputer system]. The bulk of this cost was for the 4GL/relational database and the subsequent development costs.

6. Implementation

The implementation of the MIS and DSS's were considered separately. First, as the DSS's were not dependent upon the MIS, they could be introduced as soon as the necessary personnel had received sufficient training. Second, the MIS required that the paper-based systems were streamlined before introducing data into the computer system. The implementation plan for the MIS is shown in Fig. 4.

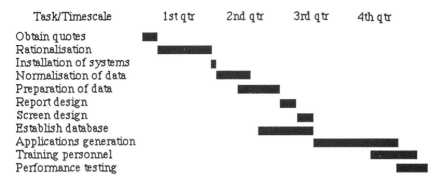

Task/Timescale	1st qtr	2nd qtr	3rd qtr	4th qtr
Obtain quotes				
Rationalisation				
Installation of systems				
Normalisation of data				
Preparation of data				
Report design				
Screen design				
Establish database				
Applications generation				
Training personnel				
Performance testing				

Fig. 4. Implementation plan for the MIS

The timescale for the implementation phase, some thirteen months, required that the department made the necessary personnel available. This was roughly equivalent to one officer on a full-time basis. The department is currently implementing the MIS.

7. Conclusions

Most of the time and effort expended during the investigation was concentrated in meeting the first and second objectives [Section 3.1 (a) and (b)]. The underlying philosophy was one of spending as long in the analysis phase as was necessary to discover the precise nature of the information flows and processes, and the improvements that could be made to them. There appeared to be no benefit in undertaking detailed investigations of perceived solutions without first of all understanding the fundamental information needs of the department. It was considered that taking solutions and then finding ways of accommodating them would have been a recipe for disaster.

The increasing availability of general purpose software has ensured that there are now more avenues to explore than was the position a few years ago. In most cases, it is unlikely that applications software would have to be written from scratch. 4GL/relational databases offer a sensible way forward for future large scale computerisation projects.

References

Date, C.J.. (1981) <u>An introduction to database systems</u>. 3rd ed. Addison-Wesley Publishing Co, Inc.. Reading, MA.. pp64-67.

De Marco, T.. (1978) <u>Structured systems analysis and specification</u>. Yourdon Press. London.

Dickinson, B.. (1981) <u>Developing structured systems</u>. Yourdon Press. London.

McMenamin, S.M. and Palmer, J.F.. (1984) <u>Essential systems analysis</u>. Yourdon Press. London.

A MAINTENANCE INFORMATION SYSTEM

R.A. BATES
Housing Department, Hong Kong Housing Authority

Abstract
The Hong Kong Housing Authority has to maintain one of
the largest portfolios of public housing in the world.
Computer based management information systems have been
developed to deal with the large volumes of information
handled, and to provide an effective medium of communication between offices responsible for maintenance, and
with laboratories. Information flows into the
Maintenance Management Computer System from the
Authorities construction programme monitoring, computer
aided drafting, and commercial and domestic tenancies
computer systems. An on line database comprises a land,
building and property element asset register. A job and
finance system transfers information through the chain of
forward planning, budget, order of works, progress
monitoring and payments to historical records. Routine
service works are ordered automatically, and the system
can provide a 'first draft' for other works orders,
programmes and interim payments. The system permits
considerable flexibility and autonomy in the way
information can be presented to assess technical,
contractual, financial and staff performance.
Key words : Maintenance management information, Computer,
Housing

1. Introduction

1.1 The property stock
In 1955 a huge fire in a squatter area in Hong Kong left
60,000 homeless and resulted in a public housing
programme that adds over 40,000 flats to the housing
stock each year. The Hong Kong Housing Authority now has
a stock of some 620,000 flats grouped into 160 estates,
together with 3 million m^2 of other property.
   Housing estates have a typical population of 30-60,000
people and contain schools, shopping centres, sports
halls, community halls and multi storey carparks all

constructed, managed and maintained by the Authority. In addition the Authority maintains 270,000 m^2 of multi storey factory buildings, 40,000 two storey dwellings known as temporary housing, and the services infra-structure in a number of squatter areas.

The majority of buildings are of reinforced concrete cast insitu. Current heights are 35-45 stories. Blocks of flats constructed in the 1960's and 70's are 16-22 stories. Domestic blocks are roofed in asphalt and non domestic with single sheet membranes. External finishes tend to be mosaic tiles, and windows either steel or aluminium. Fresh water supplies are in galvanized iron, and the salt water toilet supplies are in pvc. Drainage is pvc above ground level and spun concrete or cast iron below ground. Drainage sizes vary from 150 mm to 1.6M.

1.2 Organisation
All work is carried out by contract. Day to day building jobs valued at less than HK$4,000 each are initiated from estate offices in each estate. Other work is undertaken by the Maintenance Division. The Division is a multi-disciplined organisation with 910 technical, 150 administrative and 78 professional staff. Professional staff comprise building and quantity surveyors, architects, structural civil and building services engineers. Consultants are retained in all disciplines. In addition to a headquarters the Division operates from three Regional offices and 22 District offices.

1.3 Maintenance
The emphasis is placed on planned and planned preventive maintenance. Since 1975 the expenditure on unplanned maintenance has fallen from 50% of maintenance expenditure to around 5%. Over 10,000 jobs are planned each year.

	Expenditure	No. of jobs
Planned	HK$685M (95%)	10,000 (5%)
Day to day	HK$ 35M (5%)	200,000 (95%)

Pound Sterling 1 = HK$11

140 contracts are let each year. These include service contracts primarily for building services such as pumps and lifts, and lump sum contracts usually with bills of quantities. 44% by value of work is by works orders placed on term contracts using schedules of rates. There are a number of specialised contracts for materials testing and investigation, CCTV drainage surveys etc.

2. Maintenance management information system

2.1 Background
Since 1975 computer based accounting systems have been used by the Authority. Originally the main feature was a record of expenditure against a location, such as an estate, and the nature of expenditure, such as day to day maintenance. By 1977 it was possible to record the commitment of funds, and to compare both expenditure and commitment against forecast. The concepts of property element (lifts, roofs etc.) and accountable centre (person or design team responsible for a project) were also introduced.

There were difficulties in handling the high volumes of technical information. For example some 1600 files existed on pump data and performance, and the technical database on the 600 slopes surrounding estates required 24 meters of shelving. In 1980 a mini computer was purchased for the growing maintenance applications. The emphasis on monitoring had extended from financial monitoring to project progress monitoring.

The computer was used to develop a number of systems including works progress monitoring, cashflow fore-casting, service schedules and an elemental database. Other applications covered energy management, staff training records, and structural, drainage and lift design.

Limitations in capacity, coding systems, speed of adding new applications, as well as the need to improve communications between offices, led to the implementation in 1985 of a more comprehensive computer based Mainten-ance Management Information System.

2.2 Objectives
The computer system was designed with the following objectives
- COMMUNICATIONS
- INFORMATION
- PROJECT CONTROL

3. Communications

3.1 Computer network
An 'on line' network of 44 terminals and 37 printers are connected to an ICL 2957 8Mb mainframe with a disc drive capacity of 2640Mb. Each of the 22 District offices has at least one VDU terminal and printer. The three Regional offices and Maintenance Headquarters have local area networks comprising ICL 150, 125, 120 and 110 terminals, as well as IBM AT and Compaq personel computers. A works order may be prepared in a District Office, checked in a Regional office and receive

13

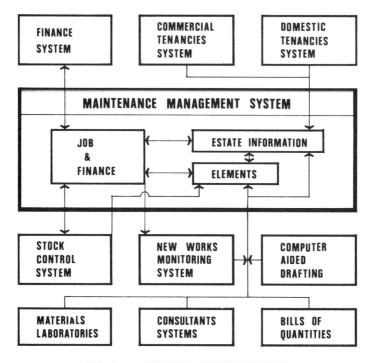

FIG. 1   SYSTEMS COMMUNICATION

financial authority at Headquarters.   There is a newsfile
system and an elementary electronic mailing system.

3.2 Interfaces
A network is being developed that will provide links with
the Authorities computers handling information on new
construction, finance, tenancy records and stock control.
Information already flows into the database from tenancy
records and computer aided drafting systems, and data
will be available from new construction monitoring and
bills of quantities systems in 1987.   (Fig. 1.)
    Materials testing laboratories operated by the private
sector undertake extensive testing for maintenance.   To
date over 325,000 test results have been transferred from
the laboratories computers to the maintenance database.
Modifications are being made to enable results to be fed
into the laboratory computers directly from test
equipment.   Computers used by consultants for maintenance
investigations and surveys are also linked into the
database.
    Plans are well advanced to access data such as acid
rain, wind direction and sulphur dioxide levels from the
Environmental Protection Department's computer.   It is

envisaged that in due course it will be possible to
communicate directly with contractors, and to permit
Academic Institutes direct access to the maintenance
database.

4. Information

4.1 Database
The main groupings of information identified are :
     a) **asset register**
     b) **jobs/projects**
     c) **finance**
     d) **stores**
     e) **staff**
   Most of the maintenance management applications are a
question of sorting and presenting information in
response to ad hoc enquiries or regular reports. In some
cases, such as in cashflow forecasts, a mathematical
calculation is also required. Wherever possible data
entry is carried out as close as possible to the source
that generates the information. About 1000 staff have
now been trained in the use of the computer and the
majority are required to use it on a regular basis.
Users of the system need to be able to question, add to,
alter or expand the database without the need to go to a
computer programmer. Users need to be able to manipulate
sorted data using programmes developed by them locally.

4.2 Asset Register
Two separate systems make up the asset register. There
is an Estate Information System and a Property (or
element) Information System (Fig. 2.) Information in the
Estate Information System is updated by other computers,
and by staff of the Planning (town planning) and
Maintenance Divisions. Information in the Property
Information System is under the direct control of the
Maintenance Division.

4.3 Estate Information System
This contains general information on an estate or
location and comprises :
     a) **estate**   - name, address, no flats,
                            financial code
     b) **land**   - land use, area, planning zone
     c) **structures** - dominant use, age, design, area.

4.4 Property information system
This is divided into elements such as structure, roofing,
lifts, pumps and so on. Information for each element is
grouped into components, inspection/works schedules,
inspection reports and defect or breakdown records.
Examples of information for each group follow :

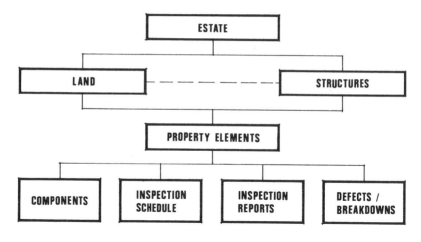

FIG. 2   ASSET REGISTER

Components for the pump records include, type, make and rating of motor, starter type, pump make, impeller blade material.

The service schedule for the 2340 switchboards determines the time for an inspection based on age, the previous inspection date, and adjusts to an appropriate date of the week. A schedule is printed out each month detailing the estates and switchboards to be inspected, and a works and inspection report docket for each board is printed.

A structural survey of each of the Authorities 620,000 flats is well advanced. Information on spalling, drainage and water supply defects are entered into the system. In addition to initiating works programmes, it is possible to present the information in a plan or elevation to examine whether problems relate to a particular zone of a building. In a parallel exercise the computer was used to calculate the critical stresses in housing blocks, compare them with the compressive strengths from the coring programme and calculate factors of safety. From the 25,000 concrete core results the computer produces graphs of depth of carbonation and age by concrete strength, cement content and density.

Each of the Authorities 3300 lifts are serviced each week and all breakdowns and cause are recorded. Performance is monitored by type and make of lift. Information is used in the evaluation of tenders for new lifts, and in the design and specification in lift components. Abnormal performances of individual lifts are brought to the engineers attention. The response time of maintenance contractors to breakdowns is checked.

16

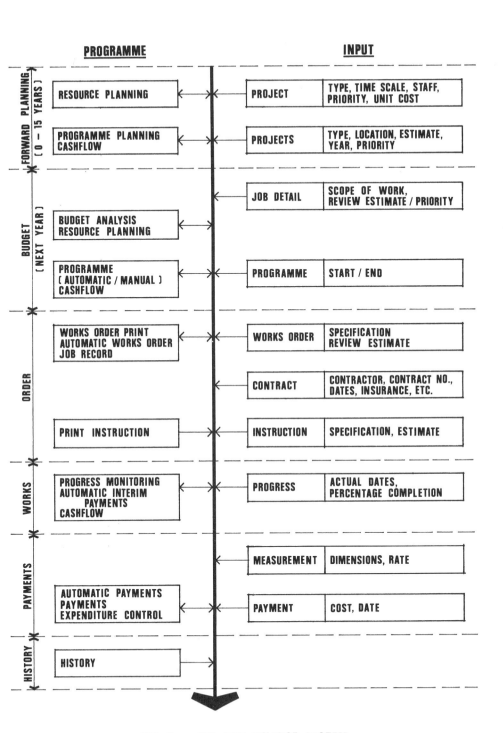

PROGRAMME

INPUT

| FORWARD PLANNING (0 - 15 YEARS) | RESOURCE PLANNING | PROJECT | TYPE, TIME SCALE, STAFF, PRIORITY, UNIT COST |
| | PROGRAMME PLANNING CASHFLOW | PROJECTS | TYPE, LOCATION, ESTIMATE, YEAR, PRIORITY |

FIG. 3   JOB AND FINANCE SYSTEM

17

5. Job and Finance System

5.1 Job information system
Information is carried through the chain of resource
planning, forward programmes, budget, programming,
issuing works orders or letting contracts, and monitoring
progress. (Fig. 3.) Much of the information stays the
same throughout the lifecycle of a project such as the
location and the nature of the work. Other information
is added such as the programme of work, specification of
work and progress of the project.

Wherever possible, data within the system is used to
generate information used in the next stage in the life
of a project by producing a 'first draft'. A works
order may be developed from budget information. The
computer generated draft of a works order will include
location, works description, estimate, elemental coding
and so on. When the name of a contractor is entered the
system will add the address. From a start and end date a
programme and a progress diary is automatically
produced.

Security systems based on staff contract responsibilities, financial authority and project responsibilities
determine who may access or change information.

5.2 Finance system
Working as part of the Job information system the finance
system provides information for Maintenance Management
and does not replace the Authorities accounting systems.

Budget modelling, cashflow forecasting, monitoring and
analysis of commitment and expenditure are carried out.
Interim payments to contractors are calculated automatically from progress information.

6. The future
Future developments hinge upon the ability to feed in and
retrieve information easily. Voice recognition is a
must, some Maintenance Division conference rooms are
already equipped with computer projection equipment and
investigation has started into the use of integrating
computers with laser discs to overcome pictorial
deficiencies in the system. Maintenance Management is
the application of knowledge which in turn is dependent
upon information.

WIMS - A SUITE OF COMPUTER SOFTWARE DEVELOPED TO ASSIST ESTATE MANAGEMENT IN THE NATIONAL HEALTH SERVICE

M. J. BLANCHARD
Estate and Property Management Directorate, Department of Health and Social Security

Abstract
The Department of Health and Social Security, in conjunction with the National Health Service, has developed a suite of information system software to assist in Estate Management tasks. The development of the software was started in 1979 and the suite now covers the majority of Estate Management applications. Recently development has begun of a "second generation" of applications. The software is largely hardware independant and is widely used in the Health Service and has had some commercial success.
Key Words: Computer Information System, Estate Management, Property Appraisal, Asset Management

1. Introduction

Works Information and Management System (WIMS) is the generic name for a suite of computerised-information-system modules each aimed at assisting in a specific area of estate management in the National Health Service (NHS). The modules have been produced jointly by the NHS (by means of the Advisory Group on Estate Management) and by the Works Group/Estate and Property Management Directorate of the Department of Health and Social Security (DHSS). System design aspects are handled by NHS/DHSS committees, program development is managed by the DHSS and validation is carried out in the NHS.

Development of WIMS began in 1979 and the availability of the first software modules was officially announced in early 1981. The applications covered include day-to-day building, plant and equipment maintenance, property registers and appraisals and building energy-usage monitoring.

The reasons for undertaking this development include a requirement to provide efficient tools to assist in NHS estate management, a need to attempt to ensure that NHS resources are not wasted in developing similar computerised information systems at different locations and, initially, to introduce NHS estate managers to the capabilities and possibilities of computers and information technology generally.

Within the last two years two major changes intended to assist the continued usefulness of WIMS have taken place. Firstly, the support of WIMS has been arranged on a more formal basis. Initially, software support was undertaken by DHSS but now each registered NHS user pays an annual support fee (£1000 in 1986/87) to a Consortium of Users which manages a support group of four full-time staff. At the end of 1986 there were 230 registered users. The second major change was the beginning of the development of a "second generation" of applications which has begun in parallel with the completion of the last of the thirteen first-generation modules. The reasons for this evolution of the software and hardware basis of WIMS are discussed later but firstly a brief description of the first generation (WIMS1) modules will be given. Most of the modules are designed not only for a specific application area but are also more suitable for different levels of management ie operational for NHS Unit/District or strategic for NHS District/Region.(There are 192 Health Districts in England grouped into 14 Regions)

2. WIMS1 Modules

       1   Asset Management
       2   Stock Control
       3   Energy Monitoring
       4   Redecoration
       5   Budget Monitoring
       6   Maintenance Contracts (ie Asset Management-Budget
                                                    Monitoring Link)
       7   Property Appraisal (includes Condition Appraisal)
       8   Property Management
       9   Annual Maintenance Plan
      10   Residential Property
      11   Contract Management (ie Capital Projects - part issued)
      12   Electro-medical Equipment Management
      13   Vehicle Management

2.1 Asset Management Module
Intended for use at the operational level of NHS estate management this module has facilities to create a register of assets (ie building components/plant/equipment), to record details of planned work, to schedule the work and to record details of work done in order to create financial/technical history of the assets.

2.2 Stock Control Module
This module is in two parts, a conventional stock control system and a method of raising and processing purchase orders which has optional links to the stock control system (ie on-order and stock levels are adjusted automatically). There is also the capability of using the stock issued data to provide parts and materials costs within the history section of the Asset Management Module.

2.3 Energy Monitoring Module
Information is held on the fuels and utility-services used on a site or buildings on a site together with estimated base-loads or space-heating-factors if applicable. The monthly quantities used are entered and, using degree-day techniques, fuel usage can be compared

month to month. If energy targets are set these can be stored and compared with actual performance.

2.4 Redecoration Module
This allows surface area information to be held for the various elements (ie walls, doors etc) of each room in a given property. Additionally, redecoration specifications and material coverage rates are recorded. The module is used to estimate total labour and material costs for any redecoration project/programme or to calculate total areas.

2.5 Budget Monitoring Module
This provides a comparison of actual expenditure and committments against allocations for specific account codes or budget centres and records each commitment and expenditure entry in a transaction file. Reports can be produced by account code or budget centre and by month or range of months. This module was introduced to provide Estate Managers with a facility to access much more up-to-date financial information than was normally available from their Finance Departments.

2.6 Maintenance Contracts Module
This module enables links to be created between the Asset Management and Budget Monitoring Modules and is designed to assist with the control and monitoring of service contracts. The Asset and Budget Modules are each stand-alone therefore when work has been carried out under a maintenance contract and an invoice is received some of the details on the invoice need to be recorded in the Asset Module (eg work done on a specific asset), some in the Budget Module (eg matching the invoice against the relevant order) and some in both (eg the cost of the work). The Contract Maintenance Module provides a simplified method of transferring data into both the Asset and Budget Modules simultaneously and was the first significant attempt to "integrate" data from different applications.

2.7 Property Appraisal Module
The Property Appraisal Module stores, allows analysis of and produces reports from, data on five aspects of property appraisal:

    1 Functional Suitability
    2 Utilisation
    3 Safety and Statutory Standards
    4 Energy Performance
    5 Physical Condition

This supersedes an earlier module which covered physical condition information only and includes a utility program for transferring data from the original module into the new module. Each appraisal is carried out over a number of elements eg for Functional Suitability -

21

Facilities
Space and Critical Dimensions
Layout
Enviroment
Amenity

and each element is given one of a range of condition categories (eg
A, B, C, CX, D, DX, 1, 2, 3, 4 etc) and additionally may have further data eg cost to repair, average remaining life etc. Cost values
may be price indexed and reports produced in location or department
order. A report generation facility is also provided.

2.8 Property Management Module
This module is a register containing details about each hospital/
property or part (block) of a property. eg types of tenure, rateable
values, sub-surface information, rights of way, covenants restricting
development, addresses of service authorities, areas, volumes etc.
The data on each property can be displayed or printed and there are
various search facilities on sub-sets of the total data to produce
reports ie Site Summary, Tenure, Technical and Tenant Reports.

2.9 Annual Maintenance Plan Module
This records details of long-term building and maintenance work that
is required over a forthcoming five year period. A number of reports
are available that analyse the estimated cost of the work under various categories and can be used to prepare annual maintenance plans
for District Management or when preparing budgets. The cost values
may be price indexed.

2.10 Residential Property Module
This module is designed to hold details on residential properties
and the tenancies within them. The data stored includes nominal
occupancy (ie maximum possible occupancy), current occupancy, rent,
facilities covered in rent (eg lighting/heating, rates, maintenance
etc), occupation commencement date, occupation termination date etc.
Two main reports are available, a property and a tenant report each
of which may be selected by a number of parameters.

2.11 Contract Control Module
This module is compatable with the mandatory DHSS advice on letting
and controlling capital building projects (CONCODE) and has the following parts:

1 Approved Contractors List
2 Tendering Control
3 Contract Management
4 Scheme Archiving

Part 1 of this module holds a list of contractors together with details of the specific types of work they undertake, the specific geographic locations they work in and the range of value of work which
they can do. The second part of the module allows a list of contractors to be produced who meet the requirements of a planned project and

allows a sub-set of these to be assigned to a tender list. Details
of the results of the tender action are stored. Part 3 holds details
of and is used progress specific schemes. Part holds summary details
of completed schemes.

2.12 Electro-medical Equipment Management Module
This module is based on a combination of the standard WIMS Asset and
Stores Modules but with additional facilities to make it more suit-
able for managing electro-medical equipment.

2.13 Vehicle Maintenance Management Module
This module is also based on the standard WIMS Asset/Stores Module
but includes additional features like the continuous monitoring of
mpg figures, the ability to schedule work on the basis of vehicle
mileage and the availability of cost information in the form of cost/
mile.

The most widely used modules are probably Asset Management, Prop-
erty Management and Budget Monitoring with the Property Appraisal
Module coming into wide use as a current NHS estate rationalisation
policy is implemented. The Asset Management Module is mostly used at
Unit (ie individual site/hospital) level, the Property Management at
District and Region level and the Budget Monitoring at all levels.
Property Appraisal is a District based activity.

3. Computer Hardware for WIMS

In 1979, when the first stages of WIMS development were underway, the
Department choose a CP/M based microcomputer version because:

a There was a wide range of makes and types of machines able to
   run CP/M

b Start up costs for a single stand-alone system were relatively
   small

c Many microcomputers could be expanded and extended at a later
   date if required

It was also decided that the MBASIC high level language would be
used. Early on, the software specification for WIMS was licensed to
ABS Computers Ltd who produced versions of the programs for their
range of mini-computers so providing a multi-terminal option for
those able to start with a larger WIMS installation.
Since that time more versions of WIMS have become available and
these now include versions to run under the ICL DRX operating system
on the range of ICL DRS computers and in PICK to run on General Automation equipment. A more recent development is a version to run on
the Dataflex database management system which is to a large degree
hardware independant. The development of all but the "standard"
MBASIC versions have been financed by commercial organisations usually

as a means of increasing their hardware sales to the NHS. The choice
of MBASIC has proved opportune as these versions of the modules will
run, with little or no modification, on any computer that supports a
high level version of BASIC, for example, with MS-BASIC or GWBASIC on
MS/PC-DOS machines.

As mentioned above, WIMS is supported by a full-time Centre of
Responsibility group which issues programs and documentation, under-
takes training and organises an annual WIMS Seminar - four of which
have been held to date. The Seminars are used to discuss current and
future software, to pass on user experience with implementations and
features a commercial hardware/software exhibition.

The fact that there are various versions of WIMS which run on
different types of hardware and are implemented in different software
enviroments obviously could cause problems for the support team. To
overcome this a policy is followed whereby any particular version
only becomes an officially supported version when it has at least 5%
of the user base.

4. Commercial Sales of WIMS

When the first WIMS module (Asset Management) was officially released
in 1981 it was apparent to the Department that there was considerable
commercial potential in the WIMS software. ABS Computers were the
first to exploit this potential and the Department also issued commercial licences to allow the CP/M microcomputer version of WIMS to be
sold outside of the Health Service. As other versions have become
available these too have been licensed to commercial organisations
and sales have been made both in the UK and overseas.

5. The Use of WIMS with Building/Energy Management Systems

There has always been considerable interest in using some of the data
available from Energy/Building Management Systems (BMS) within WIMS
applications and there are two types of data which have the most obvious applications. These are the use of "condition information" (eg
hours run, temperature, vibration level etc) for use in the job planning part of the Asset Management Module and "energy related" information (eg temperatures, meter readings) for use in the Energy Monitoring Module.

In order to transfer BMS information for use as data in a WIMS
program the BMS must somehow transmit the relevant information to the
computer running WIMS where it can then be processed. Basically this
can be done on or off-line but due to the technical problems in directly linking a real-time BMS into a computer running applications
programs such as WIMS the link-ups so far undertaken have used an
"off-line" solution where data is "dumped" from the BMS as a data
file for subsequent processing by the relevant WIMS application. To
date development of links between ABS Computers/Transmitton, CPM-
micro/ISS Clorius and IBM PC/Johnson Controls and others, has been
started.

6. WIMS Development

The first WIMS modules officially released to the NHS had been under development since 1979, these modules are therefore now coming up for their seventh birthday!. In the period since 1979 the capabilities of computer hardware and the expectations of computer users have both radically increased. As described above a large proportion of the estate management applications suitable for computerisation have been covered by WIMS modules.

Because of the rapid development of computer technology and the increased requirements of NHS users (particularly in the area of data integration) it has been realised for some time that an evolution of the software and hardware basis of WIMS is required. This evolution to what is now known as WIMS2 is underway guided by the following four main requirements:

1. A continuing high degree of hardware independance.
2. A much improved facility for integration of data across applications both in the estate management area and with the requirements of other disciplines.
3. Facilities for answering ad-hoc enquiries and for user specified report generation.
4. An ability to transfer data from existing (ie WIMS1) modules into the new applications.

6.1 Hardware Independance

This first requirement is probably the most difficult to achieve as there is no longer anything resembling the "standard" operating system/language combination that CP/M-MBASIC provided. Additionally, NHS hardware requirements are now much more varied ranging from stand-alone single-user machines to District-wide systems. Historically, the various versions of WIMS (ICL, ABS etc) have largely been developed from the CP/M-MBASIC version and from a relatively meagre amount of documentation and it is apparent that the first and major requirement for a hardware independant system is that the system should be fully documented. Full documentation allows the system to be implemented on any hardware/software combination with relative ease and this is an important consideration as it will assist Estate Managers whose Region or District have a policy of hardware standardisation to have the WIMS applications produced for other computer enviroments. To this end detailed system documentation for each WIMS2 application will be produced including user requirements, functional and technical specifications. The specifications will contain some mandatory (eg minimum data set) and some optional (eg field lengths, screen formats) requirements and will also include a suggested minimum hardware specification.

Additional to this documentation and in order to test out the new applications and provide validation software for pilot sites the system specifications are being implemented as "exemplar" applications in two forms, as a mixed "C" language and proprietary database system (UNIFY) version to run on UNIX based hardware and as a standard (SPECTRUM Manufacturers Association) PICK version. The Department and one of its consultants are producing the UNIX based exemplar together with the system documentation and the PICK based exemplar is being coded by General Automation Ltd but in a form that will enable it to be ported onto all other standard PICK based systems easily.

6.2 Data Integration

In the first generation of WIMS modules there was very little attempt made to integrate data used in different modules and no attempt to design systems to provide data for disciplines other than the estate managers. The WIMS2 development is attempting to provide one "information area" which will then be accessed by each of the estate management applications and to provide data for other NHS disciplines (specifically Finance and Supplies Departments). There are two main strands in the approach to providing data integration, one is the use of structured analysis techniques (including data modelling) to provide a low level view of the system and the other is to incorporate knowledge gained from the first generation WIMS system.

Obviously it is not feasible to produce one massive application covering all estate functions so WIMS2 is being produced as a series of applications each giving a specific functional view of estate information. Four applications are under development at the moment in the following priority which reflects the probable degree of use:

The Asset Operational Application which covers similar information areas and functions as the WIMS1 Asset Management and Maintenance Contracts Modules. The faclities provided include a detailed Asset Register with price-indexed replacement cost information and the ability to provide historical information on the cost of work done on a specific asset, building block, site, management unit etc for asset management requirements.

The Property and Land application which deals with the information areas presently covered by the WIMS1 Property Management and Property Appraisal Modules. Facilities provided include property register and property appraisal sections and an ability to access maintenance cost information for individual properties from the Asset Operational application.

The Estate Strategic Plan Application which covers the same information area as the WIMS1 Annual Maintenance Plan Module and provide similar facilities (ie long term costing, scheduling and scheme progress information) for capital and project as well as "maintenance" work. Considerable additional facilities to support the NHS estate rationalisation exercise are planned.

The Financial Control application which deals with the information areas presently covered by the WIMS1 Budget Monitoring and Stock Control/Purchase Ordering Modules but is further intended to allow the processing of all estate related ordering and invoice information and also to provide financial reports including job costing information from the Asset Operational Application.

6.3 Ad-Hoc Queries/Report Generation

The WIMS2 specification includes minimium requirements for ad-hoc query and report generation facilities and these are provided within PICK itself in the PICK based exemplar and in the proprietary database system in the UNIX/C/UNIFY exemplar by means of its SQL (Structured Query Language) facility. For example, a SQL query from an Asset Register in the Asset Operational Application might be for a list of all boilers accepted into service since 1985 and this would be of the form:

sql> select as_id, as_name, as_typ, as_accpt

                             (Fields to be displayed)

sql> from as_details

                             (From which record)

sql> where as_name='BOILER NO*' and as_accpt>01/01/85

                    (By constraints ie name starts with text shown and acceptance date after 1.1.85)

sql> order by as_accpt/

                    (Report in Acceptance Date order)

sql> recognised query!

                    (SQL accepts query)

The report produced would be of the following form:

as_id	as_name	as_typ	as_accpt
65	BOILER NO1	BB10	12/02/85
68	BOILER NO2	BB10	19/10/85
125	BOILER NO3	BB10	05/01/86

6.4 Transfer Of WIMS1 Data

The WIMS2 applications are being specifically designed so that all data held in WIMS1 modules will be catered for in the new application data structures and utilities for conversion of standard WIMS1 data to the new requirements are being developed.

7. Conclusion

At the time of writing (December 1986) there is a validation version of the WIMS2 Asset Operations Application in use in the NHS and it is planned that a validation version of the Property and Land Application will be available within the next three months. Issue of the next two planned applications is due by the end of 1987.

    Generally, the computer hardware required to run the WIMS2 applications and the applications themselves represent a substantial increase in the level of sophistication concerning computerisation that Estate Managers must possess. Hopefully, with the help of the experience gained from the use of WIMS1 this will not be too great a problem.

By and large the WIMS1 modules have been very successful and it is hoped that in the coming years the WIMS2 applications will also be taken up on a large scale to play a similar role in assisting estate management in the NHS.

CREATING A PROPERTY INFORMATION SYSTEM

IMPORTANT ELEMENTS IN AN APPROACH TO THE IDEAL

E. Ross
Scottish Special Housing Association

Scottish Special Housing Association first entered the computerised property information system arena in 1972, at a time when expertise in the construction of such systems was virtually nil. That situation is changing, though only very slowly as yet, and certainly not at the rate at which the art of the possible has moved in the intervening period, so far as the technology is concerned.

Based on that first experience, and on what the organisation has learned since then on the purpose and use of such systems, a second generation Property Information Management System has recently been introduced.

Rather than present that solution in detail - attenders at the seminar will see some illustrations of its actual operation - this paper will attempt to highlight some of the important underlying considerations. No apology is made for the fact that for much of the time it is the ideal which is discussed, since without a view of the ideal, there is no way to define a path from present state to the ideal, a path along which the S.S.H.A. is still moving.

In that context, this paper holds a great deal in common with the associated S.S.H.A. paper, which covers the much wider context of the need for and use of property information, within a philosophy which the S.S.H.A. applies to the management and care of a large existing housing stock. In that philosophy, the existence and use of a Property Information Management System, is but one arm, though a vital one, in a concerted approach to defining and solving the management problem.

The Objective

One of the main values of that philosophy, has been the extent to which the prime objective has gradually become clearer and clearer over time, so that it can now be simplisticly stated as the need to maximise the potential life of houses, or, in terms of this discussion, the need to maximise the potential remaining life of the existing stock. This is based on an acceptance that none of our aspirations for our stock, or for the successive generations of tenants who will occupy them, are achievable in practice, without the simple continued existence of the stock for as long as we can retain individual elements in a viable state.

That conclusion on the prime objective has a vital effect on the nature and form of the information systems required overall in a housing authority to achieve that objective, and in particular, on which of these contribute most to achieving the objective, since logic dictates that these must be given priority in development and in use of resources.

Almost certainly, application of that principle will produce a quite different systems development scenario from that which currently exists in most authorities, with the requirement for a Property Information System heading the list. As can be demonstrated, no other system can contribute to anything like the same extent in achieving the prime objective.

The Traditional Approach to System Design

The importance of the statement just made, is reflected in the traditional approach to system design, where it has rightly been said that any information system, manual or computer, can be designed by answering the 5 W's :-

WHY   - is the information needed.

WHAT   - kind of information is required.

WHO   - needs the information.

WHERE   - does it have to be made available.

WHEN   - does it have to be made available.

Obviously the process is one of a fully understood cause, providing a logical path to the effects necessary to achieve the objective, with answers to the question - why is the information needed - giving essential shape and form to all of the succeeding answers, and in due course, to the system itself.

In practice, answers to the 5 W's are usually produced in principle first, and then asked and answered in progressively more specific and detailed form, so that eventually the detailed data content and shape of the system become fully apparent.

A foreshortened example of the process is something like the following:-

Q. What kind of information is required?

A. Property Information.

Q. What kind of property information?

A.   All of the information necessary, to sustain application of
     a deliberate policy and practice, aimed at assessing the
     whole life needs of the stock, since such is essential to
     wholly preconsidered plans to maximise the potential viable
     life of the stock, and to ensure the availability of the
     necessary levels of resource.

In due course, logic, and a full understanding of that last answer,
would lead to a form of repetition of the 5 W's, in more specific
form for example:-

WHY   - was the property provided, to meet what need?

WHAT - accomodation is provided, is the form of
        construction, components does it have?

WHO   - designed it, built it, maintains it?

WHERE - is it located - with all the levels of place
        information which are necessary.

WHEN - was it built, did it last have/next need component
        replacement, will it reach the end of viable life?

That is only a taste of the process, but it is sufficient to
demonstrate the power intrinsic in data, within the classic
definition of the term, viz : a fact or facts, usable as information
in its own right, from which other facts can be deduced - since the
simple existence of data of the kind illustrated leads on to the
capability to calculate or analyse such as,
        How many are there and where?
        How much will it cost?
        When will it happen?
        What has happened already? etc. etc.,
with the possibility of formulating such questions on the basis of a
single field of data or on such permutations of them as may be
necessary.

The process of answering the 5 W's is a lengthy and at times painful
exercise, but then 'creation' usually is.   However, as has been
underlined in S.S.H.A.'s associated paper, the alternative of not
having such information aids to management will be far more painful
and costly in the end.   Indeed the question to be more rightly
asked is whether management can effectively fulfill their prime role
in defining the problem, i.e. the real demands of the stock, and in
obtaining maximum value for money from stock investment, without such
information tools.

In the case of the S.S.H.A. the difficulties to be faced in creating
such an information system were not lessened by the fact that, like
most Authorities who are the prospective parents of such an
offspring, we, or at least our properties, were no longer young, and
therefore 'complications' would arise, e.g. in capturing a back-log of
data on a large existing stock.

Archives

At this point, a brief word would not be amiss, with regard to the part to be played by existing archives of information, in particular, those of Contract Drawings and Documents, which should - the operative word being should - be able to play a substantial part in the data collection process.

It follows that where such archives are not already in good order, they will need to be made so, with conclusions being necessary on what forms an ideal record for individual housing developments. Subsequent study, comparing what is actually available, with the ideal, should establish a plan for making good deficiencies shown to exist.

Most Authorities will have some form of Drawings etc., archive, though perhaps few will have been driven by full and formal recognition of the inevitable re-uses of the information contained in these sources, which can not only provide the 'verbal' descriptions of property which will reside in an information system but are essential aids in extending the interpretation and application of such description outside of or beyond the system uses.

Whilst the best of such systems usually have a micro-film base - and this can be very helpful in obtaining fast access to individual housing development records - the major difficulty of this as a stand-alone system, is that any form of analysis across anything other than a very small number of houses, remains a time consuming and often impossible task.   Efficient archives must therefore be tied to an equally efficient Property Information System.

Computer based systems, which combine the storage of 'graphic' and of 'verbal' description, are now beginning to emerge, in response to fairly narrowly specified user requirements, such as those of land use or Planning etc., approval.   Though valuable in themselves and as indicators of the wider art of the possible for the future, these currently lack the width of brief which is discussed here.

Constructing a Data Model

On the basis that the various difficulties could not be taken as an excuse to do nothing, and in knowledge of the advantages to be gained, S.S.H.A. conceived and has recently given birth to a greatly improved Property Information Management System - PIMS - albeit after a lengthy period of gestation.

Looking back with the benefit of hindsight on the beginnings of that process brings the classic riposte to the question, 'what is the best way to get to such and such a place' - well if I were you I would not start off from here'.

Present day advice, would indicate that the first step, beyond firmly establishing the prime objective, would be the construction of a corporate-wide data model, the need for and benefits of which are now well documented in computer management literature. However, for the purpose of easing immediate understanding, the principle, in very simplistic terms, is one of listing every piece of data produced by an authority, and its various uses.

In terms of the present discussion, this listing would include all of the answers to the 5 'W' questions on property information, which can perhaps now be recognised as part of a much larger co-ordinated approach to data management and to necessary system design over the full range of an authorities functions.

From this foundation, one then extracts the 'data sets' appropriate to particular main uses, so that the content and shape of individual systems or data applications - manual or computer - becomes clear. Many advantages accrue from this approach.

We have a means to measure the various uses against the prime objective, to illustrate and substantiate system development priorities, as opposed to the departmental 'who can shout loudest' battlefield, which is perhaps the more traditional and wholly unsatisfactory norm.

The contribution which such a foundation also makes, to construction of an appropriate corporate computer hardware, software and communications acquisition strategy, is perhaps obvious and certainly this advantage cannot be overstated However, there are other less obvious advantages.

With the data-model as a corner stone of system design, we have a means of accurately defining the inevitable inter-connections between what, in a more traditional approach, would almost certainly have become stand-alone systems, where necessary inter-communication is an after the main event task, achieved only at the cost of re-design and considerable user aggravation, if ever.

The value of an avenue to consider reduction of the multiple handling or input of data, which can have many uses or be otherwise common across 'systems', cannot be under-rated, with not all of these being obvious at first sight, e.g. in that area of wasted effort one might cite that of Billing applications, usually seen as relatively single purpose uses of data, though nothing could be further from the truth when the use of data is looked at in the round.

The ability to see all of the uses of data, confers another advantage. That of constructing in a fully integrated fashion, the various forms of management information system related to Activity and Resource Monitoring and Calculation where such systems either extract data from, or supply data to, other main systems. That degree of co-ordination and integration is an evident feature of the highly integrated systems operating in the more advanced sections of production industry, for which there is as yet no real parallel in the housing field.

It is perhaps not the purpose of this paper to attempt to explain why this should be so, but part of the explanation almost certainly lies in the fact that, to date, computer service organisations, expert in and with the large volume of resources necessary to design and develop highly integrated database, software, hardware and communications solutions - in anticipation of multiple sales - have not yet been brought together with those who might provide a total brief of housing requirements. Such a coming together could in time lead to an ability to demonstrate solutions more readily recognisable in the housing market place, as appropriate to their problems, rather than trying to themselves establish alternate uses for 'tools' used for sometimes very different purposes.

Prime Conclusion

If experience such as has been so far explained has been hard won, the message nonetheless is that it is never too late to learn the importance of the prime objective, or to embrace the data model concept, since both are major milestones on the path to the ideal. Through understanding the prime objective more clearly, S.S.H.A. has made substantial progress in a variety of related aspects, including that of a Property Information System. A price remains to be paid, however, in the extent to which that system, in the absence of a data model, for the moment lacks the degree of co-ordination with other main data bases and systems which is necessary and might otherwise have been possible.

What Information is Required - Another Route to a Conclusion

If the answer to the question 'what information is required' is arrived at, by first establishing the full connotations of 'why is the information needed' there is a shortcut to answering that question, which produces the simple if unpalatable answer of 'every piece of information ever produced in order to put an individual property on the ground and keep it there for the whole of its life.

The simplistic reasoning behind that conclusion, is that no one, of whatever depth or breadth of experience of the housing scene, can define or prognosticate which elements out of the total will never re-appear as an information need, perhaps a need vital to early decision taking, at some future point in time. The past is littered with examples of the at one moment, insignificant, suddenly becoming very significant.

That difficulty, i.e. that of not knowing in advance exactly what tomorrow's question was going to be, has frustrated property information system designers for a very long time, since the need to pre-specify the questions in effect dictated the range of data to be held, and the exact form of the answer.

34

Fortunately, just as hardware technology has moved on to the stage
where volume data storage is no longer a primary decision factor,
software technology has defined means whereby it is no longer
essential to pre-specify all of the questions which may be asked in
the future, and these can be freely formulated and answered as they
arise, provided the data is in the system.

The ideal description therefore is everything, and the real question
to be asked is not what is the ideal, but what is the path to the
ideal within an individual Authority, over time.   That path will
vary with individual authorities, depending on what the present state
is on access to or availability of data.   In this we perhaps need to
bear in mind that the data is not a whole new range of description
and is no more than that range already required to put houses on the
ground and to maintain them.

The real trick of course, forgetting the back-log of information
gathering for the moment, is to capture data as it is being created,
preferably in such a way that the instruction to give effect to work
itself provides the means of update to the information system.   So,
we again see the advantages of the data model.   Equally, if we are
to halt any further accumulation of back-log, our system must be
capable of accommodating all new instructions, rather than some more
limited select of data elements.

The collection of back-log data is a daunting prospect, viewed as a
stand-alone task.   If however, the concerted management approach to
maximising the potential life of the stock includes, as in the
S.S.H.A. approach, an element essential and advantageous in its own
right, i.e. the cyclic physical inspection of the stock, then further
areas are opened up for the co-ordination of effort for a common
purpose.

As has been described elsewhere by S.S.H.A., it was found necessary
to apply special resources to acquiring a particular range of
elements, beyond those established by a trawl through existing
readily available sources, in order to formulate a foundation for the
stock profiling management process which is the subject of
description in that other paper.   Clearly the next step in data
acquisition for the Property Information System is the capture of
that range of data, so that it is available for alternate forms of
analysis and for the future automatic reproduction of stock profiles
within the system.

Given that the intention is the maximum possible eventual level of
description of individual houses, and lest this should appear an even
more frightening prospect than it actually is, perhaps some of the
last words of this paper, should be to underline that   part of

35

the systems analysis art is to find the most economic form of storage. The ability to describe individual houses does not demand that all of the data need be stored at that level.

The concluding words of advice however, must be a reminder that the first step on the path to the ideal must be an acceptance and full understanding of the prime objective,i.e. maximisation of the potential viable life of the stock. The rest is no more than simple logic and natural progression, within the levels of resource which can be made available. The technology is already available and is showing even more prospect for the future.

MANAGEMENT OF MAINTENANCE - THE NEED FOR AND USES OF DATA

ALAN SPEDDING,
Bristol Polytechnic

Abstract
Until such time as there is a resurgence in demand, and finance is
available, particularly for public-sector building, much of what was
built in the 1960's and 1970's will have to be maintained along with
older stock. The increasing significance of the maintenance of built
assets, as a part of the management of landed property, is requiring
public sector owners in particular to examine and re-orientate their
management structures.
This paper addresses itself to some if the problems relating to
the generation and use of data appropriate to the management of
maintenance of built assets, and the forecasting of future need.
Key Words:, management, databases, cost, accuracy, organisation,
budget, property, feedback.

Introduction

Costs of maintenance are, for many building owners, becoming more
significant. For instance, Department of the Environment statistics
show that, over even the last six years, maintenance costs have
steadily risen from just over forty per cent to over forty-six per
cent of the value of construction output for Great Britain(1). The
Department of Education & Science, in respect of educational
buildings, say that the 1965 to 1975 new-build programmes will cause
maintenance costs to rise "until the 1990s"(2). Research has
suggested that costs of maintenance of a large stock of new buildings
tend to rise as the buildings age, and may eventually attain a
somewhat stable cost profile during the middle of the economic life
of the stock. The considerable amount of new building in the mid
1960's to mid 1970's, particularly in County Council educational
properties, was followed by a fall in new-build since 1975. Thus the
inevitable ageing of the stock, should result in a general
levelling-out of total maintenance expenditure during the middle
1990s. Of course at least three major factors might affect overall
costs by that time. Firstly current shortages of money relating to
actual maintenance need (not that intuitively forecast which may be
very inaccurate) may result in a higher than anticipated general
level of failures. Secondly the increasing unsuitability of
previously built but aged properties, in economic and operational
terms, plus demographic factors may create a demand for new-build,

in new locations. Thirdly, many of the properties built in the 1960's and 1970's are likely to have a much shorter life than more traditionally built older stock.

The relationship of maintenance spending to revenue and capital budgets can be complex and "creative accounting" has been employed by many owners of built but assets to optimise their income and expenditure. The potential advantages of moving spending from capital to revenue headings has, in the past, had strategic implications for public sector as well as private sector owners. Indeed, during times of acute pressure on prices of new-build, such as in the early 1970s, particularly within cost-limit systems, it has been concluded that in the search for capital cost advantages, too little consideration had been given to long term performance factors,(3) and we are now living with many of the decisions taken during such times of high demand.

Whilst the management of landed property involves a wide range of skills, this paper deals mainly with the data needed by management for the upkeep of stocks of built assets. The wider aspects cannot be ignored, however,because several factors are combining to make it possible, particularly for some owners of large stocks, to modify or dispose of surplus buildings which will ease some of the pressure on resources. Nevertheless the question must be asked as to whether the UK Construction Industry has shrunk to a point where it might find it difficult to cope with a significant level of demand should it occur regionally or nationally. If demand on the industry increases, then prices of building work are likely to rise very quickly to levels which owners might find even more difficult to afford. Would they on the one hand have to accept lower standards, or on the other have to resort to system building again to get work done. In terms of future maintenance costs and feedback to design, would we we be in danger of repeating past mistakes?

Whatever our views on these points there is now a considerable backlog of maintenance work to be remedied in many authorities' stocks. Unfortunately some of the forecasts appear to be simply cumulative from one year to the next and one is bound to ask is this a realistic approach to the problem of forecasting the backlog of work. In the public sector,in order to convince Central Government of the seriousness of the lack of finance for maintenance, building owners need to be able to forecast when failures and breakdowns are likely to occur and this requires far better maintenance cost data than are usually available. Similarly, for forecasting and budget bidding processes within an organisation, good quality data are needed. Data are not independent of management structure and policy objectives and choices have to be made as to which data are valid and likely to be worth collecting in the light of efficiency of the overall management process.

Levels of accuracy and detail of maintenance Cost Data

The range of interest in maintenance cost data covers the spectrum from those building owners who regard the cost of maintenance as being a very minor part of the total costs of their operations, to those people whose responsibility it is to conserve large stocks of built assets, with significant cost effects, and also includes research and development interests.

All data cost money to collect, classify, store, manipulate and retrieve, and so keeping records of expenditure on maintenance should be undertaken with a clear idea of current uses and the potential needs of the future. It is clearly uneconomic to spend money on building up data banks which are either too complex for the use to which those data will be put, or on the other hand not detailed enough to inform the processes for which data are being collected.

The analysis of data for research purposes is generally undertaken at a greater level of detail than that required in day to day practice for monitoring spending and preparing budgets. Nevertheless the design of a data collection system should be such that the coding and classification system will enable data to be captured at a general or more specific level as considered necessary. For example, a broad grouping such as external walls may be adopted initially, but later on wall tie failure may need identification and thus the coding must be able to accommodate a fine level of detail. Therefore whilst some work may not ever need to be identified at other than a general level, the concept should be that of a system which is expandable in each facet.

The LAMSAC study(4) found that classification of cost data in many authorities was a mixture of significant elemental items, such as painting, as well as trivial items which probably related to a one-off query some time in the past. The same study also found that inexact terminology meant different things to different people and thus the interpretation of data could be faulty. The use of coding systems for computer, such as those developed at Bristol(5) will enable various levels of detail to be coded as required and will also reduce some variability in data by introducing more standardised descriptions and classifications of work. Whatever system is used, if one of the objectives of data collection is to facilitate feedback to the design team, then the coding system should be compatible with the classifications used for cost-planning of new-build.

There can also be little value in pursuing spurious accuracy. As an example, the writer has seen maintenance costs per annum divided by floor area given to two places of decimals. On investigation it was evident that costs might not have been completely correctly allocated to elements, nor would the authority concerned say that they believed that the floor areas, by which the costs had been divided, were accurate to anything better than within 10 per cent. Additionally, of course many costs are not incurred pro-rata to any selected yardstick, such as floor area and operational costs may substitute for some categories of maintenance work, so we should not attribute "scientific accuracy" to such data.

There are other data problems such as, in some systems in use, maintenance costs are not allocated to specific tasks, nor even to specific properties. An authority may, for instance, use named contractors or directly employed labour, on a call-out basis, to remedy mechanical and electrical faults. Whilst materials might be booked to a property and recorded in the maintenance section, the labour and transport costs may be accounted for in the accounts as global sums. Even if labour costs are identified with properties, in a spread-out rural county high apparent costs for small repairs might result from travelling time and transport costs being added on.

The nature of the organisation will also affect patterns of spending, as a decentralised organisation may allow work to be ordered by non-technical staff, such as headteachers or library clerks, usually within predetermined ranges of probable cost and sometimes within defined categories of work. The accounting system for such work, and other "fixed" costs, may by-pass the maintenance manager and prevent a full and up-to-date picture of maintenance work from being put together. Thus, the maintenance manager may not be able to monitor all proposed spending and may only be able to take a retrospective view of certain parts of what has been spent. If one of the aims of the data base is to provide early warning of failure and to reduce the level of unplanned work being undertaken, then some means of capturing such data may need to be considered. In particular, the smaller repetitive unplanned items of work may be a substitute for more major items which should not be deferred, because the real costs of deferring work may become obscured until a major failure occurs.

This is not to say that a decentralised system is necessarily inefficient because every owner of large stocks of buildings will have individual geographical, staffing, and organisational features which require costs of control and collection of data to be weighed against benefits.

Also, one should not assume that all data on repairs should automatically feed into the maintenance record system in detail. For instance, in one study of schools costs we found that Headteachers' orders for very minor works accounted for nearly thirteen percent of all maintenance orders, but less than four percent of total spending. These orders were restricted to specific damage-related items of work and so might not provide the maintenance manager with information of any particular value even if he had all the details.

Levels of accuracy and detail of maintenance cost data must therefore be chosen in the light of the efficient use of management staff and the questions which management really need to be answered.

Cost databases and management

Most studies which have examined maintenance and related costs have involved the collection and analysis of historical data, and some studies undertaken at Bristol Polytechnic(6) have been no exception. Such data can inform us on what has been spent but, taken as costs without explanation, may tell us little of actual need nor of probable future spending. Usually it is difficult to know in retrospect what factors influenced levels of prices and choice of elements which were the subject of repair or replacement. Quite apart from "need" it is most likely that the interaction of people involved in the management process affected how much money was spent. Therefore unless the database is structured so as to provide some explanatory information, it is doubtful whether collecting quantities of detailed historical cost data, beyond those necessary to establish

a broad picture of frequencies and averages of costs, for typical
elements of construction, is likely to be particularly useful.
Additionally it is of little value to collect data over short periods
of the life of buildings if it is desired to understand their
behaviour in service.

Quite apart from the inherent variability of even carefully
collected raw data there is a need for data to be collated and
expressed in terms of a yardstick which will have meaning for
management. Commonly, costs are expressed in relation to area, such
as pounds per square metre. Alternatives, such as cost per occupant,
per site, or per individual building may be easily made available in
a computerised system, but, in all cases, care must be taken in
comparisons of data. As an example it may be found that maintenance
of secondary schools costs much more than primary schools when
expressed as cost per school, but when calculated as cost per square
metre of floor area the primary schools appear to be more expensive.
This is because of the considerable differences in area which usually
occur in these two types of buildings. Additionally, when some
buildings are single-storey and some multi-storey, costs such as that
of roofing divided by total floor area are of doubful value and the
writer therefore suggests that, because of these factors, average
costs per square metre are only of use in giving approximate figures
for average spending on a large stock of buildings of similar
characteristics operating under similar conditions. They should not
be used without some explanatory detail and modification, to forecast
spending on different stocks or on individual buildings. Possibly
one of the more useful strategies to reduce uncertainty, if the
ubiquitous cost per square metre is to be used, is to group buildings
by overall size ranges, function, age and constructional type.
However, caution is needed if the resulting sample sizes are not
large enough to give some degree of confidence in the average prices
so obtained.

We now have a powerful aid to management in that using a computer
to issue orders facilitates the capture of data at the time they are
generated. For instance, a program written for research and
development purposes at Bristol is designed to allow actual,
estimated, or schedule of rate prices to be allocated to each order
so that a print-out of actual and committed spending may be obtained
at any time by management. At any time, estimated cost can be
converted to actual cost as invoices are cleared through the
financial system. As long as there is an appropriate policy on the
definition of content of orders, so that multiple orders or
combinations of elements can be dealt with, it is possible to code
work under headings specified by management and to analyse costs, in
total or property by property, against various parameters such as
£/m 2 whenever required.

Descriptive data
It is often useful to code the work ordered in such a way as will
record not only the property, the cost, and the element to which work
was done, but also other factors which may need investigation.

As an example a coded item might carry information on:-

The element or component of construction
Its location (by property or block)
The process of repair (such as replace)
The reason for work being necessary

Clearly, the system should avoid the necessity for looking-up complex codes as the data will only be as good as the people operating the system allow. Therefore care must be taken to ensure that as much coding as possible is done by the system, not the operator. The categories also must enable data to be subdivided into useful blocks within a logical structure

As an example, during an early research project at Bristol it was decided to establish a "reason code" in order to try to record why money was being spent in a particular way. An authority we were working with at that time had used such categories from time to time and co-operated with our detailed investigation of a sample of maintenance work under such headings. The result of a pilot survey is given in Figure 1 below, where it can be seen that ninety seven per cent of orders were reason-coded. The high percentage of fair wear and tear and roof leaks in unplanned work can be seen. Unfortunately whilst "fair wear and tear" may be a reason for work to be done it tells us little. Additionally "roof leaks" is not a reason, for it combines an elemental description together with the consequence of failure.

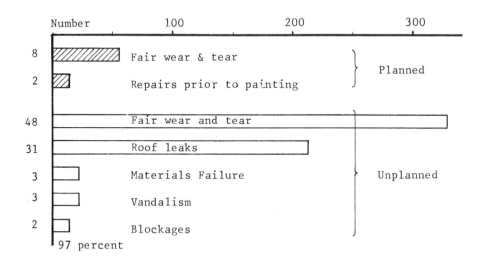

Figure 1

It was subsequently felt to be worthwhile to try to put the reason code into a more logical structure and also to ascertain if staff in the field would use it satisfactorily. A new reason code was therefore developed for a later research project on a three-digit hierarchical basis indicating:-

Level 1   Policy   (e.g. planned work)

Level 2   Cause of failure   (e.g. early failure

Level 3   Result   (e.g. water penetration)

This code, which is currently under test enables us for example to code an unexpected "roof leak" as-unplanned maintenance/early failure/water penetration-whilst the code from the order form for the work will specify the element and remedy, as in "repair felted flat roof". We can then ask questions such as "which elements are failing sooner than expected," so that we may initiate more detailed study in order to obtain a clearer view of such matters as to whether special attention is needed to those elements or whether design changes are needed in future. Even if we do not reason-code all work all of the time, the ability to collect such data when required provides us with a means of accommodating descriptive data into an existing computerised data collection system without any difficulty.

Property records

If data on maintenance are being collected, at all, then they should correspond to other data in respect of the stock and the overall information needs of the organisation. Consequentially it is necessary to know what the stock actually consists of, and what its condition is, bearing in mind that condition is not static, but dynamic, changing for the worse as a rule. Desirably, the data on maintenance costs should interlock with property records at appropriate points in the system so that, for practical purposes, management has access to a data system which is co-ordinated as far as is feasible. Generally, it is probably not economic to record cost data to a fine level of elemental detail if the system for recording of property and condition surveys does not allow for investigation of current stock at a similar level of detail. For instance, in a property with several different buildings, it is clearly important to match cost data with a particular block's constructional features. Particularly for inspection and budgeting purposes, it is of doubtful value to know that, for example, that windows type A are failing if the system cannot allow for the assessment of how many of these of what age are present in how many blocks or buildings.

The property files should include an assessment of the expected life of major components or elements. These lives are likely to be most useful if they are based upon evidence from the maintenance cost files, manufacturers' data, and assessments by staff. Clearly we

43

cannot determine the future, but we can narrow down areas of uncertainty to some extent. The large number of variables in practice make it difficult to forecast the life of elements and components, but in a large stock of buildings, we may observe some of the major features relating to failure.

As an example, we examined a number of post-1946 Primary schools over the whole of their life span. There was a range of age within which serious flat roof failure occurred, the average age being just under twelve years. However, a closer look at the data suggested that specification and size had played an important role, and we identified three main constructional types, the first two with average ages of just under eight and just under twelve years, and the third small group containing roofs of some rather untypical longevity, up to a maximum of twenty-one years.

Whilst there were other variables at work, we now have some broad observations on anticipated lives of these types. Such observations should be incorporated into the property files. These data can be used to highlight elements which have entered the danger area of life, and this should trigger off special attention at times of inspection. Inspection may then result in revision of previously assessed life in the property files, and will allow for further refinement of data for forecasting purposes.

Management processes and data

For historical reasons already noted above, the management and financial processes have tended to dominate the maintenance of built assets, whilst performance-related data have not generally been the subject of attention.

Figure 2 below indicates the broad relationships of a database system to management processes. The processes to the left of the diagram have tended to be given a high input of management resources in the past, whilst those to the right have received less. What is happening now is that management processes are gradually having to strengthen towards the tasks on the right hand side, raising the importance of the database as a management tool.

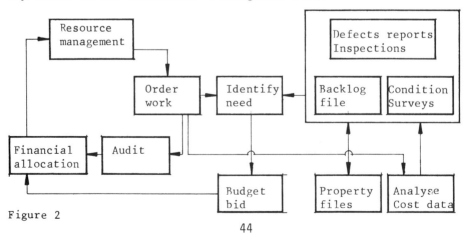

Figure 2

Whilst many of the processes above can benefit from the use of the computer, particularly the ordering of work, it is of value to set up an integrated system, even if part of it is manual, leaving the gradual expansion of a computerised system until it is felt to be worthwhile. In many cases this is being done, but we have noted that although the shift in tasks has required organisational and staffing changes, such changes are not always easy to accomplish given existing staff expertise, distribution, and departmental groupings.

Forecasting and budgeting

When maintenance is looked at in terms of the overall budget of an authority or business enterprise it is often seen to be a relatively low percentage of potential spending. Nevertheless the amounts in themselves are significant and, in the case of largely unexpected failures, such as occurred in the case of many flat felted roofs, the consequences of higher than planned maintenance costs are difficult to accommodate within tight financial planning constraints.

It is obviously desirable that the budget bid be built on reliable data and forecasts of need, but two major problems are often found. Firstly, whilst surveyors well know the properties within their area, there often is a gap between their knowledgeof properties and the recorded data. One needs to ask how are such data captured centrally and compared with other Surveyor's data. Secondly, there is often a gap between the information which is available and the budget bid. How much information collected is virtually unused because a budget bid based on assessed need will be felt to be too large to be given serious consideration at higher management level?

In such circumstances it often becomes the case that there is little correspondence between the budget bid, the amounts allocated to the budget by higher management, and the eventual spending pattern. Therefore, the budget bidding process may often be reduced to a rather mechanical formula, based on a hunch about the amount of money which might eventually be made available and also based on a pot-pourri of previous bids. As has been said(7) undetailed forecasts are in practice useless for systematic examination or the development of rational policies, and are useful in only one very dubious way - that is the support of emotional appeals. In respect of the long-term conservation of built assets it must therefore be a matter for concern if the process by which resources are obtained for maintenance is virtually independent of identified need.

Ideally, the budget-bidding process should seek to reduce uncertainty as for as possible, and to translate identified need into remedial action. There has to be a blend of knowledge of recent historical data on expenditure, recorded experience of the current assessed state of the stock and an assessment of the likely incidence of future, as yet unknown, costs. Inevitably this means that there will be a mixture of planned and unplanned work in any year's programme.

Planned work will include a mix of minor and major jobs, many of which may not be initially precisely identified, except insofar as it has been decided to tackle a particular range of problems over a period of time. Within the specific spending plans there may well be preventive maintenance programmes, particularly in Engineering Services, and for Health and Safety purposes. Many people believe that p.m. is "a good thing", possibly partly because it is planned work, although one must suggest that it be closely monitored to establish that such expenditure in certain elementsof construction actually reduces significant failures below levels which would exist if preventive maintenance were not done.

Unplanned work will always be with us and will, as we have found, include many major maintenance jobs (in our terms over £1000 per job at 1982 prices). Typically, in a County Council's annual spending, nearly sixty percent of maintenance costs are accounted for by less than six percent of the number of jobs, and a large number of these are unplanned work. A major aim of the information system should therefore be to reduce the number of major unplanned jobs, and to bring as much as possible of such work into the category of planned, even if not precisely identified.

Thus the various types of maintenance data need to be disaggregated from the general cost information,and considered in the most effective way for budget bidding purposes.

This might be:-

Minor planned work
Major planned work
Preventive maintenance
Minor unplanned work
Major unplanned work

Additionally of course there will be other work which may, in practice, overlap, but which may not be classed as maintenance, such as:-

Minor capital works and adaptation of the stock, energy conservation, conversion and inprovements.

For convenience we may keep improvement separate from maintenance, but is likely to be the case that much remedial work contains an element of beneficial improvement. Let us however consider just the maintenance headings suggested, bearing in mind that, even if we identify needs, the policy of the building owner will largely determine what goes in to the budget.

Planned work

If we possess a sound database we can decide to deal with planned works by estimation from past records and current knowledge of the condition of the stock. The minor items can be allowed as an average price per type and function of property and the major itmes will have estimated prices allocated to them. Preventive maintenance will be dealt with in a similar manner.

Unplanned work

In the case of unplanned work, minor items will have to be assessed
in the light of experience and, again, can be dealt with on an
average price basis. The major unplanned work in most Authorities is
allowed for on a contingency sum basis, based on budget rather than
assessed need criteria. Ideally this work should be statistically
based on an estimation of the likelihood of failure occurring, with
the aim of reducing the incidence of completely unpredicted
failures. Sums will thus be included in the budget bid which relate
to property file evidence on the stock as a whole.

It is this last concept which will be the most difficult to
manage in practice, although in reality it is only a small step
forward from the usual basis upon which major planned work is
forecast. If the database is adequate and computerised it should be
possible to extract the statistics, to give an indication of the
likelihood of major failures, at least in some of the observable
elements. This might be most useful where detailed inspections are
overdue. Such a process begins to transfer completely unexpected
failures into a framework where performance can be monitored.
Feedback to the design teams can then be enhanced, and even if it is
somewhat post-hoc and limited in scope it will be structured in a
manner which will enable technical staff themselves to be better
informed.

We all know that budget bids will be pruned, drastically in·many
cases, but the importance of attempting to forecast potential failure
within a data-driven structure is that we should begin to identify
more clearly what work has been deferred and how much nearer to
failure it is probably coming.We shall also improve our state of
knowledge about the longer-term costs of deferring forecast work, and
may also be more able to convince others of the economic levels of
spending required to conserve our built assets.

References

1 Monthly digest of Statistics: CSO: HMSO: October 1986
2 Maintenance and renewal in educational buildings: A & B Paper No 7;
1984: DES.
3 Design quality and cost in educational building: Spedding in
Quality & Profit in building design Ed. Brandon: Spon 1984
4 Terotechnology and the maintenance of Local Authority buildings:
LAMSAC 1981
5 A coding system for Building Maintenance: R Homes et al CIOB
Technical Information Service paper No. 47: 1985
6 Maintenance in Schools: A Spedding et al: Bristol Polytechnic:
1983.
7 The art of anticipation: Encel et al: Science Policy Research Unit,
University of Sussex:1975)

BECON - A COMPUTER BASED MAINTENANCE MANAGEMENT SYSTEM

RICHARD TAYLOR, A.R.I.C.S.
Department of Property Services, Lancashire County Council

Abstract

In 1983, the former County Architects and County Estates Departments
of Lancashire County Council were merged to form the current
Department of Property Services (D.P.S.) under the guidance of its
newly appointed Director, Mr. Gordon Brooke. The Director structured
his new Department into three Groups - Design and Development,
Estates, and Building Economics with the latter group being split
into Quantity Surveying and Building Maintenance Divisions. This
paper concentrates on the development and implementation of a comprehensive, computer based, maintenance management system within the
Maintenance Division and, it is hoped, will provide an insight into
tne work involved and the experiences gained from introducing a large
computer system.

Key words: Computerisation, Modules, Consultations, Menu-driven,
Review, Database, Phraseology.

1. Introduction

In 1984, all building maintenance work continued to be administered
through six regional offices using manual based systems that had
evolved over many years to a point where no two offices operated
exactly the same procedures. In preceding years, successive cuts in
local authority Capital building programmes,in line with Government
anti-inflation measures, had reduced the number of buildings being
replaced in a year to single figures, increasing the average age of
the Authority's building stock and producing spiralling maintenance
needs. This increasing maintenance requirement was already beginning
to expose the deficiences and limitations of the manual systems when
it was proposed to transfer to the D.P.S., the responsibility for
handling small value 'day to day' repairs, which at the time rested
with the Service Departments own District Offices. The reasons for
this decision were as follows:-

(i) It was impossible to control expenditure in a meaningful way
with fourteen Service Departments and the D.P.S. all initiating and
charging work to the same funding sources.
(ii) There was clear evidence that the £100 financial limit
applicable to Service Departments was being exceeded and works of

much higher values were being undertaken by the issue of multiple orders, not all of which related to repairs and maintenance but were improvements.

(iii) There was concern that work requiring technical expertise and supervision was occasionally being initiated without reference to the D.P.S. which if allowed to continue, could endanger the health and safety of building occupants.

(iv) The way in which work was being let by staff in establishments tended to favour particular Contractors with limited opportunity to assess Contractors workloads or quality of workmanship.

These facts were the subject of increasing concern and discussion between the Director of Property Services and the County Council's auditors, culminating in the decision to transfer the responsibility for all building maintenance related expenditure to the D.P.S. It was estimated that the 35,000 orders per annum being handled by the D.P.S. regional offices would increase to 80,000 orders as a result of the transfer. Obviously, the existing manual systems would never cope with such an increase but, nevertheless, a date was set - 1 April, 1985 and the search began for a solution to the problem.

2. Systems evaluation and identification

Two points were immediately obvious. Firstly, that the answer must lie in computerisation. Secondly, that whatever form that took, it was likely to require a considerable investment in both resources and money by the Authority, so it was important that the end product should amount to more than just an improved administrative process - Managerial benefits should also be expected.

The first task therefore was to undertake an in depth review of all functions, processes and needs of the Maintenance Division to identify key requirements and, at the same time, to bear in mind the recommendations contained in various Government circulars (e.g. DES Design Note 40 "Maintenance and Renewal of Education Building - Needs and Priorities") and particular heed was also given to the recommendations arising from the Wardale enquiry into the running of the Property Services Agency, namely:

5.3.2. Recommendations

a. All management information should be computerised to ensure that it is maintained in a consistent basis and the inefficiencies of manual recording are avoided.

b. The system needs to be on-line so that users have immediate access to current information.

c. The system must be designed to achieve the objectives of financial control.

d. User manuals and adequate training should be provided to ensure that the optimum benefits are obtained.

We recognise that in an organisation as large as the P.S.A. the introduction of a new management information system will be a complicated process. The implementation of such a system requires

urgent attention, however, in view of the need for improved
management information to achieve the objectives of financial and
budgetary control.

From this review, it was evident that, as a minimum, Lancashire
County Council should establish the following:

(i)   A property database holding details of every property in
which the Authority had an interest.
(ii) Approved lists of contractors for maintenance work and the
means to more effectively monitor performances and workloads.
(iii) Improved methods of budetary control and anaylsis.
(iv) Automation of administration processes (e.g. issue of work
orders and payment of accounts).
(v)   The means by which regional managers could more effectively
monitor and control the performances and workloads of building
surveyors.

Having thus defined our minimum requirements, an intensive search
began to identify an existing system capable of providing these
facilities; there clearly being insufficient time to develop an 'in-
house' system. It soon became apparent, however, that the choice of
building maintenance orientated systems was limited and of those
investigated, none were considered satisfactory. Until, that is, an
article in the 'Chartered Surveyor' (the monthly journal published by
the Royal Institution of Chartered Surveyors) described an innovative
system that had been introduced by Bath City Council to control its
housing maintenance work. Developed jointly, over a three year
period, by Bath City Council and Bristol based surveyors and computer
consultants, South West Systems Ltd., this system appeared to meet
most of the criteria albeit in a housing environment. Subsequent
enquiries were to confirm that, with further development, the system
had the potential to serve the differing work profile of a large
Shire authority. Accordingly, South West Systems Ltd., was invited
to submit proposals and quotations for this further development work
and for the Authority to acquire a licence to operate the system.

3. The Options

Three options were considered:

1. The development and implementation of the system in its
existing BASIC+ language running DEC PDP 11/23 mini-computers.
This was the cheapest option requiring the least work and although
favoured by the Director of Property Services was not acceptable to
the County Treasurer because it contravened the Authority's long-
standing computer policy and commitment to use I.C.L. hardware.
2. The development and implementation of the system on the
Authority's I.C.L. mainframe.
This option was the most expensive involving a total re-write of
the system into COBOL language which South West Systems Ltd estimated
could not be carried out in the time available.

3.   The conversion of the existing BASIC+ software to MBASIC to enable it to run on I.C.L.'s D.R.S. range of hardware.

On time, cost and compatibility, this was the favoured option ultimately recommended to and accepted by the County Council in July, 1984.

4.   System Development

The BECON system, as it was subsequently to be named (derived from Building ECONomics) comprises four modules:

   (i)   Utilities
  (ii)   Day to Day Maintenance
 (iii)   Programmed Maintenance
  (iv)   Reports and Analysis

It was recognised that it would not be possible to fully develop and implement all of the modules before 1 April, 1985, but it was essential that Modules (i) and (ii) should be operational to cope with the small value 'day to day' repairs. In determining how this could be achieved within the timescale two other points had to be borne in mind:

   (i) There was to be no easy option of developing a pilot scheme in parallel with existing systems. The transfer of small value orders to six regional offices dictated a 'Big Bang' approach.

   (ii) Whilst there was no precedent within the D.P.S. for the introduction of new technology on the scale proposed with the BECON system, the consequences of failing to adequately consult staff at all stages of development had been demonstrated in the past by other departments engaged on exercises of this magnitude.

To control development, a BECON Development Group was established comprising senior managers from within the D.P.S., County Treasurer's Data Processing Section and South West Systems Ltd. Chaired by Harry Edwards, Head of Building Economics, the function of the Development Group was to determine policy, monitor progress and resolve any issues raised by the workings of a number of Sub-Groups; namely:

Sub-Group	Brief
(i) Staff Training and Liaison Group	To ensure adequate training was given to staff, ensure staff were consulted and informed of all developments and to contribute to publicity material and committee reports.

Chaired by the Assistant Chief Administration Officer (D.P.S.) this Sub-Group was the principal consultative Group attended by over thirty representatives, both technical and administrative, from central and regional offices.

(ii)	Area Office Implementation Group	To organise the collection of data, rationalise existing working practices and implement alteration works to offices.

This Group comprised the six regional office managers and senior building surveyors based at County Hall under the chairmanship of the author.

(iii)	Accommodation Working Party	To resolve all accommodation issues in regional offices to facilitate the installation of the computer hardware.

Chaired by the Chief Building Surveyor, this Group was responsible for determining revised office layouts and implementing these through the regional managers. Not directly related to the BECON development but very much impacting on its implementation, was the relocation of two outlying regional offices in East Lancashire to a central office in Blackburn during the second and third weeks of March, 1985. It fell to this Sub-Group to co-ordinate these relocations.

(iv)	Contractual and Financial Systems Working Party	To review all existing procedures, coding structures, schemes of dele- gation, contractors lists etc. with particular reference to the BECON system.

Again chaired by the Chief Building Surveyor, this Sub-Group of Senior Officers subsequently produced a 103 page User Procedures Manual for the guidance of all staff.

Amongst the many tasks undertaken by the Sub-Grops were:

(i) The production and circulation of bulletins and newsletters at regular intervals to keep staff informed of developments.
(ii) One hundred and twenty nine staff, at all levels, were trained over a period of thirty five working days and forty six training sessions.
(iii) Twenty two seminars/presentations were held to explain the system to staff in establishments. Ten thousand booklets on the procedures to be observed were also distributed in support of these presentations and as a permanent reference.
(iv) Two thousand contractors were similarly circulated.
(v) The existing accounts procedures and routing of accounts were reviewed and amended.
(vi) Existing coding structures were replaced with simpler versions to improve control and potential analysis of revenue expenditure.
(vii) Office layouts were altered to facilitate the installation of the computer equipment and dedicated telephone systems were installed.
(viii) Manual records on the Authority's 2500 establishments and approved contractors were transferred to computer medium.

All of the above tasks and more had to be co-ordinated and progressed against an ongoing requirement to work closely with the consultants, to provide them with information and decisions to ensure conversion, development and testing of the software was completed in accordance with an agreed detailed workplan.

5. Staffing Review

Very early in the development of the BECON system, a policy decision was taken that the system should be operated mainly by administrative staff within regional offices and that less reliance should be placed on technical officers using the System. A number of factors led to this decision.

   (i)   The System was intended to replace manual functions being performed by administrators who, initially, were concerned about possible redundancies and were anxious to secure involvement in the new development.
   (ii)   One of the attractions of the Bath City council system was that, being menu-driven, it prompted non-technical operators to ask questions of a semi-technical nature, sufficient at least to record details of defects, if not always the action that should be taken to resolve them. Small value day to day repairs were previously administered by non-technical staff without the benefit of such computer support or ready access to technical advice.
   (iii)   It was never intended that the building surveyors already heavily committed on larger maintenance works, should be involved in trivial maintenance repairs other than to maintain an overall watching brief, nor that they should become glorified keyboard operators, although experience has since shown that some keyboard time by technical officers can be cost effective.

Having thus decided to introduce the System with a bias towards the administrative function, there was an urgent need to review the existing job descriptions and gradings of staff to reflect the changing roles and responsibilities. System Supervisors were appointed within each regional office to be responsible for the day to day management of the System and organisation of staff resources. The previously separate duties of accounts clerks, typists and general clerks were merged into the multi-function role of BECON operator. This most radical change in office practise was to meet with some resistance from staff at first as they struggled to learn unfamiliar procedures. It was necessary however for staff to be come skilled in all office activities in order that they might be rotated within the working day and thus share V.D.U. operation time (Neither the Trade Union nor the Employer considered it desirable that individuals should be expected to operate V.D.U.'s throughout the working day). The majority of staff have since expressed a preference for this method of working because the varied work pattern affords greater job satisfaction, staff absences no longer create backlogs in one particular activity and the fact that all tasks, liked and disliked are shared equally, has contributed towards the

54

creation of a greater team spirit.

6. BECON – The first months of operation

Work on the development and implementation of the system continued up to the deadline with the sixth computer being installed on the eve of 1 April, 1985.

After seven months concerted effort all that remained was to see how establishment staff would react to the System and advanced publicity. This was answered in the first week of operation with 2400 requests being received (equivalent to 120,000 requests per annum) a level of demand that was to last almost two months before slowly receding to the current level of 1600 requests per week.

During these initial months of operation, there is no doubt that the regional offices were placed under tremendous pressure because:

(i) Staff were being asked to perform new duties.

(ii) Staff were on a learning curve in operating the system and the time available for training was insufficient to prepare them fully for the 'live' and varied demands of building maintenance.

(iii) Few of the old procedures remained yet it was still necessary to maintain manual records to allow previous years works to be finalised.

(iv) The additional load of day to day repairs was immediate and 50% higher than anticipated.

(v) Traditionally the months of April, May and June are demanding as the previous years acounts have to be reconciled and the current years specifications and tender invitations prepared in readiness for current year programmed work to start in the summer months.

It is to the credit of the staff that they responded as they did during this period (and perhaps management's reward for recognising the value of full consultation with staff from the start of the development).

In order to survive this traumatic period regional resources were supplemented by central office staff, overtime was worked and some temporary clerical support was recruited (11 posts in all).

Disregarding the BECON system, a review of staffing levels within regional offices had not been carried out for many years and it was generally accepted that staff numbers had not kept pace with the increasing maintenance requirement brought about by cutbacks in Capital expenditure.

A review planned for 1984 had been postponed until such time as the BECON system was introduced as it was recognised this would have a major impact on regional offices.

An independent review carried out by the Authority's O & M section in November, 1985, confirmed the need to continue the employment of the eleven clerical assistants but also concluded that without the BECON system a further thirty one staff would have to be employed.

7. The current position

Following the successful launch of the BECON modules (i) and (ii),
budget monitoring facilities were installed in November the same
year. About this time, however, a new initiative was rapidly gaining
support with chief officers and county councillors for the creation
of a comprehensive property database on the Authority's mainframe
computer. In pulling together all property related data from the
many systems within the D.P.S. and other service departments, the
proposed database was seen as an invaluable tool for assisting with
property management and review. The BECON system would obviously
provide a major contribution on the maintenancee element of a
property's life cycle so it was imperative that the system should be
capable of communicating with the mainframe. Following the County
Council's decision to proceed with the design and creation of the
Database, all further development of the BECON system was postponed
to enable the existing software to be converted into COBOL language.
This task was undertaken by the County Treasurer's Data Processing
Section between November, 1985, and March, 1986, during which
conversion, the opportunity was taken to redesign some aspects of the
system in the light of eight months operating experience. At the
time of writing (November, 1986), the Planned Maintenance Module
(iii) and Reports and Analysis Module (iv) are nearing completion and
are scheduled to be implemented in February, 1987.

It is hoped to jointly market the COBOL version of the BECON
system in conjunction with South West Systems Ltd., commencing mid
1987.

8. Systems description

8.1. Hardware
Each regional office is equipped with the following:

1 No I.C.L. DRS 20/150 - 27 Mbt Disk
4 No I.C.L. DRS 20/110 - Satellite Workstations
1 No I.C.L. Microline Dot Matrix Printer

8.2. Software
The system is divided into four main sub-systems:

  (i)   Utilities
  (ii) Day to Day Maintenance
  (iii) Programmed Maintenance
  (iv) Reports and Analysis

(i) Utilities Sub-System
This Sub-system enables details of properties and contractors to be
established and maintained on the system together with the budget
structure and standard phraseology (used to compile work descriptions
in both the Day to Day and Programmed maintenance routines).

56

(ii) Day to Day Maintenance Sub-Systems
Also referred to as the Daywork Routine (to reflect the basis on
which much of this work is carried out), this module is divided into
a number of processes and functions to:

    a. Access a Property/Site/Building record
    b. Record the job description and other relevant information
using standard phraseology.
    c. Action the work record (e.g. Issue a work order, refer it to a
technical officer, take no action etc.)
    d. Select a contractor where the action at (c) was "Issue a work
order".
    e. Record estimated cost and budget information.
    f. Complete the record on receipt of the account.

The sub-system can print work orders to contractors, notification
letters to establishments, summary job and referred job lists to
Building Surveyors/Regional Managers, Property work histories etc.

(iii) Planned Maintenance Sub-System
Also referred to as the Tender Routine (again to reflect the basis on
which much of the planned maintenance work is carried out) this
module is also divided into a number of processes and functions:

    a. Record the job description and other relevant information
using standard phraseology.
    b. Access Properties/Sites/Building records to which the job
description applies.
    c. Input estimated costs and budget information.
    d. Select contractors invited to tender and record key dates.
    e. Record successful tenderer, tender amount, budget information
and contract dates etc.
    f. Record valuations and variations in cost up to final payment.

The sub-system can print detailed job prints and summaries of jobs by
Property, Building Surveyor, Priority, Work Stage etc., Property Work
Histories, Standard letters of invitation, Tender acceptances and
associated internal memoranda.

(iv) Reports and Analysis
This sub-system further divides into:

    a. Budget Reports - showing original budget amount, committed,
actual and residual expenditure for service committees and individual
cost headings e.g. vandalism, asbestos removal etc.
    b. Contractor Analysis - showing the number and value of daywork
orders placed with a contractor in total and by individual building
surveyors, establishment staff, etc. the number of times invited to
tender, response and success rate. The number of outstanding work
orders etc.
    c. Adhoc Analysis - a general analysis facility to answer the
'one-off' question where the user specifies the parameters using a
standard enquiry package.

Part II
Management information
and systems

DATA COLLECTION AS A BASIS FOR EVALUATION OF PERFORMANCE OF HOSPITAL
BUILDINGS IN THE DEVELOPMENT OF MAINTENANCE MANAGEMENT PROCEDURES

GEORGE T. HALL
School of Construction and Building Services, Newcastle upon Tyne
Polytechnic

Abstract
This paper relates to research into aspects of cost comparisons and
the establishment of performance targets for the maintenance of
hospital buildings and the building services contained therein.
    It discusses the relationship between data collection and the
management function in terms of
1. Identifying the nature of the organisation
2. Nature and location of data available
3. Reasons for collecting data
4. The application and analysis of data.
    Specific examples are then provided showing how the various per-
formance characteristics of two hospital buildings can vary depending
upon the method used in presenting the cost data e.g.
1. Volume of building
2. Area of building
3. Total bed allocation
4. Bed availability
5. Bed occupation
6. Building elements
7. Population served
    It will be demonstrated that with regard to the maintenance of
built assets, the identification, collection and application of
suitable data is the keynote to the success of maintenance management.

1. Introduction

For many years people involved in supervising the maintenance of
built assets have rarely been accorded the title managers, this has
been largely due to the cinderella image of the "profession" and its
work. However with the recent changes in society's environmental
requirements these people are now expected to conform to the conven-
tions implicit in the seven main processes of management, namely
1. Planning   2. Programming
3. Forecasting   4. Controlling
5. Organisation   6. Motivation
7. Communications
To satisfy these new requirements the new "maintenance manager" must
have suitable information available to allow a true management role

to be adopted. In all situations it must be remembered that maintenance provides a service and is therefore a back up to allow the main
function of the organisation to be executed to a suitable standard.

This paper:-
1. Identifies the main management functions related to data availability, its collection and application.
2. By specific examples shows the various formats in which data can
be collected and how performance measures can be varied by the presentation of that data.
3. Demonstrates that the identification, collection, analysis and
application of data is the keynote to successful maintenance management.

2. Management Functions

If it is accepted that successful maintenance management requires
suitable data then it is important that essential features, relating
to this data are identified. Consider:-
(i) Identifying the nature of the organisation. This relates to the
formal relationships between the various members of the main management team and reflects their responsibilities.
   It must be the first step as it is within the discussions with
such members that the sources of data will be established and the
format of existing data determined. The various parties must be convinced that the supplying of data will allow the maintenance team to
be effective contributors to the organisations overall objectives and
will assist each section in achieving individual targets.
   This organisation identification will determine the final format
of data which when recirculated will indicate relevant performance
levels of organisation and assets being maintained.
   (ii) Nature and location of data. The existence of data must
be established and its present format determined. This will be
achieved by analysing assets to be maintained, either through the
assets register or as a basis for the formation of such, it will
allow the manager to assess what data is available and the way it is
collected.
   Analysis of the present methods of collection and the data provided will determine whether new methods are required to ensure suitability of data for its application to the maintenance function.
   Decisions will be made as to data collection, will it be by manual
means or automatic retrieval, possibly by computer, and will data in
its raw form be suitable, if not what processing will it require.
   Are existing monitoring schemes providing adequate amounts of
data in suitable forms.
   (iii) Reasons for collecting data. It is essential that reasons
for collecting data are established at the beginning of the process,
what criteria are to be applied, what will be compared with what.
Too much data is collected because it is available, management must
be most stringent in its considerations and only collect data which
can be applied to allow objectives to be met effectively.

In the normal course of events it is performance which is important to the maintenance organisation, data collected must set criteria
and the standards of performance must be measured against these
criteria.

Possible categories for criteria and performance are indicated

(a) Establishment of cost centres within the assets maintained and
identifying those which consume the greatest proportion of resources,
these have the greatest potential for savings and/or improvement.

(b) To allow comparisons to be drawn between performance of
similar elements in different buildings and if possible establish
reasons for higher levels of performance.

(c) To provide a comparison between actual (operating) performance
and design (projected) performance to generate feedback to attempt
to improve maintainability in future asset provision.

(d) It is desirable that the maintenance organisation can measure
its performance against that of similar organisations or contractors.

(iv) Analysis and application of data. It is often the case with
such a process that the initial credibility of the organisation is
established and ultimately through which the success or failure of
the maintenance process is measured.

With modern methods it is possible to collect vast amounts of
generated data, too much data can overload systems and obscure
important factors, too little data can fail to provide pointers which
will lead to identification of the same factors. Raw data will need
to be converted into a form which will allow constructive management
decisions to be made. The adequate analysis of suitable data will
highlight the areas in which management can have the greatest impact
with regards to improving the service provided.

Correct analysis can allow predictive maintenance to be installed
alongside established preventive and corrective systems. Many
computer software packages exist to assist in such processes.

N.B. While data collection is of great importance to the manager
it must, along with all other aspects of maintenance, be cost effective. Systems which are expensive to operate but which produce few
benefits should be avoided, it is for this reason that data should
satisfy operational and managerial processes rather than administrative processes.

3. Examples

Having assessed the management functions relating to the various
aspects of data consideration can now be given to data collection and
its presentation.

Two hospitals are taken to illustrate potential variations in
performance depending upon selected criter relating to the data,
typical performance indicators are adopted.

Hospital 1
Is made up of a considerable number of different properties and is
located in the older residential part of the area it serves, its
foundation stone was laid in 1868. The construction takes many forms
ranging from natural grey sandstone, through brickwork with artifi-

cial stone dressings to reinforced concrete structure clad with sandstone bricks. Medical services of a general nature are provided in
the old dormitory type wards containing up to 30 beds.
TOTAL FLOOR AREA = 81,530 m^2
BUDGET FOR SELECTED YEAR = £411,404

Hospital 2
Is a relatively new purpose built unit of three main buildings located in a more modern residential area, its foundation stone was laid
in 1977. Its construction is to all intents and purposes traditional, consisting mainly of precast and insitu concrete frame with brick
exterior and block interior. Medical services are provided in wards
ranging from single bed to six bed size, the divisions of internal
space being created by lightweight partitioning
TOTAL FLOOR AREA = 62,815 m^2
BUDGET FOR SELECTED YEAR = £329,610.
 For the purpose of this paper Hospital 1 will provide a model
against which Hospital 2 can be compared to demonstrate possible
range of variances in performance standards due to criteria selected.
 COMPARISONS

Hospital 1 — Hospital 2

(i) Volume of buildings - 1000m^3 units
Defined as the total volume of the building considering level of
servicing but not periods or nature of usage.

Hospital 1:
Area = 81580m^2
Ceiling height = 3.5 m
Volume = 285,530 m^3
No. of 1000m^3 units = 285.5
Cost per unit = $\frac{411,404}{285.5}$ = £1441

Hospital 2:
Area = 62,815 m^2
Ceiling height = 2.5 m
Volume = 157,038 m^3
No. of 100 m^3 units = 157
Cost per unit = $\frac{329,610}{157}$ = £2099

(ii) Floor area - 100 m^2 units
Defined as total floor area, no attention to level of servicing or
periods or nature of usage.

Hospital 1:
No. of 100 m^2 units = 815.8
Cost per unit = $\frac{411,404}{815.8}$ = £504.30

Hospital 2:
100 m^2 units = 628
Cost per unit $\frac{329,610}{628}$ = £524.85

(iii) Total bed allocation
Defined as staff allocated beds i.e. the number of beds considered
when determining the staffing complement of the hospital.

Hospital 1:
No. of beds = 901
Cost per bed = £456.61

Hospital 2:
No. of beds = 813
Cost = £405.42

(iv) Area of floor to bed
Total floor area divided by staff allocated beds.

Hospital 1:
Area = $\frac{81,580}{901}$ = 90.5m^2

Hospital 2:
Area = $\frac{62,815}{813}$ = 77.3 m^2

(v) Beds available
Indicates the situation at the hospital in being the number of beds
or bed spaces available to patients if called for

Hospital 1:
Beds available = 871 (assumed)
Cost per bed = £472.34

Hospital 2:
Beds available = 580 (actual)
Cost per bed = £568.30

64

Hospital 1   Hospital 2

(vi) Area per bed
    Area = 93.7 m^2 Area = 108.3 m^2

(vii) Beds occupied
number of beds which actually contain patients at any one time
No. of beds = 845 (assumed)   Beds = 570 (assumed)
Cost per bed = £480.61   Cost = £578.26

(vii) Population served
Both hospitals serve a population of approximately 250,000,
Hospital 2 contains a regional Cardiotheracic unit which gives extra
utility to the value of this hospital costs.
Cost per person = £1.65 per yr.   Cost = £1.32 per year.

(ix) Building elements
The format for this presentation relates to the building elements,
the data can be presented in accordance with any of the above indicators, for this section costs per 100 m^2 is selected and then converted to % values for comparison.

ELEMENT	(Selected Year) CASH	%	Prev.Yr %	(Selected Yr) CASH	%	Prev. Yr %
Ext. Decoration	31.9	5.65	0.46	3.00	0.76	0.85
Int. Decoration	181.34	32.11	26.35	114.65	28.52	25.03
Main Struct.	97.08	17.19	16.97	19.53	4.92	4.27
Int. Construction	28.54	5.06	3.81	28.34	7.14	9.52
Fin. & Fitting	111.59	19.76	22.78	84.22	21.23	23.49
Sanitary Fittings	55.22	9.78	3.24	8.64	2.18	3.68
Ext. Works	16.68	2.96	8.05	8.09	2.04	10.65
Impr. & Adapts.	2.93	0.52	14.75	76.42	19.26	10.25
Overheads	38.51	6.82	3.2	53.83	13.57	12.00
TOTAL		99.85	99.61		99.62	99.74

Further comparisons
As well as comparing different buildings during the same period of
time, it is also desirable to compare the performance of individual
buildings in any one year with their performance in the previous
year. This is now demonstrated.

Hospital 1   Hospital 2
Actual budget for selected year
Budget = £411404   Budget = £329,610
Actual budget for previous year
Budget = £381,620   Budget = £229,273
It will be immediately recognised that a direct comparison cannot be
made between selected year and previous year due to the different
values of the two budget amounts. Assuming interest rate of 10% the
adjusted values of the previous year budgets are as follows:
Adjusted budget = £381,620 x 1.1 Budget = £229,273 x 1.1
                = £419,782   = £252,200

The new values for previous performance indicators are shown to be
(i) Volume of building - 1000 m^3
Cost per 1000 m^3 = £1470   Cost = £1606

(ii) Floor area - 100 m^2
Cost per 100 m^2 = £514.56   Cost = £401.60

(iii) Total bed allocation
No. of beds = 884   No. of beds = 480
Cost per bed = £474.86   Cost = £525.42

(iv) Area of floor to bed
Area = 92.29 m^2 Area = 130.87 m^2

(v) Beds available
No. of beds = 854 (assumed)   Beds = 450 (assumed)
Cost per bed = £491.55   Cost = £560.44

(vi) Area per bed
Area = 95.52 m^2 Area = 139.59 m^2

(vii) Bed occupied
No. of beds = 838 (assumed)   No. of beds = 450 (assumed
Cost per bed = £500.93   Cost = £560.44

(vii) Population served
Cost per person £1.68 per yr.   Cost = £1.01 per year.

(ix) Building elements
This has already been demonstrated in the previous section related
to elemental performance.

3. Importance of Data

When assessing the importance of information to the maintenance manager
consideration must be given to conditions within which the management
process is executed. Consider:
    (i) All of the constraints which apply to the organisation and
execution of the maintenance work already exist, they have been

created by another body (designer) who has had to meet criteria which are frequently different from those applying to the maintenance manager.

(ii) There are many situations existing where the assets being maintained were designed and installed, or erected, when the execution of maintenance work did not warrant any great priority with the client.

(iii) Maintenance previously executed can have considerable bearing upon the future maintenance requirements and subsequent performance of assets within the organisations control.

(iv) In certain situations, contractors involved in the provision of the assets make decisions and carry out work to:-
(a) overcome problems unforreseen at the design stage
(b) conform with the clients changed requirements
(c) make installation more speedy and maybe cheaper for increased profits,such options, when applied, can invalidate original design decisions relating to maintenance and its objectives.

(v) The need to respond quickly in the case of emergencies to exercise control or carry out work to minimize potential damage caused by a malfunction, is an essential requirement.

(vi) The performance of the assets being maintained must be established to allow comparisons to be made with similar elements to establish success of design.

(vii) The performance of the maintenance organisation must be established to provide a yardstick against which future effectiveness can be measured.

(viii) The formation of accurate budgets is essential with regards to providing adequate levels of funds for work to be executed and to allow satisfactory control procedures to be adopted to ensure adequate all year performance.

(ix) A sufficient case needs to be prepared to allow sound arguments to be put forward if and when cuts in budget are in the offing. Sound financial reasoning provides the best defence against cuts in resources.

(x) Manufacturers recommendations must be adhered to at all times to allow guarantees and warrantees to be utilized to their fullest extent and therefore minimize maintenance costs to the organisation.

4. Conclusions

It is noted that the previous considerations depend totally upon the provision of suitable, recorded information. Built assets are now too varied and complex in their construction,assembly and operation for information not to be collected and stored for use. Such data must be in a suitable form, technical enough to be used in understanding the "working" of the asset but simple enough to interpret and apply to allow for suitable diagnosis and repair of malfunctions encountered. Useful information in the correct quantity will encourage its application, both operatives and managers will appreciate the reason for its collection, analysis and application, usually a better service. The application of maintenance to any asset must be optimised in terms of reducing resources consumed while improving the effectiveness and efficiency of that asset, if necessary by taking opportunities to introduce improved technology. Lack of information relegates any process to the level of crisis management, this does nothing to create an environment within which essential work, maintenance, can be executed. Accurate data at the right time will allow the seven processes of management to be adopted with the resulting improvements in the decisions made.

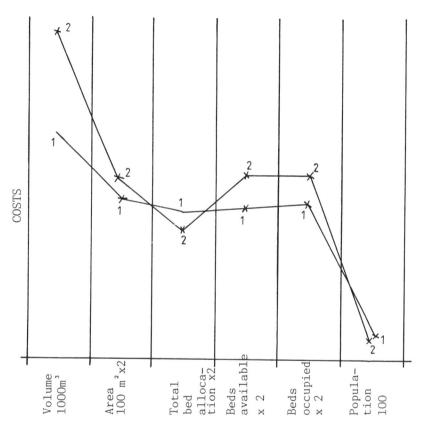

Fig.1 demonstrates the relationship between the various performance indicators illustrated earlier in the paper, the implications of the various interpretations will be readily understood. The mainten- ance manager in any organisation, however, could be expected to present performance data in varied forms to satisfy internal account- ing and external accountability processes. External bodies must be well informed as to the possible problems created by comparing raw data in isolation, e.g. comparing costs per bed, as against floor area in units of 100 m^2. Good information will establish the true worth of the maintenance organisation while its analysis and application will ensure continued appreciation of the service pro- vided.

My thanks go to the Northern Regional Health Authority and the Newcastle Area Health Authority for their permission to reproduce the information presented.

THE EFFECTIVENESS OF SMALL MAINTENANCE MANAGEMENT ORGANISATIONS

R.D. HODGKINSON
Department of Surveying, Liverpool Polytechnic

Abstract
The paper focuses on the human resources side of maintenance management. It describes research based on an analysis of the maintenace
management sections of a major commercial organisation which was
concerned with increasing the effectiveness of the sections and in
particular the efficiency of the maintenance surveyors. Models of
organisation effectiveness are described, based on organisation
structure and management style. The extent to which they can be used
as diagnostic instruments is discussed, and the modification necessary to use them for small organisations is described. The results
which emerge are analysed and found to be of value in revealing what
changes should be made. Of the models, management style is seen to
provide more information of immediate value, and the organisation
structure model found to provide a useful basis for organisation
design.
Key words: Maintenance management, Human resources, Organisation
effectiveness.

1. Introduction

The paper focuses on a study of the maintenance management division
of a large commercial company seeking to maintain a large estate of
buildings. It was organised into two sections, geographically dis-
persed, with surveyors in one section carrying out a significant proportion of their work using term contracting. The aim of the study
was to compare the effectiveness of each section and to make recommendations.

In seeking to improve effectiveness, maintenance managers typically
place their greatest emphasis on the management of financial resources
to control the standard of the physical asset. Underlying this, is
the implicit assumption that the greatest opportunities for increasing effectiveness lie in this direction. There is, however, one
other resource, the surveyors and support staff managing maintenance,
who are frequently neglected.

Likert (1973), indicates that probably the greatest incremental
opportunity for increasing efficiency often lies in adopting a positive response to improving human resources management. Potential
benefits of the order of 20-40% can be achieved by a concerted effort
from management in this direction.

71

What is needed, however, is some method of speedy preliminary diagnosis of the existing state of the health of the organisation. The
objectives of this paper are as follows:
    (a) To demonstrate that the models developed by Lansley (1974),
can be used as a diagnostic instrument for the comparison of the
organisation effectiveness of two relatively small sections of the
division of a company engaged in maintenance management.
    (b) To measure the differences between the sections in terms of
organisation structure and management style.
    (c) To interpret the results in the context of the prevailing
company climate.

2. Theoretical Background

Lansley derived two models, one emphasising the structural differences
between organisations, focusing on the control system and degree of
integration achieved. The other, on management style based on the
work of Blake and Mouton (1964), delineating four styles of management.
The structural model (Fig.1) reflects four types of organisation:

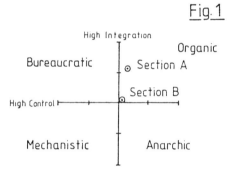

Fig.1

    (a) Bureaucratic. Personified by staff activity being prescri-
bed by rules, procedures and written instructions. At the same time
the structure is defined by a high level of integration, achieved by
the use of effective communication of overall tasks and the creation
of a sense of purpose by leaders.
    (b) Mechanistic. This is typically described by emphasis on
close control of staff activity, but lacks integration, with each sub-
unit pursuing its own objectives and failing to relate these to the
overall objectives of the main unit.
    (c) Organic. A structure with some of the features of the Bureau-
cratic structure, in terms of the level of integration. Except that
the latter is achieved by freer communication, laterally, and diagon-
ally through the organisation. It also has much lower level of control, with self-motivated staff providing the impetus, rather than
being regulated by rules and procedures.
    (d) Anarchic. This is personified by staff with considerable
freedom to pursue their own narrow goals and determine their own
activities.

The styles delineated in Fig.2, reflect four orientations:

(a) High task and low people. Personnel are viewed in a similar light as other resources available to management, to be used in a rational and economic manner.

(b) High task and high people. This implies a concern for achievement through subordinate involvement and teamwork.

(c) Low task and high people. This defines the style which encourages people to keep happy, with the hope that the results will take care of themselves.

(d) Low task and low people. Defines the situation where management is passive and neither emphasises task or people relationships.

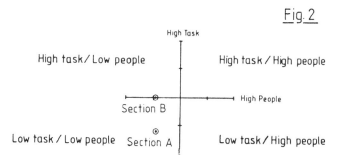

Fig. 2

3. Method

Data was obtained from each member of staff using structured questionnaires and supported by in-depth semi-structured interviews. From the variables identified in the questionnaires, data was collected and grouped according to measures of the interviewees' perception of aspects of organisation structure and style of management, level of satisfaction with their job and company, effectiveness of communication and finally the way in which the division had managed organisational change. Further data was collected with respect to respondents' perception of their and other peoples' position on the organisation chart.

4. Method of Analysis

The two sections of the division were classified according to structure and style. The control dimension for structure differed from that used by Lansley and was modified to facilitate its use for small organisations. A measure based on an analysis of the hierarchy of authority was substituted, derived from the worth of Samuel and Mannheim (1970), known as the index value of control intensity. Its value allowed the definition of control in an organisation, with compensation for its size and complexity. The scaling of the new control dimension of the organisation structure model was set by computing the theoretical maximum and minimum value for the index.

5. Results and analysis

5.1 Organisation structure

ORGANISATION STRUCTURE FACTORS   Table 1

	Effective lateral communication	Effective formal communication	Index value of control intensity × 1000	Structure category
Section A	40	53	480	organic
Section B	21	79	430	organic

Both sections achieved above average scores for integration,(Table 1) (measured by reference to the level of effective formal communication), and below average for index of control intensity, causing them to be located in the ORGANIC sector of the structure model (Fig.1). This result was suprising in view of the budgetary control procedures and systems used as a necessary element to task performance. On reflec- tion, it was felt that the result pointed towards a deficiency in the methods and means of communicating information within each section, with a need to strengthen control in this area, compatible with the needs of the task. A modification to the organisation structure, suggested as a response to an analysis of measures of human perfor- mance, required that a specialist role be created for a development surveyor and a deputy appointed, responsible to the section surveyor. Analysis of this change to the organisation, maintaining the existing level of integration, moved the structure towards a slightly higher degree of control, into the BUREAUCRATIC segment. This realignment was felt to be more compatible with the needs of the task. The above demonstrated the utility of the model for organisation development.

5.2 Human performance and management style
An examination of Table 2 columns 1 and 2 reveals the differences in scores for job and company satisfaction between each section with company satisfaction being below average in Section B, and job satis- faction below the norm in Section A. We suspect that this reversal had something to do with the fact that Section B was isolated geo- graphically from the main firm and Section A located with the parent organisation

The scores for effectiveness of communication channels (Table 2, columns 5-8) revealed that staff in both sections experienced a great deal of difficulty in obtaining sufficient information to carry out their job effectively. This was a major indicator that the systems and procedures in operation were being used ineffectively, and were not providing enough quality information to staff. Coupled with this, column 8 of Table 2 indicated the lack of willingness of superiors to listen to staff ideas for improved effectiveness, which was at a particularly low level for Section A. The high score for level of clarity of instructions registered for Section A in column 7 of Table 2,

74

HUMAN PERFORMANCE MEASURES

Table 2

	Satisfaction measures		Effectiveness of org. change		Effectiveness of communication channel			
	Job satis. (1)	Comp. satis. (2)	Improved organisation effectiveness (3)	Improved work atmosphere (4)	In picture (5)	Job information (6)	Few conflicting instructions (7)	Willingness to listen (8)
Section A	40	50	40	0	60	20	100	20
Section B	66	38	14	0	38	25	50	50

MANAGEMENT STYLE FACTORS

Table 3

	People orientation		Task orientation		Managing style	External priority	Internal priority
	Perceived style	Morale priority	Willingness listen	Diversion priority			
Section A	27·5	1	20	47	Low people Low task	13	33
Section B	26·25	10	50	5	Low people Low task	14	71

was further reinforced by staff feeling that they were better informed about what was happening in the division, compared with the much lower scores of Section B. (column 5).

The effectiveness with which each section could accommodate organisational changes is revealed in Table 2 columns 3 and 4. Staff in both sections concurred that changes had led to a deterioration of working atmosphere and further, that the changes had led to a decline in effectiveness.

Table 3, shows the factors contributing to the diagnosis of management style. Task orientation is delineated by scores of the extent to which superiors are willing to listen to ideas, to make the section more efficient. It is reinforced by the score for diversionary priority. The latter being reflected by such factors as competing with other departments/sections for more resources and fighting for positions of power. People orientation is prescribed by the staffs' perception of the centralisation or decentralisation of decision making and reinforced by morale priorities,such as considerding the welfare of employees and creating a good working atmosphere in each section

Further factors which strengthen or weaken people and task orientation, include the scores for external and internal priority. The
latter being concerned with staffs' perception of the emphasis placed
by superiors on internal efficiency and the former, with building
up of the company's reputation.

Figure 2 illustrates the model of management style, with both
sections being located in the low people segment, a passive response
to style of management. Management literature, underlines the link
between style and effectiveness, with a high task/high people orientation being recommended.

5.2 Implications of the Results

The key measures of morale, job and company satisfaction, emphasise
the need to provide stimulus by way of changes to the organisation
structure, such that a clearly defined career structure is delineated
and in this particular case, attention paid to salary levels. Experience indicates that these areas can provide a powerful stimulus to
motivation, together with enhanced committment and job effectiveness.
In further attempts to restore status and morale an enhanced staff
training and development policy was also recommended.

There appears to be a direct linkage between ease or difficulty
of obtaining information to carry out the job, with the job satisfaction. Applying this to the circumstances of each section, it is evident that there is a need for reducing complexity by greater attention being paid to standardisation and simplification of procedures
and documentation.

In the context of the organisation it was apparent that a redesign
of the organisation was necessary, to take some of the pressure away
from senior staff. It was hoped that this would provide them with
more time for listening to ideas generated by staff for increased
efficiency, and for changing their management style, towards a more
democratic approach.

An examination of the scores in columns 3 and 4 of Table 2, reveals
the negative impact of previous organisational changes. This points
to the importance of staff from both sections being consulted prior
to effecting changes. It emphasises an approach where everyone is
kept well informed and is consulted before changes are made.

6. Conclusions

The models described provide a rapid method of diagnosis of the
health of the organisation. They provide pointers to those areas
warranting further attention and more rigorous investigation. They
have the capacity of gathering relatively objective information about
the 'softer' areas of the organisation namely, human resources.
Examining each model and associated performance factors, it was found
that the human performance measures yielded the greatest benefit.
The structural measures were helpful however, for organisational re-
design and the tentative assessment of the implications of different
degrees of restructuring. Nevertheless, it must always be recognised
that there is no one best way to organise a business. The model
of structure provides guidance, and a means of monitoring structural
changes.

Effective communication was highlighted as a key factor in affecting the level of organisation performance, as was task uncertainty. However, the latter is difficult to quantify for a given situation. The adage that higher task uncertainty should be compensated by higher degrees of integration in the firm, holds good, but any moves towards organisation redesign should always be tempered by detailed knowledge and experience.

References

Blake, R.R. and Mouton, J.S. (1964) The Managerial Grid Gulf, Houston, Texas

Lansley, P., Sadler, P. and Webb, T. (1974) Organisation Structure Management Style and Company Performance. Omega 2, 4.

Likert, R. (1973) Human Resource Accounting : Building and assessing productive organisations. Personnel, May, June, pp.8-26

Samuel, Y. and Mannheim, B.F. (1970) a Multidimensional Approach Toward a Typology of Bureaucracy. Administrative Science Quarterly, 15, 216-229

MAINTENANCE AUDIT

J.D.M. ROBERTSON
The Surveyors Collaborative, Chartered Quantity Surveyors

Abstract
The principle objectives of 'maintenance audit' are, bearing in mind
the objectives of the organisation, to show whether or not value for
money is being achieved by building maintenance and to identify areas
where different systems or approach could be improved. There are
three broad areas where the audit approach is applied - technical,
managerial and design. Three broad questions are addressed: How much
has been achieved? How good was it? How much did it cost?
Key words: Costs, Performance, Condition Appraisal, Value, Budgeting,
Information, Management.

1. Introduction

Maintenance audit in practice, as its name implies, is challenging
but if dealt with sensibly will provoke constructive action, and
above all seek to make improvements which will benefit the condition
of an organisation's property assets.

In accounting, the principal object of an audit is to ensure that
the accounts on which the auditor is reporting, 'show a true and fair
view of the state of affairs at a given date and of the results for
the period ended on that date'. Audit is part of management control
which ensures that resources are obtained and used effectively,
efficiently and economically and that the organisation's objectives
are accomplished. Just like the accountant's traditional audit, an
essential feature of the maintenance audit is that it evaluates the
system of internal control in order to ascertain whether it is appropriate and to test whether it is being operated correctly.

Internal audit is an everyday part of good accountancy practice
and most organisations also have a management review section. External audit is increasingly significant, no longer limited to an audit
of accounts but now in pursuit of value for money. In particular,
the Audit Commission has made a marked contribution in local government and in 1986 published two reports specifically dealing with
building maintenance. Ideally, maintenance management would wish to
have an internal audit system supplemented from time to time by an
independent review which would act as a catalyst for change.

2. Understanding Maintenance and its Pressures

Any maintenance audit has to understand the problems of building maintenance and three aspects always need to be addressed - life expectancy, expenditure and standards.

Buildings are designed to serve a community for many years and it follows that running costs cannot be considered in the short term. Nevertheless, annual budgets dominate. Communications between finance departments and maintenance management seldom seem to give each other the information they want. Property management has little documented evidence of past performance, yet budgets are set as often as not on last year's spend. Nor is it common to have detailed estimates prepared on current and future maintenance requirements. On the other hand, there is only token acknowledgment that finance departments see building maintenance as an important part of asset management or of providing an integral part of the organisation's operations.

Maintenance management has to face up to maintenance's rate of inflation which, according to the Building Maintenance Cost Information Service (BMCIS) General Maintenance Index, was 3.9% in the twelve month period ending 1986 and 27.3% over the past five years. It has further had to defend its position against the ravages of other spending departments wishing to eat into the maintenance budget to alleviate the pressures of their own inflation and growth. There is little doubt that the pressures on revenue budgets have increased considerably. In addition, decisions on capital expenditure, none more so than new building work, have to take into account revenue implications much more carefully than they once did. More detailed questions are, therefore, being asked of maintenance management and without an information system its ability to answer, without detailed researches, is somewhat limited. It is not surprising, therefore, that over the past few years there has been much more careful consideration given to maintenance management control so that maintenance managers cannot be accused of failing to give advice on any risks that are being run.

Finding a basis of comparison of maintenance performance, far less standards or norms, is fraught with difficulties. Judging performance in all business is complicated because results are affected by complex factors, the net influence of which can vary from one job to the next: appraising maintenance performance is no different. The phrase 'standard of maintenance' has always produced long debates and 'locally acceptable standard' is open to many interpretations.

In large organisations, government departments and local authorities there are standard management control procedures. It is possible for them to collect performance data from area offices or the like in an attempt to assess performance. Intra-firm comparisons help motivate departmental heads and in smaller organisations year-in-year-out performance information can also present useful targets. Inter-firm comparisons and exchanges of data amongst different organisations also help to produce norms against which measures of maintenance performance can be appraised.

The maintenance audit team should review the management control system itself. Some organisations have unnecessarily complicated and verbose systems which would benefit from a periodical overhaul to ascertain whether proposed new reports were likely to be worth the cost of preparing them and whether existing reports continue to fill a real need. Indeed, the introduction of maintenance audit procedures might be able to reduce the hierarchy of reports which central control demands from its so called delegated areas.

The fact is there is no single measurement of performance in building maintenance but a whole series of questions and answers which have to be appraised. Judgements about performance have to be based on an imperfect standard which only time and experience will adequately determine.

3. Three Broad Areas, Three Broad Questions

There are three broad areas where the maintenance audit approach will help management achieve value for money from properties-in-use. The technical audit examines the condition of the estate, appropriateness of technical decisions, standards of maintenance work and quality of diagnosis. The management audit studies maintenance policies, control systems, information flows, budget procedures and advice given to corporate management. The third is the design audit where the lessons of occupying a building can make a positive contribution at the drawing board for new schemes.

Questions have to be answered which will show:
How much has been achieved?
How good was it?
How much did it cost?

4. The Technical Audit

4.1 Condition Appraisal
Condition appraisal is used on the occasions when a technical assessment of an organisation's property is required, often involving an overview of the whole estate. Individual surveys are unavoidable if the buildings are unique or dissimilar or where very detailed records have been requested. On more homogeneous estates e.g. housing, a sampling approach can be adopted. First, a representative sample of buildings would be selected. A check list of items would be drawn up, preferably based on a small detailed survey of typical buildings and coupled to it would be a points system for assessing maintenance requirements from zero, through minor repairs to complete renewal. An estimating system is devised to calculate probable expenditure. The report will identify the size of the mountain of maintenance that will need to be dealt with over a period of years and will in some detail identify technical maintenance requirements, in particular buildings, at a suggested timescale and for an order of cost. In some respects the condition appraisal is a 'political' document which tells management in no uncertain terms that they are facing a maintenance problem which will not be solved by the current level of maintenance expenditure. Often it leads to work being done to estab-

lish a more realistic budget for maintenance, although not necessarily one which will cope with the identified backlog. More credence is given to condition appraisals and budget reviews when comparative cost data can be supplied from other organisations.

4.2 Energy Audit

The Energy Audit is well promoted by the Department of Energy. Fuel efficiency is now an important international concern and its use during the life of properties needs to be controlled. The starting point is a simple report on energy used in each financial year. To discover whether energy is being used efficiently or wastefully requires detailed analysis, involving individual measurement of main items so that, for instance, electricity could be broken down into lighting, air treatment, space heating, hot water.

4.3 Operational Assessment

The Operational Assessment studies the output of the maintenance department - the quantity and quality of the work that is done. The technical audit examines procedures and will look at a sample of maintenance items to see how management has tackled its tasks. The following questions will help cover the subject:

o Was the job a priority item?
o Was the right maintenance standard set and was it achieved?
o Was the diagnosis correct and the method of dealing with it technically sound?
o Would it have been cheaper in the long run to replace than to repair?
o How long after reporting was the failure dealt with?
o Would it have been better to use a local contractor, direct labour or a term contract?
o Was the repair work satisfactory?

5. The Management Audit

In its search for the best value for money, the maintenance audit team would also examine management, its policies, its planning and its procedures. The management audit would seek answers to questions which would include some of the following:

o Has the organisation committed to paper a definitive maintenance policy? Is there a maintenance control plan?
o Does the plan identify preventive maintenance, corrective maintenance and emergency maintenance?
o Does it try to minimise corrective maintenance and emergency maintenance?
o Does it try to minimise corrective maintenance by increasing preventive maintenance; failing this, is planned maintenance replacing emergency maintenance?
o How does the control system monitor whether asset protection has been achieved with minimal breakdowns and acceptable maintenance costs?

o Is the internal feedback system good enough to indicate achievements, problems, defects, changes to the planned maintenance programme?
o Are costs sub-divided in a way that assist maintenance planning?
o Are planned activities and achievements fed back for performance appraisal?
o Does the maintenance department influence designs or specifications for new building works?
o Are defects logged or technical feedback analysed so that modifications can be made to design or maintenance programmes?
o Are maintenance budgets prepared on technical requirements or last year's budget?
o Is the motivation of the maintenance department in line with the organisation's objectives?
o Does maintenance management meet with the finance department at that critical period three months before the end of the financial year?
o Is there a method for establishing a manpower budget?
o How are overheads on DEL dealt with?
o Are maintenance manuals being prepared on new buildings?
o Is there a budget for research and development?
o Does the material stores inventory show what stock should be kept?
o How do you advise the managing director that cuts are not savings?

6. The Design Audit

Now that the maintenance management organisation has stood up to its own rigorous examination it can feel amply justified and capable of making a valuable contribution to the design process of new buildings. So often maintenance professionals complain about the expensive problems which they have inherited and there are too often good grounds for this. They, or their maintenance audit consultants, should be given responsibility for making a positive input at the drawing board for new schemes. The Department of Health in their Circular HN (80) 29 deals with the relationship between planning health buildings and the cost of running them. The NHS Circular lists the following example questions:

o Does the engineering design solution allow for easy access to plant and equipment which needs frequent attention and easy replacement of items whose life is relatively short?
o Is there a proper balance between buying cheap plant and equipment which needs to be replaced fairly frequently and more expensive items which will last longer and may need major overhauls periodically?
o Have sufficient guardrails and knocking plates been provided to prevent damage to walls and doors from vehicles?
o Have the relations been considered between the finishes it is proposed to specify and the cost of their maintenance, cleaning, repair and replacement? Have the various choices been considered, e.g. carpeting suitable areas?

o Have the advantages of maintenance-free metalwork over cheaper
   softwoods, which require a relatively high degree of maintenance,
   e.g. for windows, been evaluated?
o If flat roofs are to be used (and experience suggests that they
   should not), are the reasons for preferring them to pitched roofs
   sufficient to justify the much heavier costs of maintaining and
   renewing them?
o To what extent have the comparative costs of different standards
   of materials, their comparative lives and replacement costs, e.g.
   pipework, electrical cables, etc. been assessed?
o Have control systems been simplified to the maximum extent consistent with operational requirements and ease of maintenance? Has
   consideration been given to the relative claims of automatic
   regulation with its need for skilled adjustment and periodic maintenance and manual control under the hand of the users?
o Have the maintenance costs of the constructional materials been
   considered? Will their choice influence future flexibility in
   use?

7. Scope for Maintenance Audits

At the University of Bath in the late 1960's a number of detailed
studies were done by a surveyor, an accountant and an organisation
consultant. Although not rejoicing in the name at that time, here
was the ideal maintenance audit team.

The chartered surveyor prepared a technical assessment of the
buildings; the accountant examined the paperwork routines and the
financial accounting used in the maintenance management control
systems; the organisations expert looked at the hierarchy and staff
dispositions. Here was the scope of the maintenance audit. These
studies did not, however, have as part of their brief a crucial
aspect of the terms of reference of a maintenance audit, namely,
recommendations. The reports revealed many aspects of maintenance
management which demanded closer scrutiny with each organisation
throwing up different problems. Similarly, the work of Peter Brigham
into paperwork routines shows the wide variety of control systems
which exist. All these studies were published by the Building Maintenance Cost Information Service.

All aspects of a maintenance audit may not be required at the same
time. Where maintenance audits have been undertaken it is interesting to see why the studies were initiated.

One of the first was undertaken for the Bath Corporation into its
housing stock where a sample of houses and flats were surveyed, rated
and the cost of repairing shortfall maintenance estimated. This was
done in 1975 and the housing manager wanted to know the problems of
the estate he had inherited following local government
reorganisation.

A new head of department found that building maintenance policies
were ill-defined and different systems were being preserved in
various regional offices and he needed an independent review and
recommendations. A government department some years ago wanted to
compare its maintenance standards, expenditure and procedures with

similar buildings in the private sector.

A recently formed property department of a large corporation needed an independent maintenance audit to fend off the challenges of the finance department and quench accusations of empire building.

Many District Health Authorities have commissioned Condition Appraisals and some have sought outside help in getting realistic budgets to cope with maintenance backlog.

8. Conclusion

Sadly, what is common to all of these studies and no doubt would be true in most maintenance organisations is the paucity of maintenance management information. Few had a definitive maintenance policy, less had prescribed procedures and cost records were not very useful for management decisions. This leads to the suggestion for a first step towards an internal maintenance audit. Table 1, a model Property Occupancy Analysis Form contains the information which maintenance management should be able to complete without too much difficulty. It is based on the BMCIS "Standard Form of Property Occupancy Cost Analysis". If maintenance management can complete the data in the same level of detail as the example, they will get a very good idea of what their maintenance organisation is like.

References

The Audit Commission for Local Authorities (November 1986) Improving Council House Maintenance, H.M.S.O.

The Audit Commission for Local Authorities (March 1986) Managing the Crisis in Council Housing, H.M.S.O.

Building Maintenance Cost Information Service BMCIS Occasional Papers, Case Studies, BMCIS.

Brigham, P. (1978) Examples of Paperwork Routines Used in Building Maintenance Management, BMCIS.

Building Maintenance Cost Information Service (February 1984) Standard Form of Property Occupancy Cost Analysis - Principles, Instructions, Definitions and Elements, BMCIS.

Table 1 - A Completed Model Property Occupancy Analysis Form

OFFICES	CI/SfB 32
Building function: Administrative headquarters Location: North-east England urban area	Owner/Occupier: University Date of erection: 18th & 19th centuries

UPPER MANAGEMENT CRITERIA AND BUDGET PROCEDURE

Maintain building in its state within the limits of the budget allocated by the Finance Committee.

Overall annual budget estimate is prepared for all university buildings and grounds, split into 1 - elemental heads, 2a - wages and salaries, 2b - materials and contracting services. The maintenance estimate is considered along with other departmental recurrent estimates and adjusted according to allocations. Budget control is the responsibility of the maintenance officer who reviews expenditure monthly.

MAINTENANCE MANAGEMENT AND OPERATION

The maintenance officer is responsible for the maintenance of all buildings and grounds assisted by the supervisory staff (electrical, mechanical, buildings and grounds), office manager, secretary and three clerks.

Total estate comprises 90.2 hectares including several small sites away from the main campus; 134,319 m² floor area teaching and residentail accommodation. Routine inspections: regular visits made by supervisors. Maintenance implemented by PPM process and requisitions raised by heads of departments and others. Painting frequencies: 5 year cycle externally; 3 and 6 years internally depending on designated use.

Cost records and feedback: individual jobs are cost coded according to 1 - building, 2 - element subdivided between a - DEL, b - contract, c - PPM.

Work done by DEL 55% and contracted out 45%. Directly-employed labour establishment is 58 in total including 6 chargehands.

Contracted-out work is on a daywork basis, larger contracts use university form or JCT contract.

BUILDING FUNCTION AND PARAMETERS

90% office space, 10% staff facilities. 80 occupants. Design criteria: maximum office and boardroom use within given parameters. Change of use: residential accommodation converted for administration and ancillary services.

Gross floor area: 3905 m²

Area of pitched roofs (on plan): 1500 m²

Area of flat roofs (on plan): 400 m²

Area of external glazing: 315 m²

Storeys above (and including) ground floor: 3 No.
Floors below ground floor: 1 No. semi-basement
Floor to ceiling height: maximum 3.50 m
                         minimum 2.30 m

FORM OF CONSTRUCTION

Structure: Traditional construction. Brick external walls, cavity and solid of various thicknesses. Painted wood and metal windows, sash and casement, some leaded lights. Mainly clay roof tiles on pitched roof with small areas of lead and asphalt flat roofs. Brick and block internal partitions and timber framed construction. Timber floor joists and boards except semi-basement in concrete.

Finishings and fittings: Wood strip flooring, lino tiles, carpet, pvc and quarry tiles. Hardwood counter and softwood painted cupboards and shelves.

Decoration: Internally - walls and ceilings mostly emulsion, metal and wood gloss painted. Externally - gloss to wood and metal, aluminium and lead no paint.

Services: Copper water services, pvc wastes, saltglazed drains. Oil-fired boiler, low pressure hot water, radiators and fan-assisted warm air heaters 18-21°C. Keighly 5 cwt. kitchen electro hydraulic goods lift serving two floors. Cold stores, kitchen equipment, ventilation system in one room, water softener, fountain pump.

Table 1 (contd)

FINANCIAL STATEMENT: COST PER 100 m^2 FLOOR AREA   Gross floor area: 3905 m^2

Element	1978/79	1979/80	1980/81	1981/82	1982/83
0. Improvements & adaptations	£ 13.78	£ 91.22	£ 170.01	£ -	£ 170.19
1. Decoration					
1.1 External decoration	-	0.10	69.55	0.13	2.43
1.2 Internal decoration	109.58	18.21	8.22	10.24	47.35
Sub-total	£ 109.58	£ 18.31	£ 77.77	£ 10.37	£ 49.78
2. Fabric					
2.1 External walls	14.21	3.99	10.96	12.52	10.22
2.2 Roofs	31.16	89.12	21.25	68.60	101.07
2.3 Other structural items	34.19	6.76	14.49	15.19	29.68
2.4 Fittings & fixtures	7.12	14.24	9.44	21.18	13.91
2.5 Internal finishes	28.53	23.92	15.25	19.13	54.19
Sub-total	£ 115.21	£ 138.03	£ 71.39	£ 136.62	£ 209.07
3. Services					
3.1 Plumbing & internal drainage	2.53	6.58	4.84	5.28	4.76
3.2 Heating & ventilating	24.23	21.92	31.81	23.97	39.82
3.3 Lifts & escalators	-	-	-	-	-
3.4 Electric power & lighting	21.18	15.31	14.83	24.38	35.77
3.5 Other M & E services	17.80	70.88	33.62	34.39	47.68
Sub-total	£ 65.74	£ 114.69	£ 85.10	£ 88.02	£ 128.03
4. Cleaning					
4.1 Windows	5.04	5.27	8.22	7.50)	
4.2 External surfaces	-	-	-	-)	9.45
4.3 Internal	231.40	246.79	254.62	292.88	290.58
Sub-total	£ 236.44	£ 252.06	£ 262.84	£ 300.38	£ 300.03
5. Utilities					
5.1 Gas	0.15	-	-	-	-
5.2 Electricity	197.75	226.79	244.69	281.10	331.40
5.3 Fuel oil	335.06	477.87	502.07	462.61	423.17
5.4 Solid fuel	-	-	-	-	-
5.5 Water rates	25.71	27.94	34.72	37.67	33.14
5.6 Effluents & drainage charges	-	-	-	-	-
Sub-total	£ 558.67	£ 732.60	£ 781.48	£ 781.38	£ 787.71
6. Administrative costs					
6.1 Services attendants	-	-	-	-	-
6.2 Laundry	12.91	9.83	10.32	20.05	13.65
6.3 Porterage	)	)	)	)	)
6.4 Security	) 714.70	) 852.34	) 185.22	) 199.46	) 193.24
6.5 Rubbish disposal	)	)	)	)	)
6.6 Property management	85.40	93.83	117.44	120.49	129.99
Sub-total	£ 813.01	£ 956.00	£ 312.98	£ 340.00	£ 336.88
7. Overheads					
7.1 Property insurance	39.61	44.61	52.65	60.85	58.75
7.2 Rates	256.98	289.14	349.71	369.27	405.81
Sub-total	£ 296.59	£ 333.75	£ 402.36	£ 430.12	£ 464.56
T O TA L	£2195.24	£2545.44	£1993.92	£2086.89	£2276.06

MAINTENANCE MANAGEMENT IN SCHOOL BUILDINGS.

ALAN SPEDDING and ROY HOLMES
Department of Surveying, Bristol Polytechnic

Abstract
Maintenance costs in school buildings are rising rapidly and funds to
meet the perceived need are becoming increasingly difficult to secure.   The schools stock is extremely varied in design and complex
in variety of components and specifications used, therefore there is
a need for establishing a maintenance management system which will
highlight areas of work which are causing problems and improve cost-
effectiveness in decision making for maintenance. Furthermore, if
realistic maintenance programmes and accurate budgets are to be
prepared each authority must review its data recording procedure.
This paper sets out the problem, as seen in terms of variety of
buildings and the variation of specification and then goes on to show
how data can be collected and analysed to produce maintenance trends.
The paper also covers the aspect of maintenance management and sets
out the methodology for producing good maintenance management information.
Key Words Maintenance, Management, Schools, Computers, Condition
surveys, Property files.

1. Introduction

School buildings represent a substantial part of the United Kingdom's
building assets.   The post-war building boom resulted in a wide range
of constructional solutions, which were significantly affected by
developments in aesthetic perceptions.   Changes in pedagogy had their
influence, particularly in the 1960s and early 1970s, on the layout
of schools, which in turn affected design solutions.   The vast National investment in school building was controlled by a system of
overall cost-limits per pupil place and detailed cost-planning of
individual school design solutions, which resulted in quite wide
variations in quality of buildings, and area provided per pupil.
    The mid 1970s and mid 1980s have seen a reduction in U.K. con-
struction activity and a fall in pupil numbers which presents problems of under-utilised buildings in some parts of the United Kingdom.
The relatively large number of schools built during the 1960s and
1970s will remain with us for a considerable number of years, and it
is likely that a peaking of 'first replacement' maintenance is upon
us.   Maintenance of building assets in a period of lower investment

requires a greater than ever application of management expertise and the use of computer-based techniques.

2. The current stock

There are many schools still in use, particularly in rural areas, which were built before 1914, and these were compact in layout and substantially built, usually in classical or ecclesiastical styles. In the early 1930s, school architecture was influenced by a trend towards 'open air' schools which led to linear classroom layouts with access from covered verandahs or enclosed corridors, which caused area per pupil to increase significantly. Frequently such schools were built around a quadrangle, and they lent themselves to a repetitive constructional solution.

The end of the Second World War left the United Kingdom with the problems of replacing war damaged schools and of building for a rapidly rising young population.

The far-reaching 1944 Education Act, new regulations on school building introduced in 1945 by the Ministry of Education and the raising of the school-leaving age in 1947, combined with the high level of demand for building of all types, presented the U.K. with the formidable problem of providing a large number of schools within a relatively few years. From the early 1950s onwards, all types of constructional solutions were officially encouraged, ranging from the traditional unsystematised through to timber, steel framed, and concrete systems. Over two dozen systems were used in the U.K. to build schools, including eight 'schools consortia' systems formed by groups of like-minded county authorities.

Nevertheless, despite the difficulties, the schools were provided and this represented a considerable National achievement.

3. Capital Cost and Quality

Early in the post-war building programme Morrell and Pott (1960) commented on the fact that apparently comparable schools differed in price by as much as 200 per cent. These cost differences appeared in spite of the fact that a system of cost planning for new designs, related to a cost allowance per pupil place, had been instituted by the Ministry of Education (1951).

The almost immediate effect of the Ministry cost planning system was to affect design of schools and particularly to reduce circulation space, thereby achieving cost reductions. Subsequent attention to cost planning reduced cost per square metre but eventually, even with periodic increases, the levels of the cost limit lagged behind cost inflation and put very strong pressure on the finance which would be provided to build a school.

After examining initial capital cost data from over two thousand Primary Schools, Spedding (1968) concluded that quite wide variations had occurred in the quality provided in school buildings due, in many cases, to economies made in construction in order to achieve a satisfactory amount of floor area. At one time this may not have been an acute problem because if problems arose during the life of a building it was possible to rectify them. Unfortunately, changes in financial rules for County Authorities have placed pressures on maintenance budgets so that economy in this field has assumed great importance.

4. Maintenance expenditure

As a result of the increased importance in maintenance a study was undertaken for the Department of Education and Science (DES), Spedding (1983), which involved extracting maintenance cost data for the 1977 to 1982 period from the works order files and cost ledgers of a large County Authority and then coding them for computer analysis. A coding system for building maintenance cost analysis was developed, Holmes (1985), this proved capable of facilitating analysis down to very detailed levels. This hierarchical coding system is based on functional elements of buildings which can be broken down via sub-elements to individual components if desired. Figure 1 indicates in histogram form the relative costs of the elements examined in the DES study.

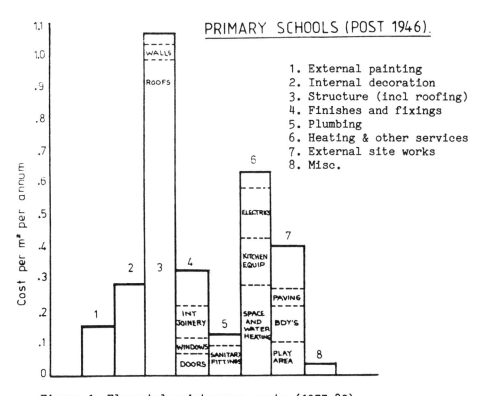

Figure 1   Elemental maintenance costs (1977-82)

Detailed examination of the data showed that policy of the County Authority and its Maintenance Surveyors had significantly influenced

the incidence of elemental costs. As the study had shown that maintenance data were available in the County's records from 1946 up to
the present day it was decided to investigate cost during this period.

Other detailed investigations followed and an histogram of relative costs obtained in one of the studies is given in Figure 2 below.

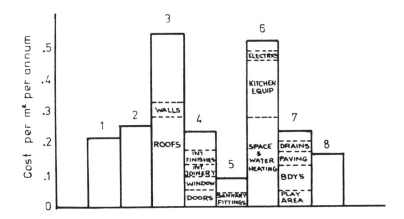

Figure 2   Elemental maintenance costs (1946-82)

Although the histograms give only a broad indication of what were
very detailed studies a cursory comparison shows the increased expenditure in more recent years on roofs, joinery, sanitary fittings.
electrical installations, and certain external works elements. It
also revealed a significant rate of expenditure on service installations over all years. A further study which involved a sample of pre
1903 schools appeared to indicate a rise and then a levelling off of
costs at a relatively higher level than the sample of more recent
schools, suggesting that post-1960s schools might reach a higher
plateau of average expenditure in due course.

5. **Maintenance data: Roofing**

It might be useful to illustrate in a much abbreviated form, part
of a study on roofing maintenance data carried out by Spedding et al
(1984).   A sample of 50 typical County Primary schools (pupils up to
11 years of age) was chosen to include 25 pre 1903 and 25 post 1946
schools. The County concerned had undertaken a programme of replacing roofs where significant problems had arisen, rather than simply
repairing them.

Table 1 (over) shows that post 1946 schools had incurred greater
average expenditure on roofing than the older schools, which was due
to the predominance of flat roofs.

Schools sample	Cost including major renewals			Excluding major renewals
	Roofing as % of all maintenance	Gross cost per school £	£/m2	Gross cost per school £
Post 1946	12	296	0.27	78
Pre 1903	8	140	0.47	44

Table 1: Costs per annum for roofing.

The apparent difference in relative costs is due to the smaller size of the older, rural schools which makes the cost per square metre appear greater.

It was found that sixteen of the post-1946 schools had undergone major renewals and seven of these had been less than fifteen years old. Seventeen of the pre 1903 schools had also undergone major roof renewal in the period under examination.

It was also found that gross costs per school of general minor repairs in the post 1946 age group were similar for flat roofed or pitched roofed buildings, but that serious failures had occurred in flat roofs relatively frequently and were expensive to rectify.

Because not all failures could be precisely identified with a particular building block in a school it was not possible to allocate all repairs, but it appeared that given approximately similar areas of flat and pitched roofing, flat roof maintenance and renewals accounted for about three quarters of the total cost of all roof maintenance. Naturally it is difficult to separate the cost of, for instance, repair of felt roof covering from repair of the chipboard decking caused by water ingress.

The study also attempted to identify the life of various elements and in the case of flat felted roofs it was found that the mean time from initial construction to the first significant repair was eight and a half years and the mean time from such repairs to substantial re-roofing was a little over a further three years. Such average figures conceal a range of significant failures from about three to twenty years of age.

6. Maintenance data and management

Detailed studies of maintenance costs have indicated to us that, annually, there is a very large number of minor repairs, costing considerably less than £500 each, and a smaller number of major repairs. In fact it is commonly the case that a small number of jobs account for over half the total maintenance costs. A very large proportion of the minor repairs as well as many major jobs will not have been foreseen when the year's budget was planned.

Clearly, management policy, such as alluded to above, will considerably affect the decision as to what level of remedial work will be undertaken for any particular category of failure, and therefore the

nature of the data which will be collected in future. Also, most
cost-recording systems were produced in the past for financial accounting and auditing purposes and not for management control and budget
forecasting purposes. This has convinced the research team, in the
Building Research Unit at Bristol Polytechnic, that the need is to
use the computer to examine current levels of spending and their
causes, and this point is considered later.

Having made the point about historical data some patterns of
effective life, and the failures rates of elements and components,
can be produced. However, it was found that the wide variety of
initial detailed specifications as well as different standards of
workmanship in initial construction, allied to varying conditions in
use, make accurate statistically-based forecasting of expenditure on
individual school buildings impracticable. Of course, average rates
of failure applied to a large stock of buildings may provide useful
indications of what might be expected when preparing budgets for
future maintenance work. Such budgets will inevitably be based on
previous spending patterns, particularly in minor repairs and unplanned maintenance, and an authority may not have enough money to cope
with the 'perceived' needs recorded by individual surveyors. This
will put increasing pressure on senior staff, who have the task of
allocating budgets, to carry out a 'comparative' need exercise; this
involves the technique of comparing the needs of one school building
against another to ensure that the funding allocation will achieve
the best value for money. To help with the comparative need exercise
management should have some answers to the following questions:

1.   What specific elements or components are causing problems, and
      why? what remedial work, if any, has been done?

2.   What quantity, of the problem elements, do we possess, where are
      they and what is their age profile and probability of failure?

The answers to these and other questions can be found if authorities
give some thought to coding procedures, to property files and to
condition surveys; these are now discussed.

7. Coding maintenance data

There are two basic stages to computerised maintenance data, first,
the ordering of the work, at this stage the work is coded by some
suitable coding system and issued to a contractor; secondly, the
costing stage, where the work done is checked against the order and
the work code changed, if necessary, and the cost entered.   The
heirarchical coding system developed at Bristol by Holmes et al
(1985) allows detail to be coded to five levels, for instance, tap
washer repairs can be coded if desired. On analysis this produces
data for various management functions, one of which may be the identification of particular high numbers of repairs, which can be followed up by interrogation into specifications etc; another analysis
might be the number of jobs costing more than, say, £250 and so on.
The advantage of a heirarchical code is that the level of analysis

can be varied to suit the management function. In particular it greatly enhances the programming and budgeting process.

8. Property files

In a current study the research team at Bristol is finding that few authorities have found it worthwhile to collect and collate detailed data on their properties, although many are now considering some kind of computerised system for such data. One of the questions being asked is 'what type of information should we collect', it appears that by concensus two aspects of property data need attention:-

1.   The physical details of the property, including the amount, the type and location of elements and components.

2.   The condition of these elements and components, updated as they are repaired or replaced.

Clearly, it is not economical to record information on every aspect of a building at the level of detail which may be useful at some time in the future. Therefore, for detail, it might be worth considering those elements or components which move or are subject to the effects of the weather. Such detail would include data to identify or order a specific component.
    In addition to element or component detail it will be an advantage to record the location by block or specific part of the building. This will, in the case of schools, take into account the age factor; often a school has extensions of varying ages and one cannot anticipate the failure rate of components if the location and age factor is not recorded.
    Having got all this information all one needs is the actual condition so that an analysis can reveal the potential work ahead. This information is obtained from condition surveys and these are now discussed.

9. Condition surveys

There are various schools of thought on the extent to which data should be collected on the condition of properties. Some authorities favour an eight point scale ranging from 'dangerous' to 'as good as new'. Most authorities, however, see the wisdom in limiting the scale to around five points, but often the points on the scale signify different things. For some the points refer to percentage scores of new condition, so that by adding the scores of all of the main functional elements of the building together one may produce a single percentage score of general condition for the building as a whole. Usually, because some elements cost more than others initially, and/or because of failure in some elements is more crucial than in others, such as roofing versus internal decoration, then further weighting factors may be applied.
    A more simplistic measure of condition, and one currently being

95

investigated by the authors, is to use a five point scale in which grade 1 means that the condition is such that it requires action within one year, grade 2 within two years and so. By using this system the computer can print out the work which needs attention in any one of five years and the overall programme of work can be established. Where the amount of work exceeds the likely budget allocation a 'comparative need' exercise can be applied. The considerable amount of technical skills expended on the condition survey, if used in the way described, might produce an initial measure of condition which regular updating will change but little. However, there must be a clear commitment to regularly updating the data on the property files, not only from the condition surveys, which might carried out every four or five years, but also when maintenance work is done. Of course, updating due to maintenance work could be left until the following condition survey thus reducing the amount of file updating. If the principal aim of the system is to improve budgeting and value for money in maintenance management, then the relatively scarce resource, technical staff, might be better deployed selectively to support these functions.

10. Budgeting for maintenance work

In many authorities, maintenance work is the responsibility of a Deputy County Architect or a Chief Surveyor. New capital work over a certain value may come under the supervision of a different Architect or Surveyor, and the maintenance budget will be in competition with many other heads of expenditure.

It must be borne in mind that, whilst the money expended on building maintenance work is significant, particularly in National terms, it is clearly insufficient to satisfy most maintenance managers that enough is being spent, expenditure must be kept in perspective. If one considers the County Council's annual revenue budget one might find up to two thirds relating to the provision of the education service, but an extremely low proportion (approximately three per cent of the budget) being spent on maintenance. Therefore, those in charge of maintenance may find that they will have to produce strong and well supported arguments if they wish maintenance to be given a higher priority in the County Council's overall budget plans. The problem will be to break out of the self-fulfilling budget based on last years spending plus adjustments for inflation and changes in the number of properties.

Inevitably, however, there will probably always be a backlog of maintenance work. It is therefore essential to have a method of quantifying the amount of backlog, many of the published figures appear to be conjecture. One way of doing this is to produce a file of those items of work could not be included in the planned maintenance programme. Figure 3 indicates a schematic view of the relationships between condition, budget, programme of work and backlog, although it is recognised that the reiterative totalling of work which cannot be afforded each year will not produce convincing evidence of real need. What is required is an assessment of the extent to which minor items of work have been pruned, together with a record, at

appropriately detailed levels, of major items which have had to be
deferred. The latter will include planned work which was not done
due to being squeezed out of the annual programme by major emergency
work which cropped up.

Backlog items must be given special attention at times of surveys,
if staff resources are available, in order to assess any relative
deterioration, so that a 'consequential damage due to deferral'
database might be produced. Thus the manager will gradually be able
to evaluate by how much the backlog has gone up and to estimate what
deferment has cost by comparison with previous years' data. This
will begin to answer the question of what is the real cost of not
doing work.

Clearly, such backlogs have to be built up against agreed standards of maintenance and upkeep, which must not be unrealistic, because maintenance work can, if allowed, consume large amounts of
human and financial resources. Completely accurate forecasting of
failure is not possible, and preventive maintenance programmes on all
elements of buildings are unlikely to be cost-effective. Therefore
there will always have to be a measure of compromise in the management of maintenance of building assets, but the heart of the system
is to obtain good information.

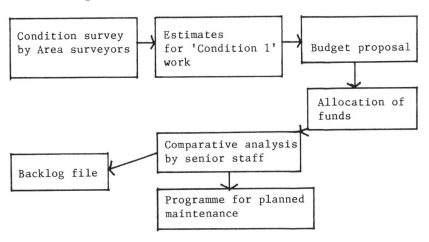

Figure 3 - Process Relationships

11. Conclusions

The stock of school buildings is varied and complex, in terms of
design options and components used. The fall in the demographic
curve means that many of our schools may have to be used for other
purposes and therefore the most cost effective schools, in terms of
running costs and maintenance costs need to be identified. This can
only be done with a good management information sytem, most of which
will impinge on the upkeep the physical aspects of the buildings. A
logical method of coding maintenance data must be developed so that
maintenance cost trends can be plotted and cost-effect solutions

prepared. Programmes of work, together with accurate budgets can be enhanced if such coding is comprehensive. The management function is further enhanced if property files and condition surveys are employed, this allows 'comparative needs' to be determined by senior staff; without such comparison there is a danger of maintenance expenditure being 'surveyor' led. An information system which allows rapid analysis of data is essential for cost-effective maintenance management.

As spending upon educational buildings in the United Kingdom frequently consumes over eighty-five per cent of a County's total budget for building work it is sensible to start with schools when setting up a maintenance management information and control system.

References

Morrell and Pott, (1960) Britain's new schools, Longmans Green 1960.

Ministry of Education, (1951) Cost study, Building Bulletin 4, HMSO 1951.

Spedding, A (1968) PhD thesis, unpublished.

Spedding, A. et al, (1983) Maintenance in Schools, Report No SUR/83/1, Department of Surveying, Bristol Polytechnic.

Holmes, R., Droop, C. and Mellor, P. (1985) A coding system for building maintenance, Technical Information Service., CIOB, Paper No. 47, 1985.

Spedding, A. et al, (1984) Roofing and Service Installations, Report No SUR/84/1, Department of Surveying, Bristol Polytechnic.

CONTROL OF MAINTENANCE IN A COUNTY AUTHORITY

ALAN SPEDDING   Department of Surveying, Bristol Polytechnic.
VIVIAN SMITH   Acting County Architect, Wiltshire.

The views are   those of the authors, not of their employers.

Abstract

Control of maintenance in a large authority must take place within
a financial discipline related to the workload and staff must work
in a clearly defined and effective system, which must allow for
transition as computing power is introduced. A geographically
spread out organisation has to allow for optimum participation by
area technical staff, in order that management information may
flow effectively. Additional, the maintenance system does not
exist in vacuo, it has to be seen in the light of the total County
Council budgetary system.
Keywords: Management, finance, span of control, computing,
information.

Introduction

This paper is based upon discussions which took place between the
authors on the subject of control of maintenance, and the introduction of computing at County Hall and in outstations of the
organisation. The intention of the discussions was to bring out
some of the key factors behind decisions which have to be taken
in any organisation which has responsibility for a large stock
of landed property to maintain. These factors relate to three
main elements of a management system:-

1. Organisation

The system must provide rapid access to information, both financial and technical, must allow involvement of technical staff
in establishing budgets, forward programmes and policies, and
must allow rapid access to higher authority when it is needed. In
particular:-
    (a) Lines of command and information must be short and
direct;
    (b) Responsibilities must be defined and made clear;
    (c) Objectives must be established, and performance monitor-
ed.

2. Staff

All maintenance systems ultimately depend on the Building Surveyor
or Area Engineer who has to make on the spot decisions, and will
decide the quality of the final product, whether it be work on
site or information passed back for future use. Therefore staff
quality is important, but also expensive and therefore numbers
must realistically relate to the tasks involved.

3. Equipment.

This must aid management at all levels, by providing storage of
information in readily usable form by technical and administrative
staff: allowing for rapid retrieval and updating of data, as well
as calculations and manipulation.
     Each element has a cost and a value, and the task of the man-
ager is to balance these elements within the overall budgetary
allowance. The paper however, does not try to separate the
elements but deals with some of the problems in the context of
the development of a new computerised system.

Costs and the organsiation.

Examination of the work done in a typical year at 1985/86 prices
shows a maintenance expenditure of just over four million pounds.
If the supervisory and management work is analysed in detail, and
costs built up on a basis in line with the RICS fee scales for
Building Surveyor's services, it can be shown that just over sixteen percent of the value of work done might be appropriate as
a total management fee. Naturally in a financial environment of
constraint an in-house organisation has to make the most effective use of money, and a figure of about ten percent, or slightly
higher might be an appropriate target.
     Such a figure gives a budget base or a starting point and then
allocations have to be considered between staff and equipment.
Equipment means anything from accommodation to computers and a
computer information system, fully developed for a maintenance
organisation of such a size could cost somewhere in the order of
£150,000 to maybe £250,00. A typical costing might look like the
following:-

Cost of installation £200,000 - over 5 years = £40,00 per year
(without interest charges)

Running cost   £25,000 per year

Maintenance and development   £15,000 per year

                                          £80,000 per year for
                                                  5 years
                                          _____

100

Subsequent costs may drop if the installation lasts a few years but when it needs replacing the costs will rise again to about the £80,000, or its equivalent at the time. The sum of money, annually could equate to three or four Building Surveyors in terms of cost.

Since any organisation ultimately depends for its quality, on the staff, whether it's the information that is brought back or the work that is carried out on site, one cannot afford to reduce the number of building surveyors too much in order to buy an information system, and a balance has to be struck. Therefore in Wiltshire, the lines of command and the lines of information are kept to a minimum, keeping the number of personnel involved in instruction-passing to the minimum with no pyramids, as far as possible. The computer information system is to be used as the information source, and information transmitter as well, and in that way one is better able to get a more balanced equation between staff and management system. The need is to reduce the numbers of levels of responsibility between the man in the field and County Hall to one.

The object of course is to improve forecasting and monitoring but this requires a considerable amount of data. If this information is held on paper it is of not much use, because it cannot be sorted and handled without huge manual effort. However, with computing at a cost of £200,000 spread over a period of 5 years plus the running costs, the manager has the job of deciding if this long term investment is justified in his present economic situation. Probably, it is, but one should attempt to spread the cost into other fields, thus, instead of charging the whole of these costs, (computing costs and organisation costs) to maintenance, one should also charge minor capital works, energy conservation and other heads, with part of these costs because, patently, the records will serve those heads as well. This is an advantage in those organisations, (it may not accrue in all) where such work all falls under one department also because the manager may distribute the costs, and provide a better service.

Management of outstations in areas of a County

Typcially with a manual system there might be five areas in a County, the organisation looking like the following:-

Assistant County Architect

3 B.S.	4 B.S.	1 B.S.	2 B.S.	3 B.S.
1 Eng	2 Eng			1 Eng
a Admin	1 Admin		1 Admin	1 Admin

The opportunity to use computing power may suggest that three areas would be more suitable, each area having a computer terminal linked to County Hall, but with micro computers attached to allow local working with central storage and data analysis. The system would allow the use of Fax to send out documents as well, so that communications will be by telephone/Fax and by computer from the centre, to three offices. Orders will be originated in both places, both in the outstations for the work which is generated locally, and in County Hall for that which is tendered for, because, for larger jobs, orders are placed by County Hall against tenders, rather than in the outstations. Of course, although there will be a financial limit below which the outstations may order materials or work, all Surveyor's orders will all come through the computer system. In fact all work will eventually come through the computer system because even that very minor work ordered by Headteachers and heads of Institutions will be brought back, at least in terms of financial information, by the new accounting system that the County Council is setting up, independent of the property system but attached to it.

Head's orders will be typed on the terminal and "WILMAS" the County System, will automatically generate an entry onto the main frame which will then be loaded into the maintenance system as lump sums rather than individual orders. The problem of the man on site wanting to write an order, whether he brings it back to his office and writes it or whether he writes it and it comes back to County Hall and it is typed centrally, is one that is not yet resolved. But the aim is, that there will be only one man (the Building Surveyor) generating the order, which comes to the centre in whatever way, where it is recorded and the totals are kept running. There is thus no intermediary, which allows overheads to be kept low.

In addition to the staff in the outstations, there are five plant maintenance engineers which are accounted for separately. Their costs about £90,000 per year are kept within a total envelope and, at present, redistributed pro rata to an area rather than to an establishment. This may be refined so that their costs are distributed to an establishment, and this is a simple accounting technique, if required, because they already record time to establishments, for management purposes, and record orders for materials for the work they do.

There must, of course, be rapid feedback, at an appropriate level, to the man in the field as well as at County Hall, because the Building Surveyor should be able to know how his budget is going; he shouldn't have too hard a job in keeping records himself, the system should keep it for him. He must be able to retrieve what data he needs, in terms such as cost per square metre to allow him to estimate in the future. Eventually, when the computer system is developed, a Surveyor will be able to call up the information from on his own terminal, and obtain hard copies whenever necessary. He will have all the financial and administrative information that he needs on his terminal; and also as much technical information that can be contrived.

There will be an up-date on current policy related matters, asbestos is an example, so that he may refresh his memory without wading through paper. The system is not as yet fully developed in Wiltshire and so there is a substantial transitional period envisaged. In the long run, however, more useful information will be supplied to technical staff to enable better decisions to be made.

Objectives for maintenance work

It has to be decided at the beginning of the year, to what level it is going to be possible to maintain with the money available, as maintenance is all budget driven. One has to establish which are the main elements of the building to sort out. In simple terms; the primary objectives are that the fabric will be kept sound, the health and safety of the occupants will be protected, the environment will be kept comfortable in terms of heat and light, but beyond that there is little money to do decoration or less essential work. The secondary objectives will be that the major efforts for the next three years will be devoted towards special programmes such as the renewal of heating systems and the restoration of rotten timber work. These objectives are defined by surveys which show where the next problems are arising and therefore dictate where major money and major effort should be expended in the future.

The surveys are, at present, done at times of visits to sites in respect of defects reports, or annually to prepare budgets. Probably a complete quinquennial survey system will be set up when staff can be made available. At present all work found to be needed is noted and listed, and this includes engineering work. For instance all circuits are tested five yearly by the Electricity Board, all gas installations are tested by the Gas Board at intervals and all boilers are examined by insurance inspectors annually, routinely. The annual survey is meant to establish what work the Building Surveyor and the engineer can identify on every building on the basis of an inspection lasting one and a half to two hours. One is well aware that he won't pick up the minutiae, and one has to accept that at the moment. However, the Building Surveyors try and pick up everything even though they know that they are not going to get the money. This provides as good a record of the work that is needed as possible. The Surveyors then giv work a priority, based on discussions which have taken place with them earlier, which then enables management to look at where the major problems seem to be.

This has enabled the flat roofing problems to be mainly remedied and has indicated the needs mentioned above, particularly boilers which have been highlighted due to their entering the age range associated with failure. The latter element is an example of where property records can play their part, in that the ages of all boilers will shortly be on record and dates of replacement can be decided in advance.

103

There is frequently an element of improvement in maintenance
work and this is desirable, although client departments must contribute out of capital funds where that happens. Lighting is an
example where, when rewiring, the change is made from tungsten to
fluorescent, obviously in many cases enhancing the lighting levels.
Thus the client Department head is asked to contribute towards
that out of his Capital fund as well as being funded out of the
central maintenance fund. Similarly the attempt is made to keep
"pure" maintenance work separate from other heads, such as Health
and Safety work.

Setting objectives for staff in the field also presents
problems of equating standards. One can broadly measure performance
of staff in relation to condition of property and money spent. One
of the ways in which it is done because standards achieved are
always subjective opinion, is for one person, say the manager, to
look at examples of the level of maintenance achieved in all of the
areas covered by each of the Building Surveyors. One can look at,
say, three comprehensive schools in each of the areas during one
period of time, perhaps in May. One monitors the condition
achieved, and then looks at what they say needs to be done, to try
to form an opinion of standards are being applied, and also what
they have done in terms of money spent. There is no doubt that
there is a wide divergence in money spent by staff. This sometimes
is an indication of the standard achieved, but not always, because
the original condition of buildings is different, and this dictates
what has had to be spent.

Even if a reasonable sum of money is available from the County
Council, the demands of people out in the field still vary, because
the man who has been used to spending money in order to catch up on
condition still feels that he has to continue to spend money. The
man who has not been used to spending money, either because he does
not feel it necessary, or because the condition of his buildings is
good, often doesn't ask for money although in some cases he should,
in order to preserve the long-term condition of his stock. It is
sometimes suggested that a group of Building Surveyors should themselves arrange to visit samples of each others stock to undertake
comparative surveys. Although this might not be at all cost-
effective an objective might well be that of stimulating staff
interest and co-operation in the whole issue of quality and value
for money.

Recording and use of cost data.

The heart of data collection is the order, and at present, in Wiltshire the orders for work are issued together with an estimated
price which goes into a commitment account. When work is due for
payment a hard copy goes to Treasury asking for payment to be made.
The commitment accounting is does by maintenance management so that
Treasury only know the overall agreed budget, and pay invoices when
requested. When the WILMAS system is in operation this process will
take place electronically.

The relationship with Treasury is crucial particularly as Wiltshire have just set up a total property related cost per pupil head, right across the County, using this for comparison purposes to try and establish where all the expensive properties are. That includes all costs in use, fuel, cleaning and the like.

Obviously it is difficult to collect that information because sometimes it doesn't come into the maintenance group at all, it goes into Treasury. One has to have a means of collecting that information and this requires a good relationship between the data system and the Treasury. Maintenance has to strip the costs for cleaning, caretaking, rents, rates from the Treasury. They come up initially, in paper, hard copy, but will shortly be input direct into the Department's own energy computer, simply because the energy computer is already set up on the basis of floor area and pupil head so one has already got the basic structure. It is an IBM PC80 which is linked to the mainframe, so access to data is straightforward. At present the maintenance database is being assembled on another IBM PC, but eventually the mainframe computer will be used to move data around the system.

Eventually the whole data system will be computerised from original estimate right through to payment. This will enable costs of repairing elements and components to be isolated, but a good data system will cost money and require staff effort. Staff are the source of data, and one relies very heavily on the Building Surveyors to input the data. They not only initiate the orders, but some time or another orders have to changed (perhaps they are not correct in the first place) and the price has got to be updated. On the system that is running now, there is an estimate at inception and then an actual tender price accepted or quotation price accepted. What is not yet on line is the opportunity to put a revised price in on work that is ordered, on either day work or on the schedule rate system, until receipt of the final invoice. This means that one is working on estimated prices for a large portion of the time but, again, this relies on Surveyor's expertise.

On the question of expressing cost data there is always the question of how to present them. As an example, supposing one has been replacing boilers would it be most useful to get out of the system the average cost of replacing a boiler per building, or some other measure? As data accumulate, say twenty, thirty, forty boilers replaced, the average price, or cost per square metre might be calculated. In practice this may not be very useful. In order to provide management information, one has to categorise into, (not in cost per square metre or cost per pupil head, as far as a specific compenent is concerned), but in cost per building type - e.g. Primary schools, 50 years old; and that is the type of grouping of most interest. The aim is to project forward anticipated property costs so that one can advise committee which ones they should get rid of, and which ones they shouldn't be getting rid of. Therefore cost per pupil head or cost per square metre, does not tell us too much, but costs of specific components, such as boilers or roof trusses, for example, attached to buildings of a certain type and age, can then generate some useful information.

105

The work done at Bristol Polytechnic has indicated some directions, but in practice one has to avoid much of the detail commonly collected for research purposes. In practice, one can show committees the cost of running a given establishment and it is quite easy to get the running cost, and show them, in broad terms, the anticipated costs in the next thirty years on the basis of boiler replacement, roof replacement and the like. There will then be enough information there to get their attention, and one can then either get broad policy decisions made, or get instructions to proceed with detailed studies.

As a general comment, the notion of a thirty year forecast raises the question of discounting cash flows in some people's minds, but the concept is not easy to put before committee, particularly as errors in discounting rates and the like may be considerable. In fact the time horizon for decision is usually shorter than five years, so although one would not rule out discounted cost flow as a concept, present day costs are usually adequate.

Comparative spending and policy

Figures of target spending are sometimes expressed as a percentage, say 1.8, of the total assessed value of the stock. This in fact can be dangerous because so much depends on what the building stock consists of. Somebody might have a building stock of all 1960+ buildings, it is not impossible to imagine. Others will have buildings of 150 years old, others will have a mix. The mix varies, the actual cost varies, the weight of use determines so much what maintenance charges are. One has only to look at the difference between maintaining per pupil head, the cost of maintaining a comprehensive school compared with maintaining a primary school to see how wear and tear varies with the type of use.

There are also suggestions that the cost of maintenance and condition should be linked to the priced assessed replacement value of the properties say on a basis of £500 per square metre at current prices and the same criticism applies. The buildings vary so much, that it is impossible to rely on such overall yardsticks. A lot of people are collecting this sort of information and building it into their computer programs, particularly on condition surveys where they are going into great detail, but is is difficult to specify a cut-off point where condition survey detail can become uneconomic. However, the caretaking costs of a comprehensive school per pupil head are roughly the same as the maintenance cost; therefore there must come a time when the effort is not worthwhile because maintenance is simply one of, and not even the major, cost of running the building.

As has been pointed out, the Surveyors will know their properties, they will submit priorities for work to be done, as they see it from their annual inspections, which we accept may not be comprehensive, but that which can be seen in the time allowed. A total list of requirements will thus be produced, even though staff will know that the money available will be insufficient, and judgements will have to be made.

If it's felt, that, for example, one cannot afford to replace twenty boilers in one area because there is only so much money available, one has to decide whether to spread reboilering out between areas, or one has to assess comparative need to say whether the twenty boilers are so bad that they really have to be replaced in that one area.

This of course requires the manager to make the decision based upon reading Surveyor's reports, analysing their performance in the way described earlier, and having a look at the comparative conditions, and then discussion, not only with the building Surveyors but also with the user Departments. As soon as the full list is assembled, the list is discussed with representatives from the Education and other Departments, their Area Officers, the persons who from their point of view know their buildings. In the end however, it is the maintenance manager who has to decide, based on the sort of broad strategy which has been agreed for the next period, such as mainly dealing with rotten timber and boilers.

The comparative allocation of money needs, of course, to be treated with sensitivity. Money is not allowed for the year to particular Departments for them to treat virtually as they wish. The maintenance fund is central one, and it is managements's job to spread it fairly, taking need into account. At present, when orders come to be written, apart from very minor Headteacher's orders, they are written by the Building Surveyors for work decided upon and specified by them. This common source of orders helps to keep a check on comparative standards between, say Social Services, and Education programmes.

County policy, of course might decide, for instance, that Education has to receive special attention next year and management will have to adjust resources accordingly. Nevertheless, the money will probably still be insufficient and judgements will have to be made. Naturally, where only certain schools can be dealt with, and others have to be deferred, management will listen carefully to the preferences of Education. However other, more overriding policies may be decided such as with a Committee Instruction, that where there is a competition for funds, all the essentials having been dealt with,residential accommodation has a priority in terms of decoration over non-residential property. Such a policy patently is meant to favour social services where people actually live the whole of their lives, rather than just term-time.

Other policy matters will affect the information required of the maintenance data system by the political members of the authority. Surveyors will collect information in one way, probably elemental, but there may be items which do not fit an entirely elemental heading, but nevertheless need collecting under headings, such as vandalism. Thus the system needs to have an element heading, and also give an opportunity for tagging certain things which are of interest to political members. Of course, it is difficult to get people to accept that it is vandalism, and such opinion is challenged by Heads of Establishments because it reflects on their control, but it is the Surveyor who makes that decision.

Obviously things like window breakages, which will be Headteachers orders are bounded by instructions and will appear on a lump sum but they are probably 50% vandalism so some items will have to be inferred. Similarly other political/sensitive matters such as asbestos, will need a code for asbestos removal, even though it is associated with other maintenance activities like reboilering.

The level of detail and categorisation has, as been said, to be kept in perspective. Maintenance has to compete in the budget with the whole County and the County's Education Service alone costs say 60% to run whilst the maintenance budget perhaps is less than 3%. One must ask how realistic is it to spend a lot of money on refining a maintenance system when bigger savings could be made by looking at the organisation and staffing. Clearly, it isn't realistic to go beyond a certain level, because the budget has to be balanced in terms of running the maintenance system, between management systems and Surveyors out in the field. A super computer-based system may be attractive to the maintenace manager, but in terms of relative priorities one might have a hard job to justify it in political terms if it costs too much for the improvements it brings.

108

THE PROPERTY SERVICES AGENCY BUILDING INSPECTION SYSTEM

T E WHYTON ARICS
Principal Building Surveyor, Property Services Agency, South West
Region

Abstract
The PSA Building Inspection System is described in detail, the
methods employed to ensure a balanced workload for the inspecting
officers and the method of recording defects on the building inspection form.

Other Building Inspection Systems are described which are set
up in response to specific requirements either the type of building
or structure or its status.

The use to which the information is put following the inspection
and the action taken. The Forward Maintenance Register, its form
and purpose.
Key words: Inspection, Technical, District, Urgent, Forward, Maintenance, Monitoring.

Introduction
The Property Services Agency (PSA), part of the Department of
the Environment (DOE) is the single largest design and construction
organisation in the UK. Its role is to provide, manage and maintain
properties used by all branches of the Government.

It has been referred to as the largest multi disciplinary group
practice in the country employing Architects, Engineers, Surveyors,
Estate Surveyors, Land Agents etc.

The variety of installations in the Department's care is vast
ranging from local office accommodation to Naval bases, Airfield,
Army Barracks and Railways.

The Department also maintains British Government installations
abroad including Military Bases.

PSA Organisation
The PSA organisation consists of a Headquarters, 8 Regional Offices
and Welsh and Scottish Directorates. The Headquarters unit has
Design Directorates to cover the main Government clients and Regional
Offices also have a considerable design capability.

Each Regional Office has a number of Area Offices reporting
to it. In the South West Regional the Headquarters is in Bristol
with Area Offices in Bristol, Cheltenham, Bulford, Plymouth and
Corsham.

The Area Offices are responsible for the management of a number of District Works Offices which are located close to the clients they serve.

The DWOs are the principal maintenance arm of the organisation and are responsible for the major part of an annual spend of £722M (85/86) on maintenance work by the PSA.

The South West Region has 20 District Works Offices strategicly placed to serve the clients. For example, Plymouth is covered by 4 DWOs serving mainly the Navy, but with responsibilities for Army, the RAF and Government Departments (referred to in the PSA as Civil). The Salisbury Plain Training Area is served by 5 DWOs, the Army is the main client followed by the RAF.

Each DWO has a spend of around £5M on maintenance. The following is a staffing chart for a typical District:-

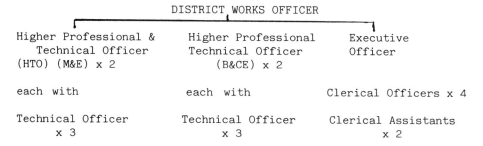

DISTRICT WORKS OFFICER

Higher Professional & Technical Officer (HTO) (M&E) x 2	Higher Professional Technical Officer (B&CE) x 2	Executive Officer
each with	each with	Clerical Officers x 4
Technical Officer x 3	Technical Officer x 3	Clerical Assistants x 2

The DWO is responsible for the regular inspection and maintenance of facilities.

To assist him in this task, he has a team of technical officers skilled in either building and civil engineering or mechanical and electrical disciplines. All Districts have a number of directly employed operatives.

Each year the District Works Officer submits a bid for maintenance funds to his Area Officer. The make up of the funds is an amount to cover continuing and inescapable committments such as DEL wages, grounds maintenance, day to day maintenance, testing and servicing of mechanical and electrical installations. The other part of the bid is made up of specific maintenance tasks identified in routine inspections by the technical officers and comprise re-decoration, renewal of roof coverings, boiler renewals etc.

The subject matter of this paper is the Building Inspection System used by the DWOs to identify defects in installations, the subsequent recording and action taken.

Building Inspection System

The PSA has for many users had a building inspection system based on a 2 yearly cycle. The inspections were carried out by technical officers and overseen by line managers. The system was updated in 1984 by improvements to the monitoring systems the inclusion of mechanical and electrical inspections (which had previously been done separately) and simplification of the inspection report forms.

An outline of the updated system is as follows:-

1   For the purpose of inspection the estate is divided into facilities and a register of these established and kept up to date. Each facility should represent about 4 hours of inspection time, thus a facility could be only part of a large building or a collection of small buildings within an identifiable unit or group with similar characteristics.

2   The standard of maintenance for each facility is established from one of 5 prescribed levels. (See below).

3   Facilities are inspected by suitably experienced staff.

4   The results of inspections and consequential actions are recorded on Inspection Record Sheets and where appropriate, in a forward Maintenance Register.

5   Each Facility has a file which contains completed Inspection Record Sheets and information relevant to the inspection.

The required standard of maintenance for each facility is set by the District Works Officer after consultation with the client and will be one of the following:-

CODE   REQUIRED CONDITION

X   Exceptional

N   Normal

L   Limited Life

W   Wind and Weathertight

D   Demolition pending

(See Appendix 1)

All facilities will be inspected at a normal frequency of 2 years. This frequency may be varied to suit the circumstances of each case.   For example an empty building will need inspection more frequently than one that is in daily use.

New buildings are inspected one year after handover and thereafter every 2 years.

The inspection is carried out jointly by a B&CE technical officer and a mechanical and electrical technical officer. The inspection is usually visual only and normally no testing or opening up is carried out though reports giving the results of M&E tests, statutory tests etc will be available. One of the results of a routine inspection might well be a request for a full structural survey or testing.

Programming and Progressing

Inspections are carried out on a running programme arranged to spread the workload throughout the year. To monitor progress of inspections each District Works Office maintains a wall chart which identifies the facilities to be inspected and indicates the progress achieved by the use of symbols.

Thus each DWO is able to assess when inspections are due, those that have been carried out and those that are overdue.

Facility Jacket

Each facility has a separate file known as a Facility Jacket which contains details of the standard of maintenance required, the inspection interval period and details of any lease repairing covenants. Floor plans and a brief description of the building would also be included, together with details of the Mechanical and Electrical installation.

Inspection Record Sheets and Checklists

A standard Inspection Report Sheet is used to record details of each facility inspection. Defects observed are entered together with recommended action and priority. The Record Sheets are kept in the Facility Jacket and so form a permanent record of the condition of the facility.

During the course of inspections officers may identify defects not due to normal wear and tear and these are made the subject of a Defects Report which is passed to Area Office for further investigation.

Often these examples of premature failure are reported to Headquarters via Areas and Regions and often form the subject of Defect Feedback Reports in Construction magazine.

Action Following Inspection

Assuming the inspectors are also the ordering officers, the following action will be taken on completion of the inspection.

All defects noted will be listed on the report form and marked according to the importance and urgency as follows:

All items noted as needing immediate attention are ordered immediately and this is noted on the form.

Items not requiring immediate attention are entered in a Forward Maintenance Register.

Items of defect requiring a more detailed inspection, eg settle-

112

ment or structural cracks the DWO would arrange for a specialist to inspect. The specialist could be a member of the DWO staff but more usually would work at either Area or Regional Office.

By this means, the PSA covers the vast majority of the estate in just 2 years and is able to determine at any time the condition of all of the facilities in its care.

Statutory, Operational Specialist and Other Inspections
In addition to inspections that ascertain future maintenance needs, PSA policy requires other regular or occasional inspections of buildings, civil engineering, mechanical and electrical installations.
  Many of these inspections arise out of statutory or mandatory requirements and fall broadly into the following purpose categories:

Examining standards of health, safety or security

Examining operational efficiency

Examining condition (by professionals or other specialists) supplementary to the general technical inspections carried out under the standard building inspection system.

The list at Appendix 2 indicated those facilities that come within the scope of these inspections, the relevant code, inspection type, focal point responsibility and inspection level.

Historic Buildings
The PSA in the South West Region has maintenance responsibility for a large number of Historic Buildings ranging from small cottages to stately homes, law courts, hangars and engineering workshops. The register currently numbers 350 but this is no real guide to the maintenance task.

One building in Plymouth Dockyard for example, covers over 4 acres. Most of the buildings are Grade II but there is one Grade I, several Grade IIs* and a large number of Ancient Monuments.
  Like all other buildings on the PSA estate, each is inspected by the DWO staff but every year rather than biennially.
  In addition, every 4 years the building or facility is surveyed by a professional in far more detail than the DWO staff have time for. This inspection would in addition to a structural appraisal would comment on past work and make recommendations on future maintenance. These recommendations if not put in hand immediately would be entered on the Forward Maintenance Register in the usual way.

Property Repayment Service
There has been a trend during the past few years to allow occupiers

of Government buildings to order minor maintenance work of a non technical nature themselves without involving the PSA. The type of work that can be ordered is strictly controlled so as not to conflict with lease obligations or interfere with the building services or structure.

The buildings are inspected by the DWO staff annually and they are available to give advice at any time.

In addition to PSA operated inspections, most clients have their own systems of inspection. Most Military establishments for example have personnel whose taks is to liaise with PSA. Each building has a focal point to whom all defects are reported and he in turn reports defects to the PSA.

Commanding Officers also make regular tours of inspection accompanied by the District Works Officer.

Married Quarters also tend to have a fairly high turnover of tenants and each time there is a tenancy change, there is an inspection of the Quarter (called a March Out).

Monitoring

Any system is only as good as the people that operate it and the Building Inspection system is no different. It stands or falls on the quality of the inspections, the initial action taken, the follow up to any requests for specialist advice and the care taken in the compilation of the Forward Maintenance Register.

The first check and perhaps the most vital is that undertaken by the Senior Technical Officer. On him falls the responsibility to ensure that the inspections are to the correct standard.

The Forward Maintenance Register is designed to be the first source of reference when compiling annual budgets and to be of real value one must be selective as to the items to be included in it. Currently, some DWOs are restricting the list to items of defect costing more than £2500 to repair. There is a growing belief in the PSA that this figure is too high and perhaps a supplementary register is needed to record the smaller value items that cannot be dealt with immediately after the inspection is carried out.

Area Officers have management teams who oversee the work of DWOs and one of their tasks is to monitor the progress and quality of building inspections every 6 months. The management team report to the Regional Works Officer who is then made aware of any major slippage.

In 1985, the PSA set up District Management Teams, Regional based staff who visit each District every 2 years.

Their task is to review all the management and operational functions of the DWO including building inspections. The team have the advantage of seeing all the Districts over a two year period and are thus able to compare one with another and ensure a uniform standard.

The Future

At present each DWO is equipped with a computer system which handles

114

all the financial information of the District. The computers are not large enough to handle planned maintenance as well but from 1988 this will change. From that date District Works Offices will start to be equipped with more powerful computers which will be able to deal with all the planned maintenance systems that districts operate. The present rather cumbersome and labour intensive systems will be refined, the Forward Maintenance Register will be automatically compiled from the findings of the building inspection reports. District Works Offices will at any time of the year be able to rapidly assess the maintenance backlog and perhaps more importantly as all items are costed in the FMR senior management will be able to assess more accurately the impact of a cut back in maintenance funds.

The PSA has always put a great deal of effort into the various systems of planned maintenance and is determined that the Building Inspection system will remain a powerful management tool.

Works Functions   DR 529 Annex A

CLASSIFICATION OF REQUIRED MAINTENANCE STANDARD

REQUIRED MAINTENANCE STANDARD CODE	DEFINITION	EXAMPLES
X	Exceptional	
	Maintenance in impeccable order at all times for reasons of operational necessity, public importance, client status or environmental quality. Classification at this Level requires the authority of the Area Officer.	Selected public or defence facilities in environmentally important areas or with irreplaceable contents.
N	Normal	
	Fully maintained in accordance with all appropriate PSA instructions and with regard to clients needs for extended use.	All facilities except those in categories X. L, W or D.
L	Limited Life	
	Maintained to allow use for a period of not more than five years. Classification to be reviewed annually by DWO in consultation with client.	Facilities awaiting a decision on continued use, conversion, modernisation etc.
W	Wind and Weatherproof	
	Disused facilities maintained only to prevent serious deterioration with due regard to safety.	Facilities having no present use awaiting decision on future use or disposal.

REQUIRED
MAINTENANCE
STANDARD CODE   DEFINITION   EXAMPLES

D   Demolition Pending

               Maintained only to a level   Facilities having no
               sufficient to obviate the   further use or value
               risk of claims or legal   awaiting demolition.
               action against PSA or
               client.

DW 529 Annex B   Variations – Guidelines

GUIDELINES FOR GRANTING VARIATIONS TO THE NORMAL
TWO YEAR INSPECTION INTERVAL FOR FACILITIES

1   All facilities are normally to be inspected every two years but
the Area Officer may vary the interval between one and four years,
having regard to the physical characteristics of the facility and
the need to optimise the use of his staff resources.

Extensions

2   The Area Officer may approve extensions up to a maximum interval
of four years provided he is satisfied that:

   (1)   the previous inspection indicated that there were no
   material defects
   (2)   the construction finishes and services are such that any
   deterioration is unlikely to occur within the period of the
   extended interval which would reduce the condition to a level
   below the required standard
   (3)   PSAs statutory of care or equivalent liability will not
   be prejudiced
   (4)   in leased premises PSAs lease obligations will be fulfilled.

3   Facilities likely to qualify for consideration of an extended
interval will generally be of a simple uncomplicated form, in good
condition and with a known record of low maintenance.

Reductions

4   The Area Officer may reduce the interval from two years to one
year where the particular circumstances justify more frequent inspections.

5   Facilities likely to qualify for consideration of a reduced
interval will generally be either classified exception (Code Xx of
the Required Maintenance Standard) or be of doubtful integrity with
a known or likely high demand for maintenance.

6   Such reductions should be reviewed periodically to ensure that
they are currently appropriate.

Works Functions   DW 529A

STATUTORY, OPERATIONAL SPECIALIST AND OTHER INSPECTIONS

1   In addition to inspections that ascertain future maintenance
needs, as described in DW 529, PSA policy requires other regular or
occasional inspections of buildings and civil engineering,
mechanical and electrical installations.

2   Many of these inspections arise out of statutory or mandatory
requirements and fall broadly into the following purpose categories:

   (1)   examining standards of health, safety or security

   (2)   examining operational efficiency

   (3)   examining condition(by professionals or other specialists)
   supplementary to the general technical inspections carried out
   under DW 529

3   Responsibility for initiation of inspections within DW 529A
does not always rest with the District Works Officer. However, the
DWO is required to refer matters to his Area Officer where
assistance is required to fulfill his obligations under DW 529 and,
where the condition of a facility gives grounds for concern.

4   The B&CE inspections covered by this Code, their authority and
frequency are as scheduled within Annexe A. For detailed information the source documents quoted should be consulted. For M&E
these inspections are covered by the M&E Planned Maintenance System
(Vol 4 - 6 of the M&E Engineering Guide), Safety Procedures (Vol 8
of the M&E Engineering Guide) and various Works Procedures Codes.
The DW 530 requires an annual M&E inspection to be carried out to
check the compliance with these instructions and uses Form W2106 as
an inspection checklist. Reference to M&E instructions have only
been included in Annexe A where a joint B&CE/M&E responsibility
exists.

SUBJECT	REFERENCE NO OF INSTRUCTION/ CIRCULAR	INSPECTION TYPE AND INTERVAL	FOCAL POINT RESPONSI- BILITY	INSPECTION LEVEL
Professional appraisal of building structures	CE93 WP101 CE119 (Large Panel System Buildings)	Defect inspection 8 years	AWO	RCE/ACE
SECO Hutting	CE92	Defect inspection 1 year	DWO	Experienced Officer
		2 years (periods may be extended in certain cases TICE 92)	AWO	RCE/ACE
Airey Houses	DCES Report Dec '85	Defect inspection 5 years	AWO	RCE/ACE
Asbestos based materials	B46 CE146 MEG Vol 8, Sect 56 A&W 24/84	Defect inspection 1 & 2 year MAX (annually for PRS Buildings in all cases)	DWO	Specialist Tech
Fire Precaution in Property maintained by PSA in the UK	WP8	Survey of Precautions normally a 5 year MAX	AWO/DWO	PSA Fire Staff
Testing and maintenance of fire hydrants and wet and dry rising mains	CE102	Test and inspect annually	DWO & FO	Specialist Tech

STATUTORY, OPERATIONAL, SPECIALIST AND OTHER INSPECTIONS

SUBJECT	REFERENCE NO OF INSTRUCTION/ CIRCULAR	INSPECTION TYPE AND INTERVAL	FOCAL POINT RESPONSI- BILITY	INSPECTION LEVEL
Sampling of Drinking Water	CE22	PHE Sampling monthly and 6 months	DWO	Specialist Tech
Periodical turnover of stores domestic water supplies	CE43 WP74C	Operational inspection Ad hoc	DWO	Specialist Tech
Protection of water supplies and water treatment works	CE148 WP45	Defect inspection Varies	)))	Specialist Tech/RCE/ ACE/Panel Consultant
	WP74 WP74C WP101	Operational insp Varies Professional appraisal of treatment works 2 years Statutory insp. 10 years MAX large dams.	) DWO/AWO) RCE)))))))	

COMPUTER-AIDED INFORMATION SYSTEM OF BUILDING MAINTENANCE

Dr. István Zeley
FÜTI, Research Institute for Economics, Organization and
Computer Technique of Building Maintenance, Budapest,
Hungary

Abstract
A planning system of maintenance works (economic planning
system and a computer-aided information system supporting
it) is to be developed by FÜTI which starts from the actual demand for the renewal of the buildings and it ranks
the renewal activities on the basis of the technical condition.
The data base of the system should contain the necessary
information on:
- the general characteristic data of buildings,
- data of types and quantities of buildings structures,
- the condition of building and of their structures,
- the resource requirement of renewal of the structures
  or buildings

The services rendered by the system are:
- planning of maintenance requirements of buildings,
- ranking the requirements
- preparation of building mainenance directory, etc.
Key words: economic planning, building maintenance, building register, condition-survey, resource requirements,
norms, computer

1. Aim of the information system

The value of the building stock is around 2.000 billion
Forints in Hungary. The annual maintenance expenditures
amount to 40 billion Forints. This corresponds to building activities through 12 years and it means three times
the magnitude of the annual national income in its value.
   The maintenance of the state-owned building stock has a
special importance. In Hungary there are 65 thousand state-owned residential buildings (from this amount 30 thousand in Budapest) and the number of rented dwellings in
these residential buildings is 800 thousand, out of this
400 thousand ones in Budapest.

The main source of the maintenance of the state-owned residential buildings is the national budget. The maintenance of the building stock is backwarded, the condition of buildings is very bad therefore the maintenance requirements set great burden to the budget. It makes necessary to elaborate such an information system which, on the one hand, supports the improvement of the maintenance of the state-owned residential buildings and their moderni- zation, on the other hand, it facilitates the economical management with the state budget sources.

The system of maintenance planning is to be developed with the above aim in mind together with the national building register serving for its base. The development is pursued by FÜTI (Research Institute for Economic, Or- ganization and Computer Technique of Building Maintenance)

2. The present state of the maintenance of residential buildings

The financial source of the maintenance (operation and re- newal) of the state-owned residential buildings comes from the rents (in a lesser part) on the one hand, and from the state budget subsidies (in a greater part), on the other hand in Hungary. The management, operation and maintenan- ce of the state-owned residential buildings are carried out by non-profit public enterprises. These enterprises are controlled by the local authorities.

Annual and five-year plans are elaborated for the rene- wal of residential buildings in the following way: ·
- the whole renewal of a building is determined in cycles by orders and by-lows. This cyclic time is 30 years at present. The enterprises managing the buildings take into account for the annual or five-year cycles the renewal of which buildings will be actual (entirely or partially) on the basis of the renewal cyclic time. They estimate the costs of renewal, too. The local authorities revise, mo- dify as necessary and accept the preliminary plan (build- ing-list) and they submit it to organs managing with the state budget in order to get state subvention;
- the compilers and managers of the state budget determi- ne the sum of subvention for the renewal of the residen- tial buildings taking into account the costs calculated on the basis of cyclic time, on the one hand, and the so- urces available in the state budget, on the other hand:
- this sum - which is generally less than the one reques- ted by the enterprises managing the buildings - is first distributed among the counties and then among the local councils which make the enterprises managing the build- ings to be renewed during the successive five years or the following year only. The task of enterprise managing the buildings is the realization of the renewal plan.

122

The above and presently being in force building maintenance planning methods are to be modified and further de-
velopped. These methods have two basic insufficiencies:
- they encourage the enterprises managing the buildings
not in the direction of reaching a greater profit or economic effect but towards the realization of a pre-determined plan and it is not in accordance with the present
system of the Hungarian national economy which is built
upon the maximum profit of enterprises:
- the planning method starts not from the actual condition of the buildings and from the actual maintenance requirements resulting from the above but from the cyclic time partly independent of the building condition of the
maintenance requirements. The technical condition of the
induvidual buildings depends on the building system, on
the building materials used, on the quality of construction, on the way of utilization and on the systematic
maintenance renewal. The planning on the basis of the
cyclic times frequently gives priority not to those buildings with the worst condition and so it constributes to
the further worsening of the building stock.

3. The basic principles of the information system

Such a planning system of maintenance works (economic
planning system and a computer-aided information system
supporting it) is to be developed which starts from the
actual demand for the renewal of the buildings and it
ranks the renewal activities on the basis of the technical condition and so it contributes to the improvement
of the renewal of the buildings and to the economical management with the state budget resources as well. Within
this, the aim of the given system is:
- to help the management activities of enterprises controlling the rational utilization, operation and maintenance of the buildings,
- based on up-to-date maintenance principles it should make possible to qualify the technical condition of building structures, to register continuosly building conditions, the possibility of continuos estimate of requirements
and the ranking of tasks. It should be adjusted to the
requirements of company management,
- it should help the requirement planning, ranking, dist-
ributional and control functions of the state control.

4. The basis of the building maintenance planning: building register and condition survey

The up-to-date economical planning system of building maintenance should be based upon a detailed register extending over every building. The building register should
contain the necessary information on:
- the general characteristic data of building,
- data of types and quantities of buildings structures,
- the condition of building and of their structures,
- the resource requirements of renewal of the structures
  or buildings.

The contents of the data base of building register

In the following the planned contents of the data base
of building register will be described in detail together
with the proposed method of surveying the buildings.

The main general data of the building within the planned
building register will be as follows:

    - building identifiers (e.g. address of building,pos-
                            tal index, street code, geoco-
                            de)
    - building lots data
    - ownership, management and value data of the building
    - main technical characteristics of the building
    - main dimensional units of the building areas and
      areas belonging to them
    - data of public utilities, services and fire protec-
      tion of the buildings

Data of building structures:

    Within the register the technical data of the main
structures generally used in residential buildings are
stored related to every building.

Different data are stored for different structures depe-
ning on their character. The data stored for every structure are:

    - name of structure group
    - way of construction
    - material of the structures
    - quantity of the structures
    - condition of the structures
    - character of renewal and maintenance work

character, quantity and costs of intervention.

The way of construction and the types of the possible materials are, naturally, different by structures.
The technical condition ranges on a scale from A to E and the condition degrees are similar by structures, they differ only in special cases. The determination of the condition takes place by visual inspection in the case of the majority of structures. For some structures (e.g. floors and ceilings) the determination can take place only on the basis of expert or instrumental inspection.
A diagnostic aid is prepared for surveying the condition which facilitates the grouping of structures into the possible condition categories.
The basic element of the system is the condition qualification because the technological norms belonging to the different conditions of the individual structures and necessary for restoring the original state will give the resource requirement and costs of the renewal of the building.
As an example, the data stored in the data base of the facade as main structures and the input sheet used for collection of data and their maintenance will be desribed.

The input sheet for collecting the data of a given structure consists of two parts:

- the right part should be filled with the values and the necessary codes during data collection,
- the left side part contains the information necessary for filling the input sheet and it gives the characteristics to be surveyed and their codes as well.

In the lower left square the following information can be found in the input sheet for the facade determining the filling-in:

- the character of interventions (e.g. repair, maintenance, temporary strengthening, enlalging)
- forming (e.g. plain, smooth, simple, decorated, richly decorated)
- material (e.g. plastered, stone, cladding bricks, aluminium, glass, wood covering)
- place and position of the facade (e.g. street facade, bulkhead, airshaft)
- finishing (e.g. lime finish, plastic finish)

Condition:

A. The condition of the structure is suitable from either aesthetical or functional point of view, intervention is not necessary
B. The structure can be made suitable by usual maintenance operations
C. The structure can be made suitable by repair or partial replace
D. The structure can be made temporarly suitable by strengthening
E. It is not suitable (it should be demolished or replaced).

For residential buildings the survey and registering of the following structural groups are planned on the basis of the above sample:

- substructural structures
- load-bearing structures
- roofs, facades
- structures of internal spaces
- structures of external spaces
- services

Way of data collection

In Hungary from the 1 st January 1987 the data collection and survey will begin for registering the state-owned residential buildings. The building register to be established will be maintained continuously by enterprises managing the buildings. They will fix every such event which modifies the registered data of the given building.

5. Computerized system of building register and the computer netwoork

The building stock of the enterprises managing buildings in Budapest requires the establishment of such a data base which can reach a 50-60 Mbyte memory capaticy by enterprise. The management of the entire building stock of Budapest can reach 1.000 - 1.100 MB disk capacity.
The computer makes it possible to connect 20-22 stored terminals according to the requirements of the system and they can directly access the data with suitable time-sharing.
A direct access to the data should be provided for the state control organs (ministries), the Council of the Capital and for 15 management enterprises operating in Budapest.

Part III
Life cycle costing
and costs over time

COMPUTER AIDED BUILDING APPRAISAL FOR THE DESIGN-IN-USE OF BUILDINGS

KEITH ALEXANDER
Building Performance Research Unit
Department of Architecture and Building Science
University of Strathclyde

Abstract
The paper presents a continuing research programme to develop
computer based design aids in the appraisal of the performance and
life cycle costs of buildings in use. The concepts of performance and
design-in-use are introduced before describing the design
methodology that has been developed. This methodology allows the
effective management and use of historical data about the running
costs of buildings. Such techniques enable the development of data
for use in design decision making. The research has specified the
adaptations necessary to existing computer software to enhance its
sensitivity to detail design changes to an existing building stock.
The paper draws upon a series of research projects to illustrate the
methodology developed, describes the computer software and proposes
future research needs in the field of facilities management.
Key Words: Performance, Life Cycle Costing, Computer Aided Design,
Buidings-in-Use, Design-in-Use.

1. Introduction

'All in all, much of the country's school building stock is in a
sorry state of repair and getting worse. Long standing defects,
allied to little sustained improvement over recent times, are
resulting in some cases in a number of school buildings rapidly
approaching the stage where repairs are impossible and new buildings
may have to be provided. At current prices, the replacement value of
the country's present school buildings is estimated to be about £17.5
billion. The continued neglect of the school building stock is not
only storing up potentially enormous bills for the future but is also
seriously affecting the quality of work and achievement of many
pupils and providing a grim environment for them and their teachers'.

The report by Her Majesty's Inspectors on the effects of Local
Authority Expenditure Policies on Education Provision in England
(1984) indicates problems arising out of under-investment in the
nation's building stock that are applicable not just to school
buildings but across a range of building types. The report relates
the effects of this economic neglect to consequences for the state of
the built environment and for the morale of the users of buildings.

In response to this state of affairs, which can be shown to extend
throughout Europe, a recent seminar organised by the Organisation for

Economic Co-operation and Development (OECD)(1986) has recommended an action plan involving the following phases :

- Establish a condition survey
- Establish realistic budget levels
- Convince politicians/key people
- Arrange Dedicated/flexible budgets
- Examine the maintenance organisation
- Establish standards
- Review performance

The action plan is principally concerned with arresting deterioration - maintaining and patching the fabric to keep buildings (in this case school buildings) in service. In many cases this action may well be counter productive, extending the physical life of a building that may be operationally and functionally obsolescent.

This paper introduces a broader approach that views maintenance in the context of building performance. Performance rather than condition is the measure, and maintenance is seen as contributing to performance over time. Performance can then be related to cost through life cycle costing. Criteria for building performance are derived from continued investigations of the ways in which people interact with buildings and the consequent requirements for fabric and environment.

A change of attitude towards buildings is necessary to the effective implementation of this methodology. It requires acceptance that buildings are adaptable and need to be designed, continually re-designed and managed to respond to the changing demands of users.

Recasting the action plan in these terms would produce similar stages to the methodology that has been developed by the Building Performance Research Unit in recent projects involving industrial and educational buildings and which is described in this paper.

In the paper educational buildings are used as the vehicle to describe the methodology, the techniques employed, and to propose future developments. The methodology is broadly applicable however to all building types.

2.   A Performance Approach

2.1 Building Performance Research Unit
The Building Performance Research Unit (BPRU) have been involved in studies of building performance and use for over twenty years. These studies are driven by the objective of completing the feedback loop in the building process, so that design is informed by an understanding of the problems that arise from the use of buildings. Increasingly design involves working with an existing building stock - adapting buildings to changing demands of users, responding to technological change, conserving scarce resources and rationalising the use of space. BPRU have adapted appraisal techniques developed for designing new buildings to the needs of design in the context of buildings-in-use.

2.2 The Performance Concept in Building

BPRU methodology is founded on a performance approach to building. Essentially this approach involves making explicit statements of what is required of the building in the context of 'climate', use, and resources. The performance criteria can then be used to evaluate designs, may be used in performance specifications for design and build contracts, and could form the basis for periodic post-occupancy evaluations of building performance and use.

2.3 Performance Over Time

The theme of the conference – the management of maintenance of built assets – can be seen in this broader context of providing building performance over the useful life of a building or group of buildings.

Building appraisal involves relating predicted and achieved levels of performance, and estimates and accounts of the resources consumed in providing and using the building over an agreed period of time, to the criteria and targets established for the project. The explicit cost and performance data generated informs design decision making – in the design of new buildings, or in re-design or design-in-use of existing buildings.

The process relies on an explicit statement of expected performance extended over the useful life of the building. Alternatively it is possible to require maintenance of a level of performance for a specified period. The need for maintenance is the recognition of a shortfall in performance. Relating maintenance to building performance provides a mechanism for establishing priorities. A contract, for design or management, for a new building or an existing building is for the delivery and maintenance of performance.

A drawback arises from the lack of an adequate and explicit statement of performance at the outset of a conventional project. However a performance specification can be drawn up at any stage in the life of the building and may subsequently used to bring the building up to standard, to meet the requirements of new users or in upgrading to extend the operational and functional life.

Key concepts are robustness – the ability of buildings to adapt and provide performance over time, and capability – the ability of buildings to accept the changing demands of those who use it over time.

2.4 A Performance Design Methodology

In considering buildings in this way BPRU have developed a computer aided methodology for appraisal of performance and life cycle costs. It provides for integrated consideration of building performance and of all the costs involved in using buildings. This enables maintenance and maintenance costs, for example, to be seen in the context of other aspects of building performance and of the other running costs. The life cycle costs are similarly viewed in the context of the building performance – the overall objective of the building process.

The methodology makes use of existing computer software as the mechanism, and performance as the language for control and collaboration in the process of proposing change aimed at improvement of building performance.

In this approach to the management of built assets, individual concerns such as maintenance are not seen in isolation from the broad task of ensuring effective use of facilities. These facilities represent investment – assets that must be managed if we are to use resources effectively and achieve value for money.

2.5 Design-In-Use

The use of buildings involves a continuous process of adaptation as people interact with them. Users strive for control over their environmental conditions, in order to feel more comfortable with buildings they use. They will personalise the spaces they use, arrange furniture and introduce fittings to the environments that they inherit. A creative tension is established, necessary to the effective use of buildings. Some of the more major tasks in adaptation of a shell to particular uses will be devolved to specialist organisations. Indeed in many circumstances the opportunity for users to influence their environment will be severely restricted.

Changes to the building fabric may be necessitated by changes in the pattern of occupancy, by expansion, contraction or reorganisation of organisations for example. Conservative attitudes towards buildings prevent this next level of adaptation occuring as regularly as circumstances might demand – buildings are buildings are buildings – a fixed asset ?

However there is an increasing need for buildings to accept new technologies to avoid functional obsolescence. As an example the advanced servicing necessary to information technology is forcing the pace of change in most building types. This means that thinking in terms of maintenance of the status quo is not enough. A building's capability can be enhanced through change so that it becomes more responsive to contemporary needs.

There are also initiatives that can be taken to influence the life cycle costs of a building – and the relative significance of each of the constituent costs. It is a matter of identifying controllable costs, and demonstrating that investment in change will lead to considerable economies over a specified payback period.

Clearly such initiatives for change must be within the remit of the team charged with the task of looking after the building or stock of buildings, and the facilities they contain. The concept of design-in-use is proposed to embrace these disparate aspects of adapting buildings to the dynamic needs of the generations of occupants that use them, and for better value for money be obtained by more effective utilisation of their potential. Through a creative and co-ordinated approach to such change, and with the development of effective tools for design and management of buildings-in-use, a greater level of user participation may become possible.

2.6 Maintenance Management by Design

Designers are urged to design buildings with maintenance in mind. Having made appropriate decisions about the building there is the need to communicate the basis of the decisions to those who will manage its use, to form the basis of a plan for maintenance.

A broader concept is necessary if we are to manage buildings as an asset, and not just maintain present inadequacies of the building stock. Even if the occupants of the building do not change, or if the organisational structure is static, there will still be the continuing process of adaptation taking place between the users and the building to be managed.

In defining maintenance in terms of the concepts of performance over time and design-in-use, the need to describe buildings in design in ways which provide the tools and mechanism for their effective management becomes evident.

For the effective use of buildings it is essential to provide the link between initial design, construction and management of its use so that the full potential is realised (maximised). The oft expressed need for a building manual may be satisfied by the common acceptance of a computer model that provides the mechanism for considering buildings as a resource.

The computer aided design models developed by BPRU provide for integrated management of buildings from initial design to use and re-use. The models suggest an active, rather than reactive approach that provides the possibility of 'maintenance by design'.

2.7 Building Performance Management ?
These concepts, and the design models developed from them, suggest a creative role in managing building performance. The processes can be seen to be part of overall task of facilities management. Does this thinking herald a new professional concerned with achievement and maintenance of building performance through design and management ? Could it lead to building performance contracting ?

Provided with responsibility for design-in-use, for initiating change to adapt to changing circumstances or to make more effective use of resources, and provided with powerful tools to improve decision making such a professional can play a much more rewarding role than 'tinkering with the titanic'.

3. A Methodology for Maintenance by Design

3.1 General Methodology
The design methodology for life cycle costing projects, developed by the BPRU, has been adapted for broader consideration of the performance and costs of buildings. The methodology was first used in a research project (BPRU 1984) that investigated the life cycle costs of industrial buildings. Analytical techniques are combined with design innovation in the complete process, although they may be used independently. The stages involved may be described as follows :

- Identify typical buildings
- Identify typical patterns of use
- Appraise performance
- Identify performance shortfalls
- Assess for each project the most costly aspects of the building-in-use

133

- Evaluate for each building (or the most common types) the
  costs and consequences (performance) of separately
  changing each of the most costly aspects of its use and of
  providing for improved performance
- Bring together from these evaluations a set of design
  guidelines of what could be cost effective to do
  differently in the future
- Design (Re-design or adapt) a 'new' lower life cycle cost
  building based on these guidelines – generally applicable
  to the patterns of use identified
- Adjust the general design to take account of particular
  requirements for specific cases
- Appraise the performance and assess the costs of the
  general design and its adaptation for each pattern of use,
  and compare ensuing life cycle costs with existing costs

The methodology is equally applicable in the design of new buildings
and in working with existing buildings. Appraisal is computer aided
using advanced, interactive models developed by ABACUS, the computer
aided architectural design research unit at Strathclyde University.
   If through this process maintenance is identified as a major
component of the life cycle costs of a building, or if inadequate
performance of particular elements of construction are identified as
being significant in the whole building performance appraisal then
subsequent procedures in design and appraisal are directed to
improvement.

4. Computer Aided Appraisal

4.1 General Outline Appraisal of Layouts
The computer programme used for the building appraisals in recent
research using the methodology was GOAL (General Outline Appraisal of
Layouts), one of an integrated suite of programmes developed by
ABACUS over the past two decades. Although the programme was
developed for use in the design stages of a new build project it may
be used in the evaluation of existing buildings and includes a useful
facility for comparison of the cost and performance of any number of
buildings similarly appraised. The general structure of GOAL is
appropriate to an evaluation of the life cycle costs of the whole
building and enables consideration of variables in their context.

4.2 GOAL Structure

The basic philosophy of GOAL assumes that a designer (or design team)
generates a design hypothesis which is transfered to the computer for
modelling. By the same process the design hypothesis could be
replaced by data about an existing building.
   GOAL models the scheme and computes cost and performance. The
cost/performance profile may be evaluated and design changes made to
investigate the potential for improvement. Further iteration will
allow a range of alternative proposals to be evaluated by further
computer runs.
   The general structure of GOAL is shown in Figure 1.

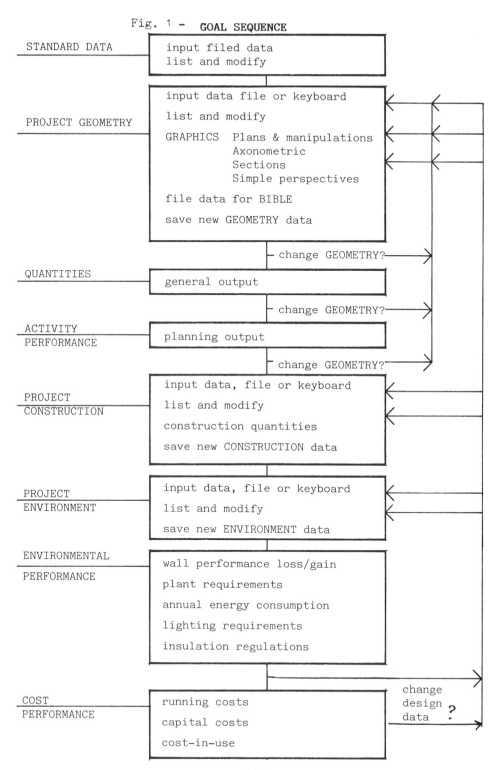

Fig. 1 - **GOAL SEQUENCE**

STANDARD DATA

input filed data
list and modify

PROJECT GEOMETRY

input data file or keyboard

list and modify

GRAPHICS   Plans & manipulations
           Axonometric
           Sections
           Simple perspectives

file data for BIBLE

save new GEOMETRY data

— change GEOMETRY? ——→

QUANTITIES

general output

— change GEOMETRY? ——→

ACTIVITY
PERFORMANCE

planning output

— change GEOMETRY? ——→

PROJECT
CONSTRUCTION

input data, file or keyboard

list and modify

construction quantities

save new CONSTRUCTION data

PROJECT
ENVIRONMENT

input data, file or keyboard

list and modify

save new ENVIRONMENT data

ENVIRONMENTAL
PERFORMANCE

wall performance loss/gain

plant requirements

annual energy consumption

lighting requirements

insulation regulations

COST
PERFORMANCE

running costs

capital costs

cost-in-use

change
design **?**
data

4.3 Standard Data
GOAL may be used in evaluation of any building type that can be
described in terms of its functional, constructional and
environmental requirements. This data is used in the construction of
a STANDARD DATA file for the particular building type under
investigation. The file includes the general data that will be used
in the evaluation of cost and performance - cost parameters, climate,
environmental criteria, functional relationships.This standard data
file also includes the range of choice of constructional types,
heating and lighting systems, fuel types and boiler capacities. Data
about occupancy regimes affecting the heating and lighting periods is
included.

      Standard Data : data about particular building type

       Functional Data - space definitions and associations
       Constructional Data - major elements -
                       floors,walls,glazing,roof
       Financial Data - running cost data
                 values and format of unit elemental
                 capital costs
       Environmental Data - plant parameters,fuel costs
                     lighting environment,fittings
       Climate Data - external climate (winter,summer,and
                        heating season)

Two Standard Data files have been compiled relating to School
buildings. PRIMSK is the appropriate file for use in building
appraisals of primary schools. Sample PRIMSK standard data is
provided as Figures 2 and 3. SECSTD is a file that has been created
to allow secondary school evaluation.

4.4 Financial Data
Of particular interest to this conference is the Financial Data that
is included.
A variety of cost structures may be described by the user in the
Standard Data file - but the general form is one of a number of cost
groups, each cost group having a number of elements. These cost
elements may relate to running cost elements as well as the capital
cost elements that are familiar in conventional cost analysis and
planning. There is associated with each cost element in each cost
group :

      - an element type index which indicates if the element is
        non-constructional, a floor, a wall, glazing, or a roof,
      - a construction type number, which is an index to the
        construction of that type held in the Standard Data file,
      - a unit cost of the element,
      - a unit quantity code. Several different quantities are
        allowed, which provide a parameter more closely
        identifiable with the element function.

In each case, the unit rate is input by the appraiser and may be updated by index if necessary. The requisite quantity is then calculated and multiplied by the relevant unit rate to give an elemental cost breakdown.

4.5 Running Cost Data

The programme automatically computes the energy related costs, lighting costs, boiler replacement costs, and water heating costs of the building from the standard data provided.

In its present state of development the programme deals with 'additional running costs' by identifying elements and attaching simple quantity codes from those currently available. By allocating a unit cost of the element it becomes possible to output running cost data which in turn contributes to the overall life cycle cost computation.

Additional running costs have to be input specifically. Available data about such additional running costs can be included and may be related to particular unit rates for calculation.

In this way it is possible to identify and specify running costs under broad running cost elements such as :

      MAINTENANCE
      REPLACEMENT
      CLEANING
      CARETAKING
      ROUTINE SERVICE
      RATES
      INSURANCE

For each additional running cost the annual rate, quantity code and energy content (if applicable) is identified. For each element identified the programme will calculate a quantity and use the relevant unit rate to arrive at a total cost.

4.6 Project Data

Once a Standard Data file is available for a particular building type it may be used in appraisals of particular buildings. The Standard Data files act as a palette from which it is possible to create project specific files. A set of PROJECT DATA files is compiled using specific data about the building form and configuration, the constructional elements, siting and financial parameters.

      Project Data : description of particular building.

      Geometry Data - geometry of each functional space
      Construction Data - particular construction types chosen
         from choices in standard data file or as exceptions
      Environment Data - specification of site parameters,
         financial parameters, building orientation

5. Computer Based Appraisal of a School Building

5.1 A Scottish Primary School

An existing school in Scotland may be used as an example of the creation of Project Data files and subsequent computer run and output. St. Francis Primary School, Cumbernauld is a typical standard primary school in the Strathclyde Region.

Using the Standard Data file PRIMSK created for primary school buildings and based upon the standard Strathclyde Region 240 place PS brief.

5.2 Geometry File :
Creation of the Project Data files commences with a description of the geometry of the project as floor-by-floor sketch plans. Each space is uniquely identified by a series of co-ordinates in three-dimensional space and labelled in respect of its functional type. The geometry of the school as presented in the Project Data files is shown in Figure 4.

5.3 Constructional File :
Each element of the building can then be allocated a discrete constructional type, selected from the Standard Data File. Elements of a construction not listed in the Standard Data file may be input as construction exceptions.

5.4 Environment File :
Finally the project environment is specified in relation to the site (its location, exposure, etc.), the building (its orientation, fuel type etc.), and financial constraints (capital cost limit, running cost limit, etc.).

5.5 Computer Output
Once the data files have been created it is possible to run GOAL to provide an appraisal of the cost and performance characteristics of the building under consideration.

        GOAL Output :

        General Output - area quantities
                        wall-to-floor area ratio
                        volume compactness
        Planning Output - activity performance - functional
                            (planning) performance
        Construction Output - construction quantities
        Environmental Performances - wall performance loss/gain
                                    plant requirements
                                    annual energy consumption
                                    lighting requirements
                                    insulation regulations check
        Cost Performance - running costs
                            capital costs
                            costs-in-use (life cycle costs)

All performance calculations are based on well established techniques, the capital cost performance is a simple simulation of the cost estimating process common in practice.

Sample GOAL output is provided as Figures 5,6 and 7.

5.6 Responding to the Output
A designer can easily and interactively modify the data in the
project data files (design data) including by graphical means, the
geometry. In the case of an existing building this represents a
process of design-in-use and enables the systematic evaluation of
alternative strategies for reducing life cycle costs. By an iterative
process GOAL can provide a wealth of explicit information for use in
comparative evaluations of different design innovations. It is
possible to engage in a series of 'What ... if' investigations in
order to improve the cost and performance profile of a particular
building and to inform decisions that may be taken in rationalisation
of the stock of buildings being considered.

It is possible to build into the appraisal process automatic
indications of the comparison in cost and performance terms of one
building against the norms of cost and performance in a population of
similar buildings.

The speed with which GOAL can provide this explicit data about the
building and about a series of proposals to improve the situation
responds to the immediacy of the design process. It also links the
user to a centralised data base, which reduces the duplication of
information by the various disciplines, and helps to overcome the
increasing bureaucracy of statutory requirements, company strategies
etc.

There are two particularly important uses of computer models such
as GOAL - in the development of data, and in the provision of a model
of the building that can be used by all those involved in design and
in management of the use of the building. Once validated a series of
runs of the program can generate data - on performance levels,
individual and overall life cycle costs - to replace the reliance on
historic data. Designers and managers can use the program to propose
design changes that may lead to more effective use of space and
resources.

5.7 Development of the Computer Model
Using the existing model GOAL as part of the design methodology in
industrial and school building appraisals and design exercises has
highlighted the deficiencies of the current generation of interactive
computer aided design models for work with existing buildings.
Particular developments of the level of detail at which the software
operates are necessary to increase the sensitivity of the life cycle
costing routines built into the program.

5.8 A Specification for a Dedicated Computer Model
If the computer model is seen as the mechanism for effective
facilities management through team working, it is possible to develop
a specification of what such a model should be able to do in the
context described.

- Allow design changes
- Promote interactive team working
- Present independant running costs in context

139

- Provide performance indicators
- Facilitate comparative studies
- Provide budgetary control and predictive mechanism
- Provide updating mechanism
- Link to existing and proposed associated programs - on a
  modular basis
  Make effective use of available databases
- Provide auditing facility - monitor performance over time,
  account for expenditure
- Accept and manage historical data

Development work is proceeding to bring such an enhanced model into
use in the design methodology described. New software - Computer
Aided Life Cycle Costing (CALCC) is being developed to meet the need.

References

Building Performance Research Unit (1984) Factory Life Cycle Costs
    University of Strathclyde.
Department of Education and Science (1985) Report by Her Majesty's
    Inspectors on the Effect of Local Authority Expenditure Policies
    on Educational Provision in England - 1984.
Organisation for Economic Co-operation and Development (1986)
    Maintenance of Educational Buildings : Policies and Strategies -
    Conclusions of a Seminar in Han-sur-Lesse, Belgium - Oct 1985.

THE USEFULNESS OF MAINTENANCE COST RECORDS IN LIFE CYCLE COST PREDICTIONS

ALLAN ASHWORTH AND PETER L.Y. AU-YEUNG
Department of Civil Engineering, University of Salford

Abstract
One of the supposedly limiting factors in the widespread application of life cycle costing is the general lack of useful historic maintenance cost information. It has long been believed throughout the construction industry that the collection and analysis of relevant maintenance statistics will provide the cost data base which is essential for the direct future cost prediction. This is a doctrine which has been borrowed from capital cost prediction.

This paper discusses some of the inherent problems associated with the collection and analysis of historical maintenance cost data. The cumulative effects from these problems suggest amongst other things, a general lack of a qualitative dimension in such data and that would inevitably discount its reliability to serve the purposes of future cost prediction.
Keywords: maintenance costs, data retrieval, life cycle costs.

1.   Introduction

The conceptual framework of life cycle costing is well recognised in offering a potentially comprehensive approach to evaluating all of the costs involved during the predefined life span of a building or structure. It is equally believed that this technique will provide for an equitable comparison on a quantitative basis amongst competing design options within the same decision-making process. Against these quantified costs, a corresponding list of perceived benefits, whether they be tangible or otherwise, should be compiled for the client so that a value yardstick can be established to allow the emergence of the design solution which best fits his predefined objectives.
Walker (1986) found that this seemingly rational approach was not widely practised within the UK construction industry. It is interesting to consider why this appears to be so.
One of the most frequently addressed problems in economic cost modelling is to determine the model's output reliability. This as such requires a separate consideration and is beyond the

scope of this paper.   However, this concern over the model's
output reliability is considered to depend relatively less upon
sophisticated modelling techniques but more upon the quality of
input data into the model.   This is also the basis of the
doctrine of capital cost prediction which depends almost
exclusively on the manipulation of cost data from supposedly
comparable projects.   Such data can then be adjusted for time,
quality, and quantity as appropriate.   This paper examines the
validity in replicating this same principle in connection with
maintenance cost data for use in life cycle cost predictions.

In the area of forecasting, Klein(1984) noted that "... there
is no separation between goodness of understanding and goodness
of forecasting".   This goodness of understanding may encompass
not only the awareness of potential changes in the socio-economic
environment, which is an important consideration in economic
forecasting, but also the awareness of what the input data
actually represented and the limitations thereof.

Hobbs(1978), Skinner(1982) and Flanagan and Norman(1983) have
indicated the significance of maintenance cost data variability.
The authors' own experiences in studying a particular type of
local authority primary schools confirms the previous researchers
viewpoints.   This paper therefore, is aimed at identifying some
of the intrinsic problems of data collection and analysis which
may account for such variability.

2.   The perceived differences in the usefulness of
            maintenance cost records.

The term "the usefulness of maintenance cost records" has many
different interpretations depending upon the various professional
standpoints.   Surveyors and other financial managers, for
example, each have different requirements to fulfill their own
distinctive tasks. The surveyors, for example, may choose to
place emphasis upon the forward projection of the data, the so
called ex-ante approach, whereas others may see it largely in the
context of solely book-keeping or accounting which is known as
the ex-post approach.   Yet, despite these differences, both
concepts do have a common ground of agreement. They both rely
upon the collection and analysis of historical cost records in
some way or other.   However, owing to this perspective divergence
in the utilization of these records this will inevitably lead to
different expectations from the level of details available from
them.

Such a disparity is likely to be further aggravated by the
fact that data collection and retrieval has long been a manual
process and data can only appear in one format which will hence
be limited to serve the intended purposes of those who have
established the system.

Moreover data collection is a costly operation which commits
and consumes a variety of resources.   The costs so incurred must
be justified for its intended purpose.   Recent data investigation
suggests that maintenance costs are currently recorded with the

142

preoccupation of ex-post concepts for two major reasons:-

a) To execute financial controllability in line with an annual maintenance expenditure target.
b) To satisfy the needs for accountability.

Data recording systems have therefore been designed and developed to meet these objectives. These data systems designs seem to have placed more emphasis on recording the magnitude of maintenance cost figures rather than the causes which give rise to maintenance needs and hence to their corresponding costs. This suggests that maintenance cost data may be available quantitatively but not qualitatively.

3.   The problems in the maintenance data collection process.

The difficulties involved in maintenance data collection process can be described in three major facets. These are illustrated in figure 1 whereby the intersecting zone represents the potentially usable data and are described below.

Data availability: manual recording of maintenance cost data is still being practised in most organisations and the average duration of this bulk data storage will normally be of five years after which this information will no longer be retained. It poses a problem therefore in statistical terms to find a sufficient sample size to detect any trend failure of components. With the gradual use of computers for this process, this weakness may be improved over time.

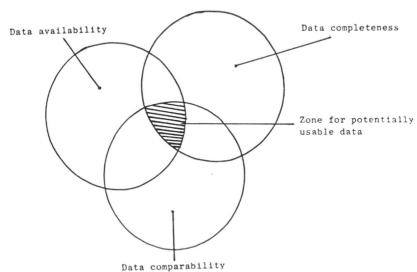

Figure 1   Facets representing difficulties in maintenance cost data collection process

Data completeness: the assignment of codes and prefixes to the various maintenance items is intended to facilitate easy and rapid idenfication. These codes, however, often represent different levels of description details in maintenance expenditure items. Attempts to decode them into sensible and meaningful description are fraught with a variety of problems.

Data comparability: different organisations tend to have their own data recording systems with varying levels of details of classification. The criteria to include or exclude certain items will vary depending upon the system adopted and the data may therefore have a limited comparability. The BMCIS may be seen as a starting point in attempting to standardize the details in data recording

4.   An intrinsic problem in maintenance cost data recording:
        the representativeness of the data

The sources of maintenance cost information together with an appreciation of the limitations which are inherent in the data generally are essential before the data can be properly used in practice.

4.1   Internal data source
The reliance on internal records is believed to be the most relevant for the following reasons which rely upon some insight of the organisation concerned.

a)   The maintenance policy adopted.
b)   The type and mix of operatives who are directly employed for this purpose.
c)   The attitude towards maintenance funding.
d)   The age, condition and geographic location of the properties.
e)   The use characteristics which give rise to the needs and frequency of maintenance activities.
f)   The density of use.

Despite the perceived advantages in using internal records they do have the following limitations.

4.1.1   A lack of indication of the extent of the maintenance
        work done.
It has been suggested that the doctrine of capital cost data collection may also be applicable for life cycle costing. This inevitably implies that the intention is to manipulate maintenance cost data in a similar way to that of capital cost data. It is worth noting at this point the fundamental differences between capital and maintenance cost data.
     The elemental unit rates derived from capital cost data do represent at least the prices at which the entire realization of those elements at a certain quality has been achieved. Whereas in maintenance, the recorded expenditure figures in themselves do

144

not necessarily represent the entire extent of repair to a component or an element. Nor is there further information to reflect the extent to which maintenance or repair work has been carried out, and no supplementary information is available to apply even 'imaginative' interpretation of the situation from these figures.

Further, Holmes and Droop (1982) noted that 'maintenance is budget orientated rather than needs orientated'. In other words, maintenance events will be carried out when and where the needs for maintenance and the adequacy in the provision of maintenance funds co-exist. This may be illustrated by means of a flow diagram shown in figure 2.

In an era of stringent government financial control, property maintenance budgets are an area to suffer early cuts in expenditure. The supply of funds for property maintenance generally also falls far short of meeting not only the increasing demand from ageing and ill-constructed properties in the past, but also from the urgent needs of a long list of accumulated backlog maintenance. A recent Audit Commissions Report (1986) highlighted some £20B of backlog maintenance on local authority housing projects. This perhaps provides a good indication about the scale of the problem. Thus, historic maintenance cost data can only represent how much was affordable by the organisation in a particular financial year, often on a make-do and mend approach, by stretching the available funds over a very wide maintenance need.

4.1.2   A lack of clarity in data categorisation
The examination of any sets of maintenance cost records from differing organisations show that there is a disparity in categorisation. The format of the records are such that it is often not possible to compare one with another, since not every maintenance category is represented in each data sets. Broad categories such as "General" or "Repairs and maintenance" disclose too little information to prospective data users on which any reasonable judgement can be made. Thus an oversimplified global approach in data recording leaves much to be desired.

4.1.3   A lack of identification on the causes of component failure
A better understanding and appreciation on the causes of component failure will help to improve assumptions on their life expectancies, which are required in a life cycle cost prediction. The causes of failure such as bad design or detailing, poor workmanship or supervision and the like, should be able to be improved upon with the benefits of hindsight. Industry should at least attempt to ensure that known defects will be avoided in the future. Other maintenance generated items such as normal wear and tear on the fabric which may be related to the degree of exposure, or fatigue of components can only be minimised but not avoided. In addition knowledge of specific causes of component

145

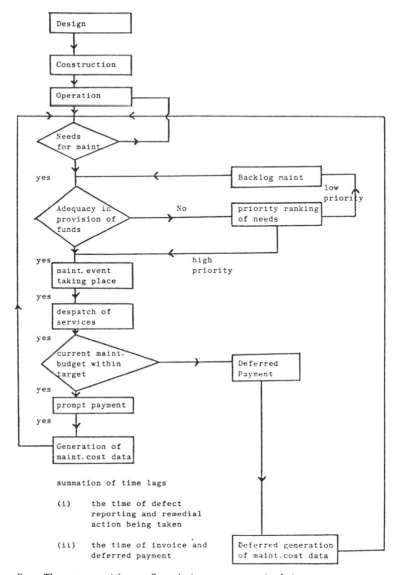

Figure 2: The generation of maintenance cost data

failure which may be the result of misuse or vandalism will
enable the data user to be aware of other factors which will
assist him with his judgement accordingly.

4.1.4   A lack of explicit information on non-identical
replacements.

The rapid advancements in technology should mean that building
components are likely to be produced with a higher degree of cost
efficiency and improved quality.   The temptation to replace
dilapidated components with non-identical new items may be
aggravated not only on the basis of cost, performance and
availability considerations, but also on the basis of changes in

146

statutory requirements.

The effects of non-identical replacements may also affect the initial life cycle cost predictions. The frequency of such and their subsequent replacement cycle will carry different cost implications. This information is generally absent from the available maintenance cost records.

This provides an added difficulty in attempting to reveal facts from figures for future model construction and model updating at a later date.

4.1.5   Potential distortion in the use of maintenance cost data as an indication of the component replacement cycle.

Defects are generally not known until they actually affect the buildings inhabitants. There are also two possible time-lag delays before such information appears in the records.

(i)   the time between defect reporting and the remedial action being taken (maintenance response time)
(ii)   the time between invoicing and actual payment.

The magnitude of these time-lags depends upon the severity of the financial constraints and the degree of urgency represented by the maintenance task. Figure 2 illustrates this point.

Where this information is used to indicate a possible observed life expectancy of components then some distortion in the results should be expected. The magnitude of such time-lags in each particular circumstance, will vary depending upon the procedures used for carrying out the work together with the availability of the necessary finance. Thus the varying magnitude of time lags inhibits the use of maintenance cost records as a potential indicator on observed life expectations of components.

4.1.6   Hidden maintenance and repair items in capital cost programmes.

Maintenance and repair items are often absorbed within a new capital works programme sometimes because of the data recording practice used or to suit budgetary requirements. Examples in energy improvement works lend themselves to illustrate this point since these works are generally classified as capital works programmes. The timing of the execution of the energy improvements work on roof insulation, for example, is done to coincide with that of roof repairs. Thus dual objectives will be achieved with the roof repair work being hidden amongst other issues.

4.1.7   Potential distortion in the timing of maintenance cycles due to the budgeting system.

Figure 2 showns that backlog maintenance is a result of priority ranking of maintenance needs within budget constraints. It is difficult to tell from records which expenditure relates to these items and for how long they have been in abeyance. This further

echoes (4.1.5) that the corresponding time of maintenance
expenditure is not a reliable indicator of the life expectancies
of components.

4.1.8 A lack of indication as to the inter-dependency of certain maintenance items

Delayed action in certain types of maintenance work will have a
'knock-on' effect upon other components. For example, a roof
leak which was left unattended would create maintenance problems
elsewhere, for instance on decorations. The cost savings
momentarily made on the roof could also create considerable
expenditure which may be out of all proportion to the initial
maintenance problem. It would also have little to do with any
maintenance cycle for these other items. This represents a
further weakness in existing maintenance cost records which might
be used for predictive purposes.

4.2 External Source

Where internal maintenance cost records are unavailable then
other external sources of data may need to be examined for a
potential use in life cycle costing. The identified and
perceived advantages outlined above will need to be factors to be
considered when using this type of data. Amongst these factors
the maintenance policy and operation are crucial considerations
but particularly difficult to accurately ascertain.

Another possible external source of data which can be used is
that derived from rental properties such as service charge data.
Caution needs to be exercised with the method of service charge
apportionment (whether it is based on rateable values, gross
floor areas, nett lettable areas or some combination of these
factors), the terms of the service charge arrangement and the
taxation status of the clients.

5. An intrinsic problem in maintenance cost data analysis: measurement distortion

In addition to the above, which affect the representativeness and
accuracy of the maintenance cost data recording, the exhibition
of data variability will be further amplified at the analytical
stage. This will depend upon the way in which the raw data is
considered. Furbur (1985) has described this as "measurement
distortion". This can be considered from two standpoints.

(a) A mathematical view. It has often been assumed that linear
relationships exist between cost and other variables such as
floor area, This presumption is questionable. Au-Yeung's (1985)
earlier work in presenting painting costs on hospital projects in
different ways showed different results. Figure 3 shows total
painting costs against the volumetric dimension of hospitals (in
health buildings painting costs are often represented in this

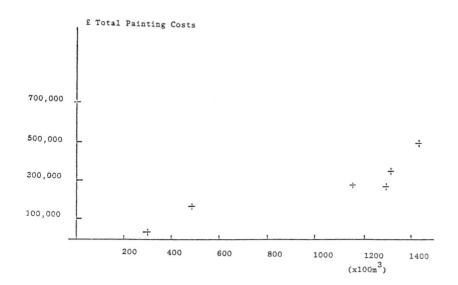

Figure 3.   Overall painting cost is plotted against overall Volumns in hospitals.

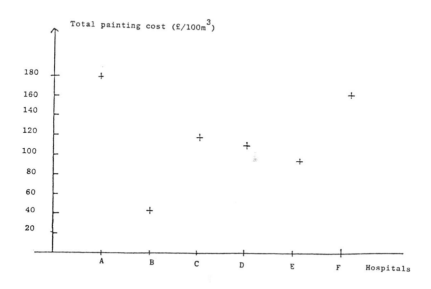

Figure 4.   Painting costs expressed in £/100m³

149

way rather than with the superficial floor area). Figure 4 represents the same data expressed in terms of £ per 100m^3. Data variability here was considerable and no meaningful trend could be detected. This preliminary study suggests two things;

(i)   Presenting data in their raw form may help to establish a mathematically predictable trend which is not necessarily linear.

(ii)   The presentation and treatment of raw data is just as important as the representativeness of data itself.

(b) A buildings measurement characteristics view: Furbur(1985) noted that: "With the peculiarities of the service charging method and the different types of costs, some area related, some non-area related, and certain on different areas or additional areas to net lettable areas.   It is inevitable that, with buildings all having unique characteristics, the final rate unit charges will vary".

    In some non-area related costs such as caretaking costs and lift maintenance, large sized buidings with small circulation areas will clearly have the edge of advantages on unit rates which tend to be low over its rivals.   It is simply because of measurement characteristics alone.   Thus, one of Furbur's conclusions was "recognising a buildings measurement characteristics against other buildings is an essential first step to gain a better understanding".

6.   Some missing maintenance cost generating characteristics

Knowing 'how costs are actually incurred on the site' is perhaps a renowned principle in any cost prediction exercise.   In order to improve understanding on how maintenance needs arise, six maintenance characteristics can be identified.

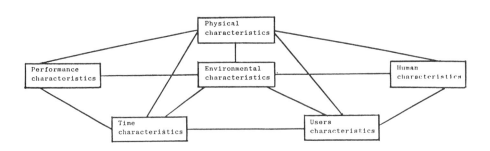

Figure 5 shows the inter-relationship of these characteristics.

150

(i)   Physical characteristics: superificial areas, type
         of heating and boiler, physical conditions, age
         etc.
(ii)   Performance characteristics: thermal
         performance/conductivity.
(iii)   User's characteristics: hours of occupancy,
         frequency of use, type of use.
(iv)   Human's characteristics: workmanship and design
         quality, vandalism, attitudes towards maintenance
         funding, attitudes of maintenance staff and
         workforce, attitudes of tenants, rewards system.
(v)   Time characteristics: time interval of component
         failure, maintenance response time.
(vi)   Environmental characteristics: organisational
         decision making environment, architectural fashion,
         change in statutory regulations.

It is perhaps important to note that maintenance needs arise not
necessarily because of normal wear and tear of components but, in
the main due to the quality of workmanship and design and the way
in which the building is to be operated and cared for. The main
problem therefore seems to relate to human aspects and yet this
is perhaps the least explored area in maintenance cost research.
Apart from physical and performance characteristics which are
available from maintenance records, all other characteristics are
virtually non-existent. Thus the data user cannot even make the
broadest subjective allowance in his or her prediction task
without knowing some background information of the data.

7.   Conclusions

This paper has exposed the fragility of maintenance cost data
which is currently for use in life cycle cost predictions. Before
the questions of predictive accuracy can be addressed the
fundamental problems in maintenance cost data reliability
discussed in this paper need to be resolved. The following are
suggested:

(a) A short-term solution: In order to avoid the problem, Morley
(1986) argued that the only reliable sources of data are those
which the project generates itself. The emphasis of his proposal
is not towards the reliance of a one-off prediction but more
towards fine-tuning of the estimate using self-generating data.
This refined estimate may also be used as a management tool.

(b) A long-term solution: The necessity for refinement of the
maintenance cost data base in the provision of meaningful inputs
to already existing robust life cycle cost models is of paramount
importance. This data base refinement process may be achieved by
the universal adoption of standard data recording formats using
an agreed framework. These numerical data must also be
accompanied by qualitative characteristics as previously

151

outlined. Alternatively, Flanagan (1986) suggests a simulation approach which allows for variations in costs across the range of data sources.

To diagnose the barrier and to scale down accordingly the ambition of what is achievable, are already a realistic way ahead. Both of the above suggestions are not mutually exclusive; the former being a stop-gap approach until the latter can be realised.

Acknowledgement

The authors acknowledge the assistance provided by SERC for research to be carried out on which this paper is based.

References

Au-Yeung L Y (1985) "Life cycle cost predictions in hospital buildings" undergraduate dissertation, Liverpool Polytechnic.
Audit Commission (1986) "Improving council housing maintenance" HMSO.
Flanagan R and Norman G (1983) "Life Cycle costing for construction" Surveyors Publications.
Flanagan R (1986) Conference Paper on "How much do your buildings really cost" RICS.
Furbur J D (1985) "The measurement distortion factor and services charges" Property Management, Volume 3, No 1, pp25-40.
Holmes R and Droop C (1982) "Factors affecting maintenance costs in local authority housing" Building cost techniques new directions (edited by P S Brandon).
Hobbs S (1978) "Collection and use of maintenance cost data" BRE CP 3/78.
Klein L R (1984) "The importance of the forecast." Journal of forecasting, vol 3,pp 1-9 (1984).
Morley D A (1986) "Maintenance data reliability" Deloitte, Haskins and Sells Construction and Property Group (internal paper).
Skinner N P (1982) "Local authority house maintenance - the variation in expenditure" Housing Review, May-June 1982.
Walker D (1986) "Life cycle costing: is it worthwhile ?" undergraduate dissertation, Salford University.

LIFE CYCLE APPRAISAL - FURTHER CONSIDERATIONS

P.S. BRANDON
Department of Civil Engineering, University of Salford

Abstract
The paper traces the need for considering the economic future
within design decision making and explores the problems associated
with applying life cycle costing to this end. It discusses some of
the psychological issues involved and raises the question as to
whether life cycle costing is there merely to provide information
or to advise on the decision to be made. The problems of risk and
future aversion are referred to as well as the underlying
assumptions upon which the technique is based. It suggests that
the relative stability of the public sector is likely to make LCC
more acceptable than the private.
Key words: Life Cycle Costing, Risk, Risk Aversion, Future
Aversion, Design Decision Making.

1. Introduction

The past three decades or more have seen a cyclical interest in
techniques which view the total cost of an asset over its lifetime
as opposed to the cost of its initial provision. With each cycle
there has been a change of name and a slight change of emphasis.
Stone (1967) published 'Building Design Evaluation - Costs-in-Use',
Southwell (1967) gave us 'Total Building Cost Appraisal', the
Department of Trade and Industry in the 1970's, set up a Committee
for Terotechnology which produced many publications and more
recently the RICS (1983 and 1986), RIBA (1985) and the Society of
Chief Quantity Surveyors (1984) have each produced publications on
Life Cycle Appraisal or Life Cycle Costing. The subject is not
confined to the UK for among others the United States Department of
Commerce, National Bureau of Standards has been working effectively
in producing publications, computer programs and workshops on the
topic for the benefit of a wide range of personnel.
    A number of questions arise from this burst of activity which
are worth asking. For example, "Why has it taken so long for the
techniques employed to be adopted?" After all they have changed
very little in concept or detail over the thirty year period.
"What is the underlying concern that brings the topic to the fore
at regular intervals?" Is there something fundamental in the

methodology which prevents widespread acceptance of the results?
The rest of this paper will touch on some of these issues.

2. Conflict and Guilt

Hilgard et al (1975) suggest that where impulses conflict with
moral standards, violation of these standards may generate strong
feelings of guilt. It may be that the normal processes of business
decision making are in conflict with the longer term view required
by LCC resulting in a corporate guilt complex by members of the
design team. There is always the nagging doubt that if we don't
take LCC into account then we are not really providing the best
solution for our clients. If we don't consider the future then are
we doing a disservice to future generations who have to pick up the
legacy of our decision making? It is brought into sharp focus when
cost studies employing the technique, usually on a single component
or operation, 'prove' that one alternative is 'better' than
another. Should we ever pick one of the rejected options? The
answer depends on the user's view of the technique and the other
criteria to be employed in evaluation.
    The issues raised lie at the heart of economic decision making.
Economic choice depends on a number of assumptions including the
belief that the decision maker is acting rationally. In LCC
'acting rationally' is usually assumed to be a discounting of
future expenditure in an identical way to the shape of the
reciprocal of the compound interest table that has been selected.
Can such a numerical technique accurately reflect the myriad of
factors which influence the decision maker's perception of the
future?

3. Numerical Techniques

One argument for LCC is that the figures produced by the method
provide a more substantive case for certain choices than merely a
description. There is some empirical evidence to show that humans
are more likely to believe in figures than words because the former
imply measurement. Consequently an argument containing figures is
supposed to provide the stronger case. Most research involving
cost involves numerical information but if we are to use this
information for forecasting then a number of issues need to be
addressed.
    For example, where should we obtain the data? Without data
there is little information (i.e. structured data) but in LCC,
historic information in terms of costs and performance is dependent
on the constraints imposed on the maintenance manager. The data is
largely 'budget led' i.e. dependent on the finances made available
by the building owner. While it provides evidence as to how money
was spent in the past it gives little information as to what will
or should happen in the future. In work undertaken with Salford
City Housing Authority we are investigating the experience of

154

maintenance managers and the workforce as a basis for assessing
component performance, rather than rely on past records. Even so
are we recording prejudice rather than fact?

Without some form of structured data there is no knowledge (i.e.
the links between pieces of information which helps make sense of
the world). We therefore need a standard way of classifying data,
irrespective of the way it is collected, to aid in communication
and analysis. A common language needs to be developed but what
part should numbers play in this language?

Knowledge whether descriptive or numerical is essential to
making forecasts but decisions about the longer term future are
meaningless unless we can exercise control. The alternative is an
expectation of the forecaster that is not unlike that of the
prophet! A greater emphasis on management within the framework of
the initial forecast is likely to be of greater benefit to the
client.

Decision making is not always entirely logical or rational and
many psychological factors must come into play. In the experience
of most people numerical information is a useful starting point but
decisions are very often based on other criteria.

The desire within life cycle costing to bring both initial and
future costs to a common unit of measurement is fraught with problems and dangers. These costs reflect assumptions about the future
behaviour of people in terms of their use of, and response to, the
building. Much of this behaviour will relate to non-economic
issues and will be difficult to measure. Schumacher (1973) in an
attack on cost benefit analysis stated "... to undertake to
measure the immeasurable is absurd and constitutes but an elaborate
method of moving from preconceived notions to foregone
conclusions". However the objective of LCC is to obtain one all
embracing figure which represents the investment position of the
client.

LCC measures future performance in monetary values based upon
assumptions of human behaviour and decision making which cannot be
calibrated with precision and if imposed could create an oppressive
tool.

The purpose of identifying these issues is to raise queries on
the use of a numerical technique like LCC as a suitable tool for
decision making. At best the technique needs to be seen as a
reference point, at worst we should recognise the possibility of
undermining other values. The weight given to one all embracing
figure is dependent on the level of expertise which interprets that
figure within the overall design decision making process. A
skilled design team may be able to use it profitably whereas a
naive client may find severe problems. Even the skilled user may
find difficulty in interpreting the LCC results of a complex
complete building. He has to be confident that his assumptions
about the future are true, that the 'weight' given to initial in
relation to future costs reflects the client's decision making, and
that the behaviour of the occupants will remain stable throughout
its lifetime.

4. A naive example

Figure 1 shows a simple example to illustrate the point. Buildings A and B have their present value calculated and the difference appears to be around 5%. A difference in this magnitude over sixty years is trivial. We know that contractors and quantity surveyors can only estimate within the region of plus or minus 10% on initial costs (Beeston (1974), Morrison (1984), Fine (1974)). What chance is there of being within this figure over a much longer life span and with considerably less control over the human and material performance? If we change the interest rate, include tax assumptions, change the building use (all highly likely) then we would get a totally different result. The author used a simple monte carlo simulation program (Brandon 1985) to simulate the LCC of a single component which required replacement but no other future cost. The building life, interest rate and component life were allowed to be sampled from hypothetical but not unrealistic distributions and the end result varied by a factor of six. Variability of this kind gives very little confidence to the decision maker.

	Building A			Building B		
	PV Factor	PV		PV Factor	PV	
1. Initial Cost		100,000			130,000	
2. Cleaning & Oper Cost	9000	9.967	89,700	7000	9.967	69,770
3. Redecoration	8000 @ 5 yr	1.63	13,040	7000 @ 5 yr	1.63	11,410
4. Roof	20000 @ 20 yr	.171	3,420	22000 @ 25 yr	.101	2,220
5. Heating Inst	6000 @ 15 yr	.310	1,860	7500 @ 15 yr	.310	2,330
		Total PV	208,020		Total PV	215,730

Figure 1

156

5. The Assumptions

The assumptions in any LCC are enormous. Let us look at some of them which affect the calculation.

(a) Component performance.
This will depend on design detailing, workmanship, building use, client attitude to maintenance, exposure, climatic conditions etc. It is often said " ... if only we had data ... " but virtually every comprehensive collection of data has demonstrated the extreme variability of cost or performance of components. Even where a single client with a homogenous set of buildings has attempted to collect information (e.g. MPBW study of 24 Office Buildings (1971) the results are almost worthless due to the wide variability caused by the factors mentioned before.

(b) Building life
This is usually assumed to be the economic life of the building. For one retail chain this is taken to be eleven years because it is assumed that by the end of this period the market will have either disappeared or grown to the point where a larger store will be required. Templeman Plat (1986) tried to establish 'period of interest' in relation to 'preferred calculated life' as a way of understanding the decision making process of clients when viewing the future. Figure 2 shows what he saw as a conflict between the two. While the concept is interesting the actual scales will need to be determined by further research.

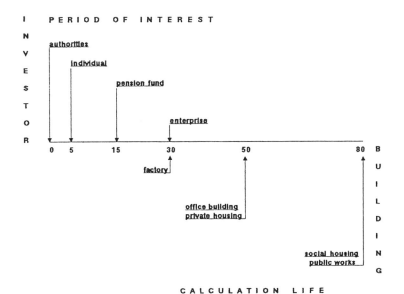

Figure 2   The conflict between period of interest and preferred calculation life as basis for design and construction

Irrespective of these matters there is little doubt that location, population trends, economic climate, planning initiatives are
likely to have the greater effect on economic building life and
these are notoriously difficult to predict. We know that because
of the exponential function in present value tables it is better to
overestimate rather than underestimate building life. However,
with the instability in markets and the mobility of the population
this may be an unwise act.

(c) Inflation
One argument is to ignore inflation (Stone 1967) but the experience
of the 1970's in the UK is to undermine this view as for some time
real interest rates were negative. Predicting what will happen
over the building lifetime is virtually impossible. The matter is
aggravated by differential inflation among commodities as
demonstrated by the changing relationship between fossil fuel
prices over the past twenty years. The next fifty years are likely
to be even more erratic as the scarce non-renewable resources of
the world are subjected to differential demand patterns.

(d) Technological change and fashion
Of increasing importance this particular assumption is almost
impossible to predict. Changes in fashion already have a dramatic
effect on future perceptions and one clothes store expects to
change its shop front every 3-5 years so as not to appear outdated.

(e) Taxation
This has a dramatic effect on future expenditure and in recent
times has resulted in a 50% reduction on many future costs for
those paying corporation tax. It is interesting to note that while
the government was encouraging industry to save on energy it was
effectively giving a huge discount on fuel bills through the tax
system. Any change in tax relief will have a substantial effect on
LCC and the importance of considering future costs.

6. Uncertainty and Risk

All of the above factors create uncertainty in predicting the
future and contribute to the risk involved in decision making. A
distinction between risk and uncertainty is sometimes helpful but
as Hertz and Thomas (1984) point out that while the distinction is
useful, in conceptual terms it has little value in the practical
process of risk assessment and analysis. They go on to say that
" ... concepts of strategic risk must reflect the realities of
strategic decision situations. That is, they must recognise such
issues as the quality of information available to decision-makers
and the importance of outcomes and organisational goals. Therefore, our concept of strategic risk recognises that strategic
decision-making situations involve 'structural uncertainty'. In
other words there is considerable uncertainty about the formulation

of the problem in terms of its structure and underlying assumptions".

In terms of LCC the quality of information is extremely poor and some doubt must be cast on the possibility of great improvement due to the time scale of prediction and the enormous number of external variables acting upon the objects of the calculation. Assessment of risk becomes a hazardous business but must be preferable to deterministic methods even if they include sensitivity analysis.

Sensitivity analysis places the user in the unusual position of being able to assume that everything is stable except for the one or two variables he is examining. The real world is never like this and to oversimplify in this manner is to distort that reality. It is the interaction between events and commodities, between time and deterioration, and between behaviour and building performance which distinguishes the real world from the deterministic model.

Probabilistic distributions achieved from risk analysis do provide a means of comparison for LCC performance but it is unlikely except in extreme cases (which would probably be recognised without calculation) that these could be used with any great confidence for comparing complete building alternatives. The problem of disaggregating an integrated set of interactive and dependent events makes the underlying assumptions obscure to the user. However for simpler situations involving individual components or operations it may prove profitable particularly where the item is clearly significant such as cleaning, energy or supervision/ security.

Even so other factors must come into play if the technique is to reflect the user's approach to decision making. The manner in which he views the future and his attitude to long term loss or gain must be considered.

7. Risk Aversion

Bon (1986) in a paper investigating the psychology of choice uses the work of Kahneman and Tuersky (1984) and others to demonstrate that there is a fundamental assymetry between gains and losses. He argues that there is risk aversion in the domain of gains and risk seeking in the domain of losses. In other words the majority of people prefer a sure gain to a gamble and a gamble to a sure loss. He then extends the argument to the subjective value of gains and losses with respect to time i.e. present and future.

He suggests that when time enters the calculation that most people are likely to prefer present over future gains (future aversion) and future over present losses (future seeking). However there is unlikely to be symmetry between the two and that it is plausible on intuitive grounds that a postponed loss is less aversive than a postponed gain of a similar amount is attractive. The concept is shown diagrammatically in Figure 3.

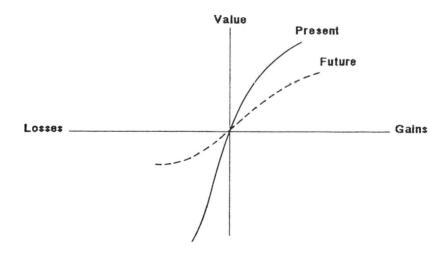

Figure 3

In the case of LCC where the emphasis is on reducing future
losses this assymetry could be important in reflecting the
psychology of the decision maker within the technique.

8. Summary

The discussion contained in this paper has highlighted once again
some of the problems associated with LCC as a technique. The
'structural uncertainty' of the problem it addresses due to the
gaps in our knowledge about future events and the lack of full
early design information means that we can only talk in terms of
probability. The attitude of the decision maker to future gains
and losses appears to be an important function and suggests that
the technique should reflect the psychology of the user group.
There seems to be little evidence to suggest that users conform to
the pattern of the discounting curve when making future judgements.
In many ways this presents a rather negative case against the
technique. However it is important that we give consideration to
future matters for the reasons given earlier in the paper. A
surveyor going before a committee of his local authority or
government department is expected to have used his expertise to
assess the future and make a judgement between alternatives. He
cannot refuse to try because of the complexity of forecasting. He
is expected to make a reasonable guess.
     So what can be done to improve things? Perhaps a starting point
should be a clear view of what the LCC process is trying to do:-

- is it merely a provider of information from which the user draws upon together with other factors to make his decision? If so does a composite figure including a wide range of assumptions, with a theoretical view of the future based on the discount function really provide the answer.

- or should the technique reflect the psychology of the user, i.e. his attitude to risk, his aversion to the future and his need to justify and investigate his reasoning.

If it is the former then why attempt to bring all factors to a common present value? Surely it is unnecessary to use a single figure in an attempt to equate initial and future costs. There are different constraints and objectives relating to the two different time scales. Sources and methods of finance vary and this in itself provides an argument for separation. If deterministic methods are employed then at least three figures should be given i.e. total initial cost, total future cost and total future cost discounted. In addition a further breakdown into significant cost headings should be used to identify problem areas. The decision maker is then in the position of being able to judge the weight to be given to each figure bearing in mind the constraints and objectives to which he is subject. Probabalistic approaches could provide further information in terms of range although the problem of dependencies should not be underestimated.

If it is the latter then a greater problem arises in capturing the attitude of the decision maker. The techniques employed in expert systems to elicit and represent knowledge may have a useful part to play. However, it is doubtful whether the knowledge is stable, except perhaps in the public sector. In the private sector where entreprenurial activity is involved, it is the ability to take good commercial opportunities in competition which identifies success and this may make LCC a low priority. To try and capture attitudes in a technique, so that it reflects the way in which the user makes a decision would be extremely difficult and possibly counter productive in a competitive market. For example in a different domain recent stock exchange selling appears to have been the result of a number of computers using a similar model with a similar perception of the future.

If LCC is to establish itself it must gain the confidence of the decision makers. In the public sector where the objectives are more stable there is evidence to suggest that the technique has been accepted. In the private sector the major cost centres are beginning to be explored in LCC terms although there is some way to go before total lifetime costs are considered as the basis for economic decision making.

Finally economic forecasting is undermined if control is not exercised over those aspects of the completed building which are within the remit of the building owner. We need to enhance and develop management techniques alongside LCC to ensure that some form of budgetary control can be employed. Realistically this is unlikely to extend over the lifetime of the building or relate to

the original budget. However, a regular review with a rolling
financial plan, projected for say five years, could result in major
benefits to the client.

References

Beeston, D. (1974) One Statistician's View of Estimating, BCIS,
    Cost Study 3, July 1974.
Bon, R. (1986) Choices, Values and Time - the psychology of cost-
    benefit assessments, in Building Research and Practice
    (ed. E.& F. N. Spon for CIB), 19, No.4, pp 223-225.
Ferry D.J. and Brandon, P.S. (1984) Cost Planning of Buildings,
    Granada, pp 277-287.
Fine, B. (1974) Tendering Strategy, Building, 25.10.74, pp 115-121.
Flanagan, R. and Norman G. (1983) Life Cycle Costing for
    Construction, RICS, London.
Hertz, D.B. and Thomas, H. (1984) Risk Analysis and its
    applications. John Wiley and Sons Ltd. pp 3-4.
Hilgard, E.R., Atkinson, R.C. and Atkinson, R.L. (1975)
    Introduction to Psychology (6th Edition). Harcourt Brace
    Jovanovich Inc. p434
Kahneman, D. and Tuersky, A. (1984) Choices, Values and Frames,
    American Psychologist, 39, No.4, 341-350.
Morrison, N. (1984) The Accuracy of Quantity Surveyors Cost
    Estimating, in Construction Management and Economics,
    (Ed. J. Bennett) Vol. 2, No. 1, pp 57-75.
MPBW, Directorate of Quantity Surveying Department (1971)
    Cost-in-Use. A Study of 24 Crown Office Buildings. Department
    of the Environment, HMSO.
RIBA (1986) Life Cycle Costs for Architects. A draft Design
    Manual. RIBA, College of Estate Management (Pub)
RICS (1986) A Guide to Life Cycle Costing for Construction, RICS,
    London
Schumacher, E.F. (1973) Small is Beautiful, Abacus, pp 35-38.
Southwell, J. (1967) Total Building Cost Appraisal. RICS, London.
Stone, P.A. (1967) Building Design Evaluation - Costs-in-Use.
    E.& F.N. Spon, London.
SCQS (1984) Life Cycle Cost Planning, Society of Chief Quantity
    Surveyors in Local Government, OCM Publishing Ltd.
Templeman Plat (1986) Housing Cost Calculation and Decision Making
    Depending on the Character of the Building and of the Inventor.
    Paper presented to CIB W65, Hungary 1986.

A RATE OF DEPRECIATION AS AN ELEMENT OF MANAGEMENT OF MAINTENANCE
OF CONSTANT CAPITAL IN THE POLISH BUILDING ENTERPRISES

MAREK BRYX
Department of Building and Investment Economics, Central
School of Planning and Statistics

Abstract
In this article the issue which arose from the inadequate
application of depreciation rates and the lack of incentive to efficiency in the utilization of capital assets in
Polish building enterprises is presented. At first there
are stated - a method of capital assets amortition, some
of the depreciation rates used in building companies and
the growth of their capital assets in 1970-1985.
The second part concentrates on a question of the consumption coefficient of capital goods. The application of the
above quoted rates, a decrease in supply of new assets,
maintenance of old completly amortized goods in exploitation are the reasons which provided for high level of consumption of capital goods in builders. From this fact, to
which there is statistical evidence the two sides, the
Government and the enterprises, arrived to the contrary
conclusions.
    This article indicates that:
i/ Depreciation rates have not great impact under the conditions of centralized management of the economy. However,
in the Polish reform target its significance is considerable and it must be applied with due caution.
ii/ Improvement in the utilization of capital assets as a
part of a general improvement in effectiveness is closly
related to the cosequent implementation of a new Polish
economic system.
Key words: Depreciation Rates, Consumption Coefficient,
Concealed revaluation of Assets, Ineficiency.

1. Introduction

There are 1227 state building enterprises and 273 cooperative building enterprises in Polish building industry.
More than two third of them employ more than 5 hundred
workers each. There are also about 90 thousand small private building firms employing as a rule 1 - 2 people,
because tax poliecies make those firms reduce the number
of employees. The constant capital of these firms is very

163

small; it accounts for means of transport mainly. Therefore a question of using a rate of depreciation as an element of management of the maintenance of constant capital
concentrated only on big state-owned and cooperative building enterprises. They are namely those companies that are
to be considered in this article.

In accordance with the recent Polish rules a capital
asset includes:
 i/ means of production utilized longer than one year pre-
serving its substantial forming the process, and
ii/ its value is not lower than 150 thousand zlotys.

2. Method of calculation and hights of rates of depreciation

The rates of depreciation are set by the Government as uniform for all enterprises, and differentiated for certain
kinds of capital assets. These rates are used irrelevantly
of the real terms of utilization. However in case this
principle is abandoned the exceptions refer to a particular
group of assets. For instance - vehicles used in building
enterprises are depreciated according to higher rates than
the average ones. The sole exception for which individual
depreciation rates are calculated is the fixed infrastructure of the construction sites. The above mentioned rates
is based on costs of the fixed infrastructure and forecast
period of exploitation.

The Government quoting the depreciation rates embark on
research of the real average utilization capital assets,
assuming for building enterprises utilization of fixed capital during one and half working shifts i.e. 12 working
hours. On one hand this simplifies the process of calculation, on the other - it provides an incentive to better
utilization of the building capacity. Therefore as Bień
/1981/ had stated:

The depreciation of capital assets utilized in a number
of shifts less than the above mentioned Government--set increases the unit costs of production. On the other hand a
number of shifts exceeding the state indicate one result in
a reduction of the unit costs.

Some of depreciation rates used in building enterprises are
shown in Table 1.

Table 1. Exemplary depreciation rates in building companies

The kinds of capital   annual rates in %
ussets
----

manufacturing buildings:
    - permanent construction   1.5
    - temporary construction   3.0

```
offices buildings:
    - permanent construction                          1.0
    - temporary construction                          3.0
mobile compressors                                    10.0
excavation and fundation laying machines              17.0
    - excluding compressed air hammers                50.0
road building machines                                17.0
    - excluding road-rollers                          10.0
raill lifts                                           14.0
trucks with load capacity bellow 2.5 t                20.0
trucks with load capacity from 2.5 t to 7 t non
tipping-lorries                                       17.0
tipping-lorries                                       20.0
trucks with load capacity from 7 to 14 t              17.0
trucks with load capacity above 14 t                  14.0
-----------------------------------------------------------
```

It is worth mentioning that the depreciation of a capital asset starts from the first date of the month in which
it has been delivered for exploatation, no matter whether
it is practically utilized. Depreciation ceases after the
total amortization of the assets. If the asset is liquida-
ted before its complete financial amortition the difference accounts for the losses of the company.

Capital assets are not depretiated only in case they
are not utilized for over six months.

3. Capital assets resources in the Polish building enterprises

The capital assets resources of the building enterprises
grew at a high rate in 1970's, the highest in the whole
economy. This rate has slowed down during the economic
crisis since 1980. The relevant data are quoted in table 2.

Table 2. Gross value and growth rate of capital assets in
building enterprises in current prices.

Years	Gross value in mln zlotys	previous year = 100
1970	55.4	--
1971	58.2	105.1
1972	67.9	116.7
1973	84.7	124.7
1974	107.5	126.9
1975	127.9	119.0
1976	148.8	116.3
1977	170.4	114.5
1978	202.7	119.0
1979	233.2	116.2
1980	252.0	108.1

1981	257.8		102.3
1982	273.5		106.1
1983	267.4	762.8$^{a/}$	97.8
1984		779.3	102.2
1985		792.7	101.7

a/ The revaluation point of capital assets

4. Analysis of the deegre of consumed equipment in building enterprises

4.1 Level and growth rates of consumption coefficient
Despite the considerable growth in capital assets in building enterprises in 1970's an advancing process of consumption of these assets has been observed since 1974. This
degree of consumption is measured by the ratio of the amortized value to the purchase value. This index is summarized in table 3.

Table 3. Consumption coefficient of capital assets in %

Years	Total	included		
		buildings	machines and instalations	vehicles
1970	35.4	16.7	46.3	51.0
1971	33.4	15.8	45.8	50.2
1972	31.8	15.0	43.1	46.6
1973	30.3	a/	38.7	45.2
1974	28.8	13.9	36.9	40.7
1975	30.5	13.7	40.2	42.1
1976	31.9	13.0	43.7	44.7
1977	33.4	12.8	46.8	46.4
1978	33.7	12.2	48.4	48.4
1979	34.3	12.5	47.7	50.2
1980	36.1	13.2	50.1	51.6
1981	38.7	13.9	54.3	56.4
1982	40.4	b/	b/	b/
1983	38.7	17.0	66.5	62.8
1984	41.4	18.3	69.5	65.9
1985	42.8	19.3	70.1	67.5

a/ misprint in the Statistical Yearbook
b/ unpublished data

   The consumption coefficient of the total capital assets
in the building enterprises measured by the ratio mentioned
above increased from 28.8 in 1974 to 42.8% in 1985.
   Two different trends can be observed in the presented
period:
 i/ the decrease in the buildings' consumption coefficient
which has been reversed since 1979, and

ii/ the decrease from 1970 to 1974 and then the boost in
the boost in the machines and equipment consumption coefficient /a 32.4 points in 1974 - 1985/ as well as in vehicles /a 26.8 points rise over in the same period/.

From 1970 to 1983 /i.e. to the revaluation point/ the
purchase value of capital goods in the building enterprises grew more than 5 times. Therefore the quick process of
their consumption brings us to some doubts as to the reasons of this issue. We asume that this state of matters
was caused by the sustained exploitation of completle amortition capital assets, despite their considerable supplies
in the 1970's.

These assets were maintained for two reasons:
 i/ bacause their physical consumption lagged behind their
financial amortition, and
ii/ because of the need to maintain reserves under the central planning procedure imposing objectives on the enterprises.

This precautions proved out to be adventageous to the
enterprises in the 1970's as well as in the 1980's when
the supplies of capital goods slumped.

4.2. The Government view-point

Such a high level of amortization of capital assets on the
companies' accounts and the simultaneous task fulfil ment
utilizing those assets proves, in the opinion of the Government officials, that the depreciation rates are simply
too highly set up. Therefore the latter should be veryfied
and eventually reduced. That is why these rates should fit
more adequatly the real level of capital goods disuse, the
more so the enterprises do not liquidate their assets when
the latter are run down physically not to mentioned their
moral out-of-dateness. Besides the Government argues that:
 i/ these capital goods are being utilized in one shift
only whereas the depreciation rates were calculated for
1.5 shift utilization, and
ii/ the enterprises utilize their assets in 70-75% of the
operational time only.
The Government concludes therefore that the capital assets
are not as disused as they may seem when considering the
capital consumption coefficient, but this is due to highly
set depreciation rates.

4.3. Building enterprises approach

It is quite pragmatic, in fact. The companies acted according to the Government-set depreciation rates which result
in a 70% disuse of the equipment. On the other hand employment is being reduced, but the tasks set for the building
industry in the current five-year plan systematically increase. Under these terms the enterprises are unequivocal -
- these tasks are not feasible unless considerable supplies
of new, more productive machines are provided.

167

At present the firms are equipped with out-dated even 20 year-old machines, which are more often being renovated than operational.

A question is therefore asked of whether and how long can this equipment be utilized?

5. Latest solution - the end of dilemma?

By the end of 1985 the Government passed a regulation enabling the enterprises to reestimate amortition degree of their assets. It referred to both total depreciated and those which were to be depreciated in 1986. Commissions were summoned in the companies. They decided as to how long these assets could be exploited. The prolongation of the depreciation term meant a decrease in depreciation level by the same percent which practically revalued the capital assets concerned. This allowed the enterprises to continue to depreciate the above mentioned assets.

As a result their depreciation would increase funds nevertheless transferring half of it to the budget. The Government expects to have a better view on the state of the assets.

6. Summary

It is difficult to judge which side is right or wrong in this situation. There is some truth in each side as far as this approach concerned i.e. both rates can be too high and there is also a major deficiency of capital goods.

Will the latest moves solve the dilemma? - rather not. So far there is no empirical data on the number of enterprises which have revaluated their assets. As a matter of fact none of the sides has changed its standpoint.

It is also worth mentioning that the rate of depreciation which practically played no role in the centralized management system, will be an important and sophisticated instrument and should be treated with caution.

The above mentioned conflict of interest between the Government and the building enterprises may be solved in the process of consequent implementation of the Polish economic reform The latter had to result in creation of a building market and competition among builders. Only when pressed on by the market a profitable firms would get rid of their dispensable capital assets. On the other hand the companies' demand for a capital goods would reflect the real operational needs. Therefore enterprises maintaining big reserves of utilized capital assts would not have to hide out with them, but would simply have to incur the maintainance cost. The demand for capital assets would therefore possibly drop and the exploited assets would be more efficiently utilized. Then the effectiveness of the

168

building enterprises capital assets as well as the other
means of production is determined by the process of the
implementation of the new economy system.

References

Bień, W. /1981/ Economics and Analysis of Building Enter-
    prises, PWE, Warsaw, 168-180.
Bryx, M. /1983/ Amortition on a Paper, Fundamenty, 23.
Bryx, M. /1985/ Costs and Prices in Housing Industry,SGPiS
    Warsaw, 115-120, 152.
Statistical Yearbooks from 1971 to 1986, GUS, Warsaw.
Resoluticn of the Council of Ministers number 95 from 27
    April 1973 as to depreciation of capital assets, Moni-
    tor Polski, /Official Gazette in Poland/ 25.
Disposition of Ministry of Finance numer 1 from 31 January
    1986 referring to rescheduled of capital assets as mova-
    ble assets and correction some of capital assets. Dzien-
    nik Urzędowy Ministra Finansów /Official Gazetta of the
    Minister of Finance/ 1.

CONDITIONS FOR OPTIMALITY IN PERIODIC PREVENTATIVE MAINTENANCE

CHRISTINE S. GROVER
RICHARD J. GROVER   Department of Surveying,
                           Portsmouth Polytechnic.

Abstract

Planned preventative maintenance in buildings is capable of being achieved by a number of different policies of which periodic preventative maintenance is one that has been recommended in guides to good practice. Periodic maintenance involves maintenance at set intervals of time or after a set number of cycles of operation. It is not optimal under all conditions. The principal variables to influence this are whether maintenance restores an item to a state in which it is as good as new, the form of the failure rate function, the nature and behaviour of failure costs, maintenance costs, the effects of maintenance on the risk of failure, the discount rate employed, the time horizon of the decision maker, and his degree of risk aversion. The variability in these makes it unwise to recommend the policy for adoption for specific maintenance tasks but rather the context in which maintenance takes place needs to be considered. In order to assist in this, a simple model for optimising periodic maintenance is presented. This can be used to assess the sensitivity of the conclusions to the assumptions made about the variables, and to revise the decision in the light of changing information.

Key words: Preventative maintenance, Periodic maintenance, Optimisation, Failure rate functions.

Introduction

In recent years there has been support expressed for the idea of planned preventative maintenance of buildings (e.g. Bushell, 1985). Preventative maintenance is carried out at predetermined intervals or according to prescribed criteria, and is intended to reduce the probability of failure or the performance degradation of an item. This contrasts with corrective maintenance which is only carried out after failure has occurred, and is intended to restore an item to a state in which it can perform its required function (BS 4778: 1979). One preventative maintenance policy, which has been recommended for use under certain circumstances, is the policy of periodic maintenance whereby maintenance takes place at set intervals of time, or after a set number of cycles of operation. For example,

171

the Chartered Institute of Building's guide to good practice in maintenance management (C1OB,1982,app B) advocates periodic maintenance in painting and decoration, the servicing of appliances and equipment, cleansing of refuse disposal equipment, horticultural work, and the replacement of electrical wiring and gas water heaters. Since there are a number of alternative preventative maintenance policies, and it is possible for corrective maintenance to be the optimal policy under certain conditions, it is necessary to establish the circumstances under which periodic preventative maintenance is likely to prove optimal. These are discussed in the first part of the article. Decisions about maintenance policies have to to be taken under conditions of uncertainty, using assumptions that may need revision. The second part of the article presents a method by which a cost-effective policy of periodic repair or replacement can be determined and revised in the light of experience.

Influences on the optimality of periodic maintenance

The factors that principally determine when periodic preventative maintenance is optimal are its costs compared with the benefits it offers from the avoidance of unplanned failures and from savings in the costs arising from delays in treating failure. The benefits can be examined by reference to the failure rate function, which shows the probability of failure at different stages in the life cycle of an item. If maintenance results in the condition of an item being returned to a state in which it is as good as new, because, for example, maintenance takes the form of replacement, then the form of the failure rate function plays an important part in determining the most suitable maintenance policy to adopt. Failure rate functions can be divided into three principal forms, burn-in, wear-out, and useful life, but the failure rate function for an item can also be a composite of two or more of these.
  Burn-in failures occur when there is a decreasing failure rate so that the proportion of survivors to fail in each time period declines as the age of the component increases. The probability of failure amongst newly installed items is therefore greater than that amongst older items. Burn-in failures are typically the result of poor workmanship or design. Once the items with defects have failed the failure rate amongst the survivors declines. Butler and Petts (1980) found evidence of burn-in failures after the maintenance of boilers. Reliability in boilers was reduced after being serviced, with plants taking several months to settle down again. A burn-in failure function when maintenance results in the item being returned to a state in which it is as good as new means that failures will be more likely to occur after preventative maintenance than before. A policy of periodic preventative maintenance, therefore, cannot be cost-effective. However, other policies of preventative maintenance, such as design-out maintenance to replace defective items by ones fit for the stated

172

purpose, may prove cost-effective.

Useful life failures occur when there is a constant failure rate. Failure is equally likely at all stages of the life cycle so that it is just as probable immediately after periodic preventative maintenance as before. Consequently periodic preventative maintenance that restores an item to a state in which it is as good as new cannot be cost-effective, since there are no benefits in the form of the prevention of failure to be gained. Other preventative maintenance policies, though, may prove cost-effective. For example, inspections may be used to monitor the conditions of the item with preventative maintenance taking place once the early signs of failure have been detected. In this way any disruption from unplanned failures may be avoided and failure prevented from spreading to other parts of the system.

Wear-out failures occur when there is an increasing rate of failure with age. Periodic preventative maintenance that restores an item to a state in which it is as good as new can be cost-effective since the probability of failure after maintenance is lower than prior to it. Failures and the consequential costs from failure could be reduced by preventative maintenance that takes place before the main part of the cohort is likely to fail. In figure 1 the majority of failures could be prevented if maintenance took place at time such as Otl. Periodic maintenance at intervals of Otl should keep the risk of failure to Ofl. However, whether a policy of periodic preventative maintenance actually proves cost-effective or not depends upon the precise form of the failure rate function. This determines the relative costs and benefits of preventative maintenance. Where the probability density function of failures is unimodal, has a low dispersion about the mean, and is leptokurtic, periodic preventative maintenance can be scheduled to take place shortly before the probability of failure increases substantially. The result should be a reduction in the probability of failure without substantive costs in the form of losses in the productive use of prematurely replaced items or overhauls. A higher dispersion about the mean or a more platykurtic probability density function means that the risk of failure can be kept to a given level only at a higher cost in terms of premature replacements and overhauls, as is illustrated by figure 2.

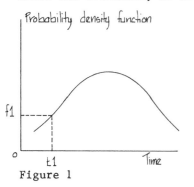

Figure 1

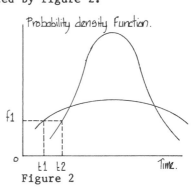

Figure 2

The influence of the failure rate function on the optimality of periodic maintenance may be modified by contractual arrangements following installation. Where installation is followed by a warranty period, there is a safe-life period during which there are no failure costs to the owner of the building. The cost of any failure within this period falls on the supplier. Unless periodic maintenance during the safe-life period is a condition of the warranty, there is little point in carrying it out during the warranty period, since the benefits from preventing failure are gained by the supplier rather than the building's owner. A policy of shifted periodic maintenance, whereby periodic maintenance does not commence until the end of the safe-life period, is likely to prove more cost-effective.

If maintenance does not result in the item being restored to a state in which it is as good as new, periodic preventative maintenance can be optimal in circumstances other than an increasing failure rate. The decision whether to adopt periodic maintenance will depend upon its costs relative to the benefits. For the policy to be effective, it must alter the prognosis of failure. The failure rate must therefore be different after preventative maintenance than before. However, in this case, it does not return the failure rate to that found when the item was new, but could result either in a return to a point on the failure rate found at a younger age than that at which the maintenance took place, or in the creation of a different failure rate function. The benefits from the revised failure rate must be compared with the costs of achieving it in order to determine whether periodic maintenance is the optimal policy. Evidence can be found of occasions when preventative maintenance does not alter the prognosis of failure. For example, Armstrong et al (1983) found that there was little change in boiler efficiency between their being clean and dirty.

A programme of preventative maintenance that succeeds in reducing the risk of failure can benefit an organisation in a number of ways. It should reduce the costs arising from unplanned failures. These include the disruption to the activities the building accommodates from unplanned failure and corrective maintenance. With preventative maintenance policies, maintenance work can be scheduled to take place at times that are convenient to the organisation. Whether expenditure on preventative maintenance is worthwhile depends, in part, upon the behaviour of the cost functions after failure. If failure is liable to spread to other parts of the system, then the costs of remedying it will increase with the time from failure. Depending on how rapidly costs rise after failure, it may prove cost-effective to pursue a policy of preventative repair or replacement. The policy can also result in less idle maintenance capacity having to be kept in readiness to meet peak demands for corrective maintenance. Variability in the maintenance work carried out and in the maintenance expenditure between different accounting periods can also be reduced (Milner & Wordsworth, 1978). If the costs of failure are borne by another party, for example, a tenant, and are not reflected in the costs

174

of the owner, for example, a loss of rent, a policy of preventative maintenance is not likely to be cost-effective for the owner of the building, since many of the benefits will not accrue to him.

Preventative maintenance increases certain costs. These include losses of productive use as a result of premature replacement or overhaul. It is possible that a policy of preventative maintenance may increase the downtime by resulting in more frequent maintenance than would be the case with corrective maintenance. However, the decision as to which policy to adopt does not depend upon the total downtime but rather on which policy minimises the disutility of downtime. Preventative maintenance can still be the more cost-effective even if it results in reduced availability, if the availability at times when it is most valued is increased. Access to and maintenance of parts of systems and structures can result in damage and wear, and so be a cause of failure. Preventative maintenance can result in a higher failure rate than would occur in its absence. Maintenance often involves fixed costs, such as access and setting up costs. Average maintenance costs can be reduced by spreading these fixed costs over a number of different tasks. Since maintenance takes place at discrete intervals, such economies of scale can be lost if maintenance is scheduled to take place at the times best suited to minimise the costs of failure for each component or system in isolation. The ideal preventative maintenance policy can therefore result in costs in the form of a loss of the complementarities to be obtained from scheduling different maintenance tasks to take place at the same time.

One of the most significant costs of preventative maintenance is that it results in expenditure taking place earlier than would be the case with corrective maintenance. The earlier payment of a cost or a delay in receiving a benefit results in a loss of interest. The costs of preventative maintenance are incurred before the flow of benefits. Different maintenance policies can result not only in different costs and benefits but also in different timing of the costs and benefits. In order to examine whether periodic maintenance is cost-effective, its costs and benefits and those of alternative policies must be placed on a time equivalent basis by means of discounting. The higher the discount rate adopted, the greater the weighting given to the earlier costs and benefits. Higher discount rates favour policies such as corrective maintenance, by which the costs are postponed to a later date, rather than preventative maintenance policies, which tend to bring forward expenditure.

The period over which the benefits are to be measured is also significant. If a longer period is allowed for the recovery of benefits after maintenance has taken place, this favours the use of preventative maintenance. Short time horizons favour corrective maintenance since the probability of failure occurring must be reduced by the length of the time period under study. The implication is that different policies are likely to be optimal according to the time period over which the premises are to be maintained. Christer (1976) found that the optimal painting cycles for new premises differed from those for established properties.

In determining the optimum policy, the costs and benefits should be considered in terms of the utility to be derived from them. This may cause particular costs or benefits to be given a higher weighting relative to their expected monetary values than others. The probability of an occurrence may be small but its consequences can be so disastrous that it is felt to be worth spending a sum of its prevention disproportionate to the expected monetary value of its cost. This is particularly likely to occur where human safety or the survival of the organisation may be placed in jeopardy by an event which has a low probability of occurrence. The choice of policy must, therefore, be influenced by the degree of risk aversion experienced by the decision maker.

The variability encountered in the factors influencing when periodic maintenance is optimal cautions against recommending it for specific maintenance tasks. Rather, the context within which maintenance is to take place needs to be considered.

A simple model for optimising periodic maintenance

When periodic maintenance should take place can be represented by a simple optimisation model. Attention is restricted here to items where there is gradual degradation or deterioration rather than sudden failure. Therefore, it is necessary to define the point at which the item is no longer fit for its purpose. The maintenance standards chosen will be influenced by legal requirements and social and economic considerations. The deterioration rate can be modelled by a function similar to the failure rate used above. This shows the degree of degradation or deterioration present at different ages.

For the estimation of an optimal policy for the maintenance of a item over a time period t, it is necessary to know certain information about the costs

Let   x = the fixed costs of a maintenance
      c1 = the unit cost of repair i.e. for 1 per cent of the item
      c2 = the replacement cost of the item
      r = the discount rate

so that the present value of future costs is

$$pv = \frac{1}{(1 + r)^t} \qquad (1)$$

176

The item is assumed to have a deterioration rate over its lifetime that can be modelled by the cumulative Weibull function

$$F(T) = 1 - \exp - (T/a)^b \qquad (2)$$

where a and b are parameters giving the scale and shape of the
deterioration rate. A three parameter model could be used with a
location parameter, g, when there is a initial period with no deterioration, that is a safe life period. As has been noted above, a
safe life period would favour the use of shifted periodic maintenance policies.

It is assumed that repair does not restore the item to a state
in which it is as good as new but reduces the deterioration to
that expected to be found at a younger age. Replacement is assumed to restore an item to a state in which it is as good as new.
Repair could reduce deterioration by a constant factor or by a
factor that varies according to the age of the item when the repair is undertaken. In either case the effect is to cause the
age of the item to be reduced. For example, deteriorated wood
is replaced in a window frame, and the entire surface painted.
The painting retards further deterioration but inherent weaknesses remain so that the frame is not as good as it was when new.
Let g(T) be the affect of repair on age at time T in the unit's
life.

The variable cost of repair is

$$100 \; cl \; F(T) \qquad (3)$$

that is the level of deterioration multiplied by the unit cost.
This may be unrealistic and the costs incurred may rise more
steeply as deterioration increases. Thus, for example, a 40 per
cent repair may cost more than twice a 20 per cent one. Hence,
the variable costs of repair may need to be represented by

$$100 \; cl \; H(F(T)) \qquad (4)$$

for some function H to permit a non-linear relation. If H (F(T))
is linear, then discounting will favour putting off the repair
until later.

At each time period t, which may be any discrete interval, one
of three decisions can be made:

$$d_{1,t} \quad \text{wait, that is do nothing}$$

$$d_{2,t} \quad \text{repair}$$

$$d_{3,t} \quad \text{replace}$$

Alternative models may depend on condition-based decisions whereby
inspections initiate a certain action.

The cumulative cost of a policy over t years depends on the cost of past decisions and the cost of the present decision. Decisions depend upon future costs as past ones are sunk and cannot be altered. Past costs can be regarded as fixed costs but future ones remain variable.

Let
$$D_{t-1} = (d_1, d_2, \ldots\ldots\ldots d_{t-1}) \tag{5}$$

be the vector of past decisions. Then

$$\text{Cost } (D_t) = \text{Cost } (D_{t-1}) + \text{Cost } (d_{k,t}) \text{ for k=1,2 or 3} \tag{6}$$

The present value of each decision is

$$\text{Cost } (d_{1,t}) = 0 \tag{7}$$

$$\text{Cost } (d_{2,t}) = (x + 100 \ c1*F(T)) \ * \ pv \tag{8}$$

$$\text{Cost } (d_{3,t}) = (x + 100 \ c2) \ * \ pv \tag{9}$$

The age T of the item depends on past decisions and their effect on the unit. Let Age_{t+1} $(D_t$) be the unit age at t+1 with past history D_t . Therefore after decision

$$d_{1,t}, \quad \text{Age}_{t+1} \ (D_t) = \text{Age}_t \ (D_{t-1}) + 1 \tag{10}$$

$$d_{2,t}, \quad \text{Age}_{t+1} \ (D_t) = \text{Age}_t \ (D_{t-1}) + 1 - g(T) \tag{11}$$

$$d_{3,t}, \quad \text{Age}_{t+1} \ (D_t) = 1 \tag{12}$$

When deterioration reaches a defined level, the unit is not fit for its purpose. There are then two paths the model may take. Firstly, this vector of decisions is not viable and is eliminated from further consideration. Alternatively, extra costs of corrective maintenance are incurred as a result of the failure of the unit. The second option may not be considered if such costs are high or if the decision maker is averse to the risk of failure. If failure does not incur extra costs, a policy of operation to failure may be indicated.

The optimal policy over t years involves minimising the costs of a decision path:

$$\text{Min } (\text{Cost } (D_t)$$

The solution involves estimating the present value costs along each decision path. This method allows for sensitivity analysis of the effect of changes in the variables to be incorporated. Such changes may include a different deterioration rate than was expected; a different effect on deterioration following repair; varying relative repair and replacement costs; and different dis-

178

count rates. An optimal solution for a policy over t years may not be optimal over t+n years. An optimal policy over t years may involve doing little repair or replacement. If the units are then in place for over t years, this could lead to large scale failure which will involve additional costs and hence a sub-optimal policy. To be certain that this does not happen, a model should consider the effects of a longer life. The model must allow for the re-estimation of future costs and the derivation of the new optimal policy when assumptions made in optimisation are found to be invalid and the situation needs reappraising.

References

Armstrong, J., Gibbons, C. and Morgan, P. (1983), The effect of maintenance on boiler efficiency, Building Services Research and Information Association, Technical Note TN 5/83, Bracknell.
British Standards Institution (1979) BS 4778:1979, Glossary of terms used in Quality assurance (including reliability and maintainability terms).
Butler, H. and Petts, C. (1980) Reliability of boiler plant, Building Services Research and Information Association, Technical Note TN 1/80, Bracknell.
Bushell, R.J. (1985) Preventing the problem - a new look at building planned preventative maintenance, in Managing Building Maintenance, Chartered Institute of Building.
Chartered Institute of Building (1982) Maintenance Management : a guide to good practice.
Christer, A.H. (1976), Economic cycle periods for maintenance painting. Operational Research Quarterly, 27, 1-13.
Milner, R.M. and Wordsworth, R.C. (1978) Maintenance and operating costs of modern boilers, Building Research Establishment, Current Paper CP 59/78, Garston.

MONITORING THE MOVEMENT OF MAINTENANCE COSTS

J.L.N. MARTIN
Building Maintenance Cost Information Service

Abstract
The comparison of occupancy costs over time, requires the use of
indices. This paper describes the models used as the basis for the
BMCIS series of occupancy cost indices for redecoration, fabric
maintenance, services maintenance and cleaning.
Key words: Maintenance Costs Indices, Cleaning Costs Indices, Oc-
cupancy Costs Indices, Building Maintenance Cost Information Service
(BMCIS).

1. Introduction

The object of this paper is to describe the method used to derive and
the input materials used to update the BMCIS Occupancy Costs Indices.
   The indices have been prepared primarily for adjusting the
relevant sections of the BMCIS Occupancy Cost analysis. The series
consists of:

   Redecorations;
   Fabric Maintenance;
   Services Maintenance;
   Cleaning.

   These element indices are compiled from weightings of labour and
material. A General Maintenance Cost Index has also been compiled
from a weighted average of the building element indices i.e.,
Redecoration, Fabric and Services indices. Definitions of the occupancy cost elements are given in Appendix 1.
   The weightings for an index which attempts to chart average movements in general costs can only give guidance on the order of the
costs for any specific building in any specific year. It is unlikely
that the make up of costs for any one building will exactly fit the
model used in the index. It should be noted for instance, that the
level of services maintenance contained in the General Maintenance
Cost Index makes it less applicable to housing than to other types of
buildings. However, the indices do give a guide to the movement in
occupancy costs and with competent interpretation should assist in
comparing expenditure in different years and in updating budgets.

181

2. Building Indices - Models

There are widely different patterns of maintenance expenditure on individual buildings in different years and so inevitably a General
Maintenance Index has to be broadly based.

By studying the maintenance expenditure patterns from BMCIS occupancy cost analyses and from other published sources the cost
relationships of redecoration, fabric and services maintenance were
derived. The relationships obtained were, however, neither conclusive nor compatible. For example, Appendix 2 shows the wide range
that Services Maitenance represented as a percentage of general
maintenance.

A similar study was undertaken of the more detailed element list-
ings in the occupancy cost analyses. However, as the available data
did not represent a random sample of building types or expenditure
periods, the average results could only be considered to be
indicative. The final weightings were arrived at after studying all
the available sources of information and tempering the results with
reasoned judgement. For example, Table 1 shows the breakdown
produced for Fabric Maintenance:

Table 1. Analysis of Fabric Maintenance Expenditure.

External Walls	-	3%
Windows and Doors	-	18%
Roof and Roof Drainage	-	9%
Internal Doors	-	2%
Ceiling Finishes	-	1%
Wall Finishes	-	9%
Floor Finishes	-	4%
Joinery	-	40%
Ironmongery	-	14%
Total Fabric Maintenance		100%

The expenditure on the major items of materials and labour were then
estimated and the labour and material inputs were abstracted to give
the weightings shown in Table 2.

A slightly different approach was adopted for redecoration, since
accurate labour and material constants were more readily available.
A painting cycle of 4 years externally and 5-6 years internally was
assumed and overall labour and material weightings were calculated
from constants for common items of work.

3. Building Indices - inputs

For materials costs, indices prepared by the Department of Industry
and the Department of the Environment have generally been used. The
Index for electrical materials is a composite index of installation
materials produced by the Department of Industry. The cost of
mechanical engineering materials is taken from the Cost of Material
Indices issued for use with the NEDO price adjustment formula for

182

Table 2. Weightings for Building Element Indices

General Maintenance

Redecoration	32.0
Fabric Maintenance	30.0
Services Maintenance	38.0
	100.0

Redecorations

Item	Weightings
Paint	11.0
Labour (building)	89.0
	100.0

Fabric Maintenance

Item	Weightings
Cement	1.0
Mastic	1.5
Imported softwood	2.0
Joinery	10.0
Glass	3.5
Steel sheet	1.5
Tiles	1.0
Asphalt	1.0
Roofing felt	1.5
Metal furnishings	4.0
Plastic building materials	2.5
Plaster	3.0
Blocks	2.5
Materials total	35.0
Labour (building)	65.0
	100.0

Services Maintenance

Item	Weightings
Plastic building materials	1.5
Copper tubes	1.0
Sanitary ware	2.5
Plumbers brass	2.0
Electrical materials	10.5
Mechanical engineering materials	17.5
Materials total	35.0
Labour (services)	65.0
	100.0

183

heating, ventilating and air conditioning installations and lift installations.

Because different building owners employ labour on different wage agreements separate indices have been prepared based on the National Health Service, Local Authority and Private Contractors agreements.

The labour input indices have been calculated from all-in hourly rates for various operatives which include allowances for National Insurance payments etc.

The local authority and private sector services indices are based on rates for electricians, heating and ventilating operatives and plumbers, while the health index contains a single rate for N.H.S. services operatives.

4. Cleaning Index - Model

A study was undertaken to establish the pattern of expenditure on cleaning windows, internal and external surfaces. An analysis was made of the BMCIS occupancy cost analyses and the results are given in Table 3. A similar breakdown taken from the DOE study "Cost-in-Use - A study of 24 Crown Office Buildings" is also shown. The only expenditure on external surfaces was for shops which also showed a high level of expenditure on window cleaning.

Table 3. Breakdown of Cleaning Expenditure.

Building Type	Windows	External Surfaces	Internal Surfaces
BMCIS Occupancy Cost Analyses			
Factories	5%	-	95%
Offices	5%	-	95%
Shops	25%	6%	69%
Health & Welfare buildings	1%	-	99%
Halls etc.	4%	-	96%
Education and research	3%	-	97%
Residential	2%	-	98%
Hotels	11%	-	89%
Average	4%	-	96%
24 Crown Offices	6%	-	94%

The report of the National Board for Prices and Incomes on "Pay and Conditions in the Contract Cleaning Trade" gives the following breakdown for cleaning costs:

Wages	56%
National Insurance etc.	9%
Materials and Equipment	7%
Admin. and Overheads	18%
Profit	10%
	100%

Expressed as Labour (i.e. Wages and National Insurance) and Materials the breakdown becomes:

Labour	90%
Materials & Equipment	10%
	100%

This breakdown does not differ significantly from the other information available, and it has therefore been used in the index. Several sources give a reasonable split between Materials and Plant as follows:

Materials (all consumable stores)	60%
Plant	40%
	100%

The weighting used in the index are as follows:

Labour	90%
Materials	6%
Plant	4%
	100%

5. Cleaning Index - inputs

The labour index is based on the wages promulgated for local authority cleaners. An index of basic wages under this agreement is shown in Table 4 together with an index of cleaners' earnings compiled from the Department of Employment's New Earnings Survey. An allowance for National Insurance etc., has been included to give an overall index for labour costs.

185

Table 4.

Date*	Index of Local Authority Cleaners' Basic Wages	Index of New Earnings' Survey - Caretakers/ Cleaners
1980	100	100
1981	108	112
1982	117	117
1983	126	132
1984	132	136

*October in each year.

The basic materials and equipment indices are obtained from the Department of Trade and Industry. The materials weighting is as follows:

Synthetic detergents	65%
Polishing cloths	10%
Brushes, mops etc.	25%
	100%

The Department of Trade Index for vacuum cleaners and polishers has been used to monitor the movement of plant costs.

References

BMCIS   Section D, Occupancy Cost Analyses   BMCIS
BMCIS   Standard Form of Property Occupancy Cost Analysis - principles, instructions, definitions and elements   BMCIS
Department of Employment   New Earnings Survey   HMSO
DQSD   Cost-in-use a study of 24 Crown office buildings   DOE
National Board for Prices and Incomes   Pay and Conditions in the contract cleaning trade   HMSO

186

Appendix 1

The indices are intended to represent the movement of expenditure on the relevant elements of the Occupancy Cost Analyses. The definitions of Decoration, Fabric Maintenance, Services Maintenance and Cleaning are as follows:

1. Decoration

1.1   External decoration: decoration or redecoration externally.
1.2   Internal decoration: decoration or redecoration internally.

2. Fabric

2.1   External walls: repairs to external structural walls, curtain walls, cladding, glazed screens, external doors and windows.
2.2   Roofs: repairs to flat and pitched roofs, roof lights, lean-to roofs and the like, including work to flashings, dpc's, gutters and downpipes.
2.3   Other structural items: repairs to ducts, internal doors, borrowed lights, frames, stairs, balustrades, dado rails, gantry rails, ironmongery, external fire escapes, floor structures etc.
2.4   Fittings and fixtures: repairs to fitted cupboards, seats, notice boards, shelving, worktops, fireplaces, grillages, blackboards etc.
2.5   Internal finishes: repairs to internal finishes, such as floor finishes, wall finishes and ceiling finishes.

3. Services

3.1   Plumbing and internal drainage: repairs and servicing to plumbing and internal drainage including work to: rising mains, storage tanks and cisterns, hot and cold water services; sanitary ware, W.C. pans, urinals, sinks, taps, valves; waste, soil overflow and vent pipes; internal manholes, rodding eyes, and access covers; and the cleansing of interceptors.
3.2   Heating and ventilating: repairs and servicing to fuel tanks, boilers, flues, plant, pumps, motors, filters, switches, expansion tanks, pipework up to and including calorifiers, radiators, ducts, valves, fans and equipment associated with heating and ventilating installations and air conditioning.
3.3   Lifts and escalators: repairs and servicing to lifts and escalators.
3.4   Electric power and lighting: repairs and servicing to electrical switch gear, fuse boxes, busbars, casings, wiring and conduit to lighting and power supply.
3.5   Other M & E Services: repairs and servicing to other mechanical and electrical services which are part of the building.

4. Cleaning

4.1   Windows: cleaning windows, glazed curtain walling and glazed screens etc.

4.2   External surfaces: cleaning external surfaces of the building, e.g. cladding or stonework faces etc. Exclude the cleaning of external wall surfaces which is accompanied by restoration (e.g. stonework); this should be included in Element 2.1 External Walls.

4.3   Internal: all internal cleaning, other than windows, e.g. cleaning floors, vacuum cleaning, shampooing carpets, dusting and cleaning ledges, furniture and fittings. Include all costs of materials and allocate machine costs. Exclude washing down walls or paintwork done in lieu of redecoration, which is included in Element 1.2 Internal decoration.

Service Maintenance as a Percentage of Total Maintenance

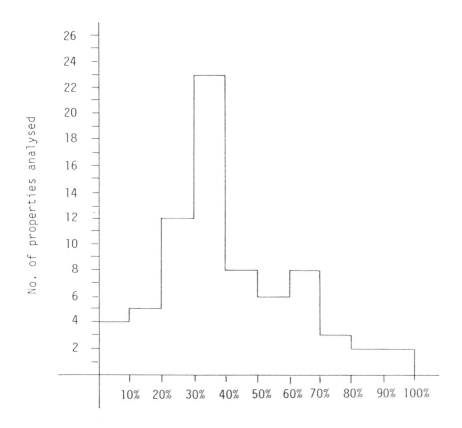

Services maintenance expenditure as a percentage of redecorations, fabric and services maintenance. For example, in the case of 23 properties the services and maintenance expenditure was between 30% and 40% of the combined expenditure for redecoration, fabric and services maintenance.

Note These figures are for more than one year's expenditure and in some cases for expenditure on estates of more than one building.

LIFE CYCLE COSTING AND RESOURCE OPTIMISATION

CRAWFORD W MORTON
Department of Surveying, Glasgow College of Building and Printing

Abstract
The modelling of an economic life cycle is problematic due to the
high number of variables to examine and the lack of certainty
regarding the application of reliable numerical data to these factors
which may change erratically over the chosen time scale. With the
aid of computers it is possible to apply techniques (Monte-Carlo
simulation to name but one) which in statistical terms may prove to
be more reliable than previous methods, but the "Theory of
Uncertainty" will remain valid. It is therefore dependant upon the
compiler of the data to present the final findings in a manner which
takes cognisance of this theory.
    In addition to these previously mentioned factors further research
into performance factors concerning the effect of the completed
building upon the intended activity process and resulting output has
to be undertaken if a complete interactive model of the building
system is to be created. From this model the resource optimisation
can be considered.
Key words: Discounting, Uncertainty, Optimisation, Failure.

1.1 Life Cycle Costing Definition

Life cycle was originally a biological term used to describe the
series of phases through which an organism passes from a specified
early stage (eg conception) to the identical stage in succeeding
generation. Consequently the term life cycle applied originally to
life forms and not inanimate objects. Linguistic scientists, who
deal with the meaning of words and with the development and change in
these meanings, view language as non-static, and observed the biological meaning of life cycle change such that when applied to
inanimate objects it was purely an analogy. The object being
described is considered as undergiong a cyclical existence from
inception to destruction and possible renewal through re-cycling of
material. In modern business economic terms life cycle is applied to
the part of the cycle over which the client has a financial interest
and therefore the term life cycle cost has the implied prefix of
economic within that context. This is the definition of life cycle
used in this paper when applied to heritable property.

Life cycle costing (also known as cost-in-use, total cost or ultimate cost) is an approach aimed at establishing the total cost of a building (or part thereof) including initial capital expenditure, maintenance costs, replacement costs and residual value or residual cost. One of the basic attributes of this technique is discounting whereby all sums of money are transferred to a common point in time, allowing comparison between different design solutions to be made. Discounting involves reducing future money to its current money equivalent (also known as its present value). To obtain the present cost implications one approach is as follows:

Using the formula

$$NPV = \frac{\pounds x}{\left(1 + \dfrac{i}{100}\right)^n}$$

where NPV   is the nett present value

   £x   is the projected cost

   i   is the interest rate expressed as a percentage

   n   is the number of years in the future when the anticipated expenditure will occur

On the basis that £100 today is greater value (ignoring inflation) than £100 in a year's time, discounting is undertaken applying a realistic level for interest rates. When choosing a level it is the "real cost" of finance that should be considered and not the rate that includes for inflation — a rate of 10% may consist of approximately 3% for the "real cost" and a 7% allowance for inflation.

The basic assumption is therefore that inflation and interest rates move in phase all be it that temporary distortions may take place due to specific economic forces. Consequently once the differential between rates has been assessed it is envisaged that on average the differential will remain constant.

Often in life cycle examinations inflation will be ignored on future costs yet inflation will be (incorrectly) incorporated within the discount rate. Even when this basic error does not occur discount rates are often too high to be realistic, with the affect of favouring low initial costs linked with high running costs.

With present rates of interest fluctuating rapidly the problem does arise as to what reasonable discount rate should be applied. Some researchers consider that the most optimistic and pessimistic figures should be used and presented to the client along with the most likely figure.

In addition to inflation and discounting a considerable amount of additional data is required including calculation of initial capital costs (an examination of accuracy levels and time factors in producing results are outwith the scope of this paper) maintenance costs, life spans and residual value all have to be examined. They are considered separately below.

2.1 Maintenance Data

Maintenance manuals are supplied when purchasing most inexpensive
items yet manuals applicable to particular buildings are a rarity.
This basic omission appears to set the stage for the inattention and
lack of data available for building products. General information
can be obtained for certain components but how the maintenance
requirements vary due to location and use is often omitted.
   Any particular piece of data may be suspect and it will therefore
be necessary to seek data from a significant number of projects to
ensure reliability in results. Recording of maintenance data is at
present fraught with difficulties as minor items that cannot be
regarded as maintenance are often included – minor construction
faults may be remedied and allocated to the maintenance budget. To
ensure useful maintenance data capable of comparison it is necessary
to define standards and criteria by which data is collected and
presented, together with detailed reports providing relevant data on
exposure, design of buildings, use of building and any other abnormal
factors effecting maintenance.

2.2 Life Spans

The anticipated life span of the building, or part thereof, should be
carefully examined as this figure will fundamentally affect decisions
regarding capital cost expenditure and future costs – a project
requiring a life span of ten years may be best suited for low capital
expenditure and high running costs as any benefits resulting from
increased capital expenditure may not be recouped in the subsequent
ten years. It is therefore important that the requirements of each
project is considered independently and that generalities are not
applied.
   Furthermore Goodacre (1978) considers that with life cycle
calculations the appropriate figure for the life span is the economic
life as opposed to the actual physical life span. This may mean that
in buildings such as supermarkets the period to consider may be under
ten years, simplifying to some extent the question of variability of
rates of discount, inflation and escalation. Only maintenance
occurring within the economic life should be considered.

2.3 Residual Value

This is the anticipated value at the end of the anticipated economic
life. The value assessed is subject to the discounting process and
is therefore dependent upon the variables affecting maintenance
costs. The residual value may be either positive (a value to the
client), or negative (a cost to the client) or may have no value
(demolition and removal equals value of material).
   Apart from these areas the problem of predicting future
expenditure is further affected by government action. The introduction of "Value Added Tax" (VAT) and its implications to maintenance had a considerable affect on the anticipated expenditure on

193

maintenance. Some projects which were constructed based on certain levels for maintenance (exclusive of VAT) would have been altered if VAT had been allowed for within the calculations.

3.1 Towards Greater Accuracy

Many clients have become disillusioned with the predictions of future expenditure, pointing to classic examples where external forces have totally altered the viability of a project – hydro electric power (HEP) would not have gone ahead on the basis of future anticipated costs for power generation, yet due to the rapid energy cost escalation in the seventies HEP is one of the cheapest forms of electricity production. The findings of a life cycle study have in the past been presented as indisputable facts instead of probable estimates based on assumptions and statistical probability.

Through the use of computer modelling, statistical analysis and refined and more comprehensive data collection it will be possible to improve the accuracy of results. The variability inherent within the factors can (through Monte Carlo Simulation or complex computer modelling) be predicted to a higher level of accuracy. In addition by performing a sensitivity analysis (1983) the making of design decisions regarding life cycle costing of differing design solutions can be undertaken allowing for the most desirable option.

Bennie (1977) however gives a warning on future cost predictions in his statement "one point we can tend to loose sight of sometimes when dealing with calculations and statistics is that, however you are trying to evaluate costs tomorrow with costs today you are ever working against certain basic assumptions on inflation, rates of interest, life etc". Hence there is nothing absolute in the figures obtained, they are by nature of their creation based on probability.

When pursuing an increase in accuracy the researcher must be constantly aware of the "Gaussian" curve in which the scatter of inaccuracy can be summarised as a deviation or spread of the curve (figure 1). From this curve Gauss proposed that theory of "uncertainty", in that we are not sure that the true position is the centre of the curve, all we can deduce is that the correct position lies in the area of uncertainty.

Hence a truly perfect model is unobtainable, a myth, and in the words of Bronowski (1975) "errors are inextricably bound up with the nature of human knowledge". This "area of uncertainty" or "principal of tolerance" is based on the concept that all knowledge is limited and that we are always at the edge of the unknown.

Any model will be limited by this concept and the tolerance will always be calculable from the observed scatter of results.

We can therefore conclude that life cycle costing requires considerable additional research if greater accuracy is required. The question however that many clients are asking are not solely within the domain of traditional life cycle costing exercises. Clients are now requesting data on resource optimisation whereby the resource of construction, maintenance and the building's effect upon the activity and production output of the organisation are all investigated and the most cost effective overall design solution produced.

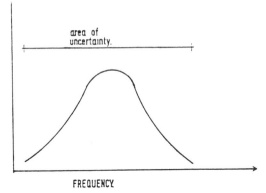

ESTIMATED LEVEL
OF OCCURENCE

area of
uncertainty.

FREQUENCY

FIGURE 1   GAUSSIAN CURVE SHOWING THE AREA OF UNCERTAINTY
AFTER BRONOWSKI

4.1 Resource Optimisation

Researchers at Strathclyde University (1983) have developed a model
which considers the cost of initial provision, cost of maintenance,
cost of the activity process within the structure and the value of
achieving the objectives of the organisation. Hence the designer is
made aware of the fact that he is dealing with a complex interactive
system where four basic systems interrelate. (see figure 2)
    Due to the complexity of this model researchers have tended to
concentrate on the first two systems (where relationships are at
least partially understood) when considering a whole building. Some
attempts have however been attempted with regard to specific parts
of a building.
    The following example illustrates this attempt with regard to
windows.
    The methodology created envisages the situation where the initial
size of the window opening has been decided upon by the imposition
of certain constraints. These constraints will have been formalised
and applied prior to the application of the methodology described.
Markus (1983) represented these constraints diagrammatically as
shown in figure 3.
    As the area of the window increases the cost of provision
(inclusive of initial capital cost, energy balance and maintenance)
increases and the effect of noise penetration increases. The cost
of failure due to the sunlight, the view and other visual
characteristics will decrease as the window increases in size. By
adding all such costs the resultant total cost curve can be
ascertained. The daylight constraint (A), cost limit (B) and noise
constraint (C) restrict the feasible search area for design solutions

195

to the area which is hatched which results in all possible solutions
being above the optimum cost solution (D).

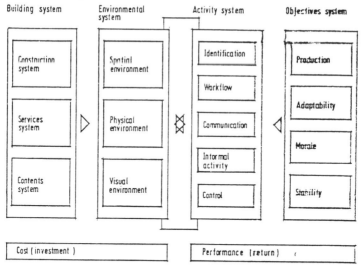

FIGURE 2   THE BUILDING - ENVIRONMENT - ACTIVITY - OBJECTIVES
SYSTEM.   AFTER MAVER

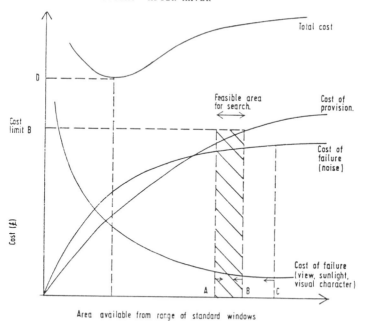

A - Daylight constraint
B - Cost limit constraint
C - Noise constraint.
D - Optimum cost solution.

FIGURE 3   THE GRAPHICAL LOCATION OF THE FEASIBLE SEARCH AREA
FOR A WINDOW AFTER MARKUS

196

Within the feasible search area the architects may add their own constraints based on carefully considered criteria which may result in the feasible area being reduced until only one size of window can be considered. From this one size further decisions of window type, glass type, ironmongery type and window surface treatment will have to be considered.

This example is simplistic in its operation in that objectivity cannot be attained when dealing with subjective values. The financial inducement paid to the building occupants, to tolerate unfavourable conditions, is a variable and very difficult to quantify without extensive research into this area.

5.1 Future Goals

The ultimate goal of resource optimisation will require considerable research and commitment if ultimately advancement is to take place. We should not attempt through resource optimisation, to dictate design solutions as design is only partly logical analysis. In addition it is dependant upon the creative spark which must be left to burn brightly.

References

Bennie, F G (1977) Quality and Total Cost in Buildings and Services Design. Edited by Croome and Skerratt, Construction Press.
Bronowski, J (1975) The Ascent of Man. British Broadcasting Corporation.
Flanagan, R and Norman, G (1983) Life Cycle Costing for Construction Surveyors Publications.
Goodacre, P (1978) A Re-appraisal of Cost-in-Use Calculations, Building Technology and Management - May.
Markus, T A (1983) First Cost - or Life Cycle Cost. Seminar organised by RIBA Services Ltd.

MAINTENANCE COST MODELLING FOR RESIDENTIAL HOUSING ESTATES IN
MOMBASA, KENYA

P.M. SYAGGA, Ph.D.
Housing Research and Development Unit, University of Nairobi

Abstract
This paper constitutes an investigation into determinants of costs
of maintaining buildings in use. The study is mainly concerned
with impact of design on maintenance costs of residential housing
estates in Kenya.
    The study, first analyses the overall cost of housing estates
into three cost areas of grounds, cleansing and building fabric.
It then breaks down the building fabric into elemental cost areas.
This is compare with the incidence of repairs by elements.
    Given the complexity of the factors that may influence
maintenance costs, as well as the incidence of the workload,
it was found necessary to employ the technique of multiple linear
regression analysis to measure the degree of association between
some possible causal factors and maintenance costs. Thus, the
study used a mathematical model in the form, $Y = f (X_1, X_2 \ldots \ldots Xn)$ as
framework within which to study how the annual maintenance costs over
a period varied with building design and other relevant factors.
Some 19 independent variables were identified for regression against
maintenance cost as the dependent variable. They were tested at
95% confidence level using F values.
    A final model incorporating seven independent variables was
developed, accounting for 98.84% of the variations in maintenance
cost per room. The study concludes that building design accounts
for 12% of the variations in maintenance costs.
Key words: Maintenance, Cost, Model, Residential, Housing estates,
Kenya.

1. Introduction

The following case study is drawn from research carried out in Kenya
between 1976 and 1983 to determine the maintenance failure
characteristics and costs of publicly-owned residential housing
estates within some selected geographical regions. Only one region,
that of the Mombasa Municipal Council is described here. The
research emphasises the quantitative rather than the qualitative
aspects of maintenance management. It also uses the case study

199

approach as a guide to other researchers on this aspect of building maintenance.

Mombasa is an area with an extreme climate, which conditioned the need for and approach to maintenance by the authorities concerned. In other cases, one could envisage emphasis on atmospheric pollution (in an industrial city), socio-cultural factors or shortage of key resources such as materials or skilled workers. With this emphasis on the effect of climatic conditions in mind, the study was made under the following headings:

- description of area and climate
- effect of climate on design
- effect of climate on structure and finishes
- sources of data
- data base
- cost codes
- overall cost analysis
- building fabric cost analysis
- relative incidence of maintenance and repairs by elements
- maintenance cost model.

Mombasa is the second largest town in Kenya, and is located in a hot and humid equatorial zone bordering the Indian ocean. It covers an area of 275sq.km, extends a maximum of 50km inland, and its altitude is less than 150m. The population density in excess of 1630 persons per sq.km. It has the largest harbour on the East Cost of Africa north of Durban.

Both day and night temperatures in Mombasa are high, the mean maximum and minimum being 30.1°C and 23.4°C respectively, with a low diurnal range of 6.7°C. The mean annual relative humidities are high, being 93% in the mornings and 66% in the afternoons. The annual rainfall is 1182mm with the highest precipitation of 235mm falling in May. There is an incidence of driving rain from April to October when South East monsoon winds cross the Indian Ocean.

2. Effect of climate on design

Due to the high humidity, natural ventilation is essential in the majority of buildings where air conditioning cannot be economically justified. The prime objectives of design are accordingly to exclude solar heat, to facilitate air movement in and around the building, and provide protection from the rains and other extreme climatic conditions. These aspects affect site planning, the house plan, structure and materials, as well as the location of openings such as windows and doors.

Several alternative design solutions are possible. Whatever

choice is made, it will affect both the initial construction cost and the cost of maintenance, as well as the durability and economic life of the building. For instance, the need for air movement and ventilation may be met by generous spacing between houses or, if land is in short supply, increased building height in preference to increased ground coverage.

The extreme climatic conditions in Mombasa affect both the durability of buildings and the comfort of the occupants. Many materials are affected by high humidity and the high atmospheric salinity of the sea air. High humidity, for instance, encourages the corrosion of items such as galvanised corrugated iron sheets and steel pipes and window frames. Under continuous high humidities and temperatures moulds and algae disfigure painted surfaces and cement-based products. Thus, in Mombasa, concrete walls, cement mortar rendering, concrete tiles and asbestos sheets in exposed surfaces are susceptible to intense blackening.

The biological decay of timber and other materials is greatly encouraged by humid conditions. The driving rain during the South-East monsoon winds not only damages external finishes, but if continuous over long periods leads to the saturation of outer walls and subsequent internal dampness. This may result in moisture movement which causes cracking in concrete blocks.

Mombasa's low latitude gives rise to a high ultra-violet content in solar radiation. This causes chemical deterioration in bituminous materials, and also causes paints to fade rapidly with resultant cracking and flaking.

3. Data base

3.1 Source of data
The data for this study was collected from about 8,000 conventional housing units on estates owned by four major public institutions in Mombasa. The data collected included maintenance costs, relative incidence of maintenance and repair requirements, and causes of maintenance problems. The ownership pattern was as follows:

Institution	Housing units
Municipal Council	3,398
Central Government	2,016
Railways Corporation	1,412
Ports Authority	1,157
	7,983

Data on maintenance costs was analysed for each element in each house owned by the institutions for the period 1974 to 1983, based on maintenance work instruction sheets, annual reports and abstracts of accounts. Each year's maintenance expenditure was raised to 1983 constant prices, using published residential building cost indices from the Central Bureau of Statistics. These figures represent the money equivalents of each year's expenditure for both labour and materials at constant prices.

The expenditure for each year was divided into the number of units on which the money was spent, and this was summed for the study period of 10 years to arrive at an annual average maintenance cost per house or per room. Although there were variations between different houses owned by each institution, and between houses owned by various institutions, the data was analysed statistically, to obtain mean results as a guide for budgeting and the control of expenditure.

3.2 Cost codes
Items of expenditure were analysed according to the following cost codes:

(1.) External and internal decoration

(2.) Plumbing and sanitary fittings

(3.) Electrical works

(4.) Roof repairs including chimneys and ceilings

(5.) Windows and doors

(6.) Floors and staircases

(7.) External walls and partitions

(8.) External siteworks, including repair and cleaning of spaces around and between buildings

(9.) Miscellaneous works not included in the above codes

3.3 Overall cost analysis
The average annual expenditure per house (of about $100m^2$) was approximately US$100. When total maintenance costs for each housing estate were considered, the expenditure on the building fabric, general cleansing and grounds respectively was as illustrated in Fig. 1. The heading 'grounds' includes siteworks and estate roads which accounted in this case for less than 6% of total costs. Naturally these latter costs vary with site slope, house layout and orientation, as well as site size and density.

Cleansing accounting for nearly 18% includes refuse collection, street cleaning, bush clearing and gully/cess pit emptying. The most expensive area of expenditure was related to repairs and maintenance of the building fabric accounting for nearly 77%. The cost of maintaining the building fabric depended on the size of the building, the materials used in its construction, exposure to climatic conditions and user needs.

Fig. 1.:   Overall cost analysis

Fig. 2.:   Building fabric cost analysis

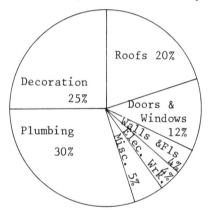

Fig. 3.:   Relative incidence of maintenance and repairs by
           element

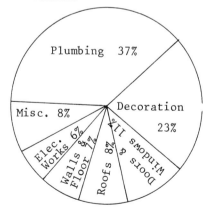

3.4 Building fabric cost analysis
Within the building fabric itself costs were analysed by element.
Figure 2. shows the overall analysis for all the houses for the
whole period. The most expensive element was plumbing including
water and sanitary fittings, followed by decoration and roofs.
Plumbing fittings such as toilet cisterns, covers and seats, as
well as water taps are particularly vulnerable to intensive use and
abuse by occupants, in cases of overcrowding as often occurs in
rented apartments. The relatively high cost of decoration was
affected by the adverse climatic conditions.

Roofs accounted for nearly 20% of maintenance costs, and were
boosted by the expensive replacement of finishes such as asphalt
and bitumen on flat roofs, which are very vulnerable to extreme
climatic conditions. Where pitched roofs were used, timber decay
at the verges and fascia boards was a frequent cause of trouble.
Timber doors and windows also suffered from exposure to the rains
unless regularly repainted or recoated with varnish. Metal window
frames were by no means trouble-free, and corrosion due to
atmospheric salinity was frequently serious.

3.5 Relative incidence of maintenance and repairs by element
Figure 3. shows the relative frequency of repair works for each
element as a percentage of all maintenance and repair works carried
out during the period. The most frequent source of expenditure on
repairs was plumbing, followed by decoration. They were also the
most expensive elements to maintain.

4. Maintenance cost model

4.1 The previous sections have described the areas where money is
spent within a housing estate, as well as within the building fabric.
However, it is also necessary to find out why, for instance,
different sums of money are spent on maintaining different
buildings. This may be achieved through explanatory or predictive
statistical modelling, which if successful could be used to predict
future maintenance cost levels. This section will therefore
attempt to develop a theoretical model based on some building design
characteristics. The study, however, recognises that during the
life of a building other factors such as management policy, economic
considerations, mode of use, climate etc. may singly or
affect addtively or multiplicatively the maintenance needs of a
building. This study will hold some of the factors constant by
choosing one organisation which is located in one climatic region.

4.2 Multiple Regression
The study used multiple regression analysis, assuming that a linear
relationship exists between some 19 independent variables and the
annual maintenance cost per room as the dependent variable. The
regression model is therefore of the form
  $Y = f(X_1, X_2, \ldots \ldots \ldots, Xn)$,
so that $Y = a + b_1 X_1 + b_2 X_2 + \ldots \ldots .f \quad b_n X_n + E$

where Y = average annual maintenance cost per room over a period of
10 years

a = intercept, i.e. value of Y when X_1 - Xn
    are in each case zero.
$b_1...b_n$ = partial regression coefficients
    assuming linear relationships
$X_1...X_n$ = independent variables
    assumed to affect maintenance costs
E   = error term

The data for this model was collected from 14 housing estates with
a total of 3301 rental housing units containing 7578 habitable
rooms. The annual maintenance costs per house were therefore
reduced into costs per room, Y, and regressed against each of the
19 independent variables in table 1.

4.3 Step-wise Regression Analysis
The data in Table 1 were analysed using step-wise regression
analysis with the aid of Statistical Package for Social Sciences
SPSSH Version 5.01 on ICL 1900 Computer. The preferred measure of
relationship between the dependent variable and the independent
variables is the coefficient of multiple determination, R^2, which
indicates the proportion of variation in Y explained by all the
independent variables.
    In order to test the significance of the relationships between
the Y and the X_s, the study used the statistic F at 95% confidence
level. That is, based on the data available, the study would be
95% confident with 5% margin of error to accept of reject the null
hypothesis Ho. The null hypothesis was rejected in each case where
the F value calculated exceeded F value expected i.e. that there
is a relationship between the independent and the dependent
variable. The alternative hypothesis H_A was accepted in each case
the F value calculated exceeded the expected F value, i.e. that
there is a causal effect between the independent and the dependent
variable.

5. The Results

5.1 The results giving the final regression model are given in
Table2, while the residual differences are given in Table 3. It is
evident from the tables that out of the 19 independent variables
only 7 were found significant at 95% confidence level. They
accounted for nearly 98.8% of the variations in the maintenance cost
levels i.e. R^2 = 0.98840.
The most important single factor is, however, the rental received
per room which accounts for 69% of the change in R^2. The next most
important factor is replacement cost of the building per room which
accounts for nearly 13% of the change in R^2. Thus the two economic
variables are responsible for nearly 82% of the variations in

maintenance costs. The fourth most important factor, age may be related to the economic factors as well as the remaining factors which are the physical characteristics of the building. These can directly be traced to design considerations, and so it can be stated that design considerations account for 12% of the variations in maintenance costs.

5.2 Economic considerations
From detailed analysis it was found that the rentals per room varied with the quality of housing provided i.e. location of the property, standard of finishes and the facilities available. In many cases high rented properties were located in good residential areas such as Kizingo, and they were detached houses or large three/two bedroomed self-contained flats. These units were in many cases occupied by chief council officers and senior civil servants working in Mombasa. In many cases such estates did not only spend large sums of money in absolute terms on maitenance, but that also as high as 22% of the rents were spent on maintenance instead of 15% generally considered reasonable expenditure on maintenance. Possible reasons for this high spend are that high rental units are occupied by people with influence who may be requiring too high a standard of maintenance, as much as they reserve the power to order the execution of repair works. Secondly, theoretically high rents are a measure of the quality of houses which have higher amenities to be maintained. Because high quality buildings command high rents, it is possible that more money is available in absolute terms to carry out repairs. The converse is true of estates charging low rents because in many cases they are neglected.

It is in the light of the foregoing that a positive relationship has been established between rental values and maintenance costs in the form of simple repression $Y_m = 26.87 + 0.0158 \ X \ 8$. The intercept and the coefficient will, however, change in the multiple regression. The replacement cost on the other hand has a negative relationship to maintenance cost because in theory high replacement cost could imply that a building is new and therefore requires little maintenance or that a building has been constructed to high standard of workmanship. There is, however, no evidence to suggest that quality of **any** construction is necessarily related to cost of providing the facility.

5.3 Building age
The age of a building is measured from the date of occupation certificate to the base date when age comparisons are being considered. The building life depends on conditions of exposure to climate and use. Individual parts within a building respond in varying degrees to these conditions so that while some parts may need replacement within only one year, others may last five or a whole life of a building. Maintenance is therefore required whether to replace, repair or service a facility. The magnitude of maintenance necessary will depend on the rate of depreciation or

206

Table 1:   Maintenance Cost Determinants for Mombasa Council Housing Estates

Variables (X_1 - X_{19})

Estates (1-14)

	Y	X 1	X 2	X 3	X 4	X 5	X 6	X 7	X 8	X 9	X 10	X 11	X 12	X 13	X 14	X 15	X 16	X 17	X 18	X 19
1.	427	35	287	652	2.3	96	3.0	12113	1899	154	218	5.8	40	2.6	0	0	0	1	1	0
2.	1530	32	18	36	2.0	70	3.5	30373	2700	241	808	8.8	96	2.6	1	0	1	1	0	0
3.	261	29	905	1394	1.5	48	4.7	17986	1720	87	225	5.8	40	2.9	0	1	0	1	1	0
4.	1734	29	6	18	3.0	105	2.5	100715	4800	288	397	9.3	64	3.0	1	0	1	1	0	0
5.	477	26	598	1098	1.8	45	3.9	19956	1294	198	396	5.8	70	2.9	0	1	1	1	1	0
6.	623	27	24	96	4.0	140	2.0	36850	2400	481	808	8.4	96	3.0	1	0	1	1	0	0
7.	1005	26	12	46	4.0	24	2.0	70815	3938	141	144	3.5	48	3.0	1	0	1	1	0	0
8.	295	16	144	432	3.0	120	2.5	28392	1700	1234	1137	11.8	98	2.9	1	0	1	1	0	0
9.	363	13	12	30	2.5	45	3.0	24408	2040	575	397	9.8	64	3.0	1	0	1	1	0	0
10.	188	13	50	200	4.0	24	2.0	17665	1650	91	153	3.5	48	3.0	0	0	1	1	0	0
11.	184	12	100	300	3.0	18	2.7	28920	1800	61	122	3.5	35	2.9	0	0	1	1	0	0
12.	256	10	300	720	2.4	96	3.0	23325	1880	241	397	8.4	48	2.6	1	0	1	1	0	1
13.	279	8	344	784	2.0	105	3.5	24600	2087	525	638	12.0	49	2.6	1	0	1	1	0	1
14.	221	8	300	600	2.3	50	3.5	36360	2250	241	397	8.4	48	2.6	1	0	1	1	0	1

Variables for the model:

Y = Maintenance cost per habitable room in Shs.

X_1 = Building age in years

X_2 = Total number of housing units per estate

X_3 = Total number of habitable rooms per estate

X_4 = Number of habitable rooms per unit

X_5 = Number of habitable rooms per hectare

X_6 = Number of persons per habitable room

X_7 = Building cost per room in Shs.

X_8 = Rental value per room in Shs.

X_9 = Building area in square metres

X_{10} = Wall area in square metres

X_{11} = Wall height in metres

X_{12} = Perimeter length in metres

X_{13} = Room height in metres

X_{14} = Roof types (pitched = 0, flat = 1)

X_{15} = Wall materials (stone/block = 0, bricks = 1)

X_{16} = Window types (shutters = 0, glazed = 1)

X_{17} = External finishes (not painted = 0, painted = 1)

X_{18} = Facilities (self-contained = 0, shared = 1)

X_{19} = Eaves (with eaves = 0, without eaves = 1)

TABLE 2: Final Model for Main tenance cost per Habitable Room

VARIABLE		MILTIPLE R	R SQUARE	RSQ CHANGE	SIMPLE R	B	BETA
X8	RENTAL VALUE PER ROOM IN KSH.	0.82931	0.68775	0.68775	0.82931	0.46298	0.87916
X7	BUILDING COST PER RM IN KSH.	0.90386	0.81697	0.12921	0.52173	-0.00674	-0.34043
X1	BUILDING AGE IN YEARS	0.93246	0.86948	0.05251	0.60918	30.02252	0.57562
X10	WINDOWS	0.97112	0.94308	0.07360	0.18153	618.87068	0.44536
X14	NO. OF HABITABLE RMS PER UNIT	0.96663	0.97344	0.33036	0.11114	-188.75991	-0.31159
X13	ROOM HT IN M.	0.98722	0.97461	0.00117	0.11554	283.65074	0.10206
(CONSTANT)						-1701.81615	

TABLE 3: Residual Differences

SEGNUM	OBSERVED Y	PREDICTED Y	RESIDUAL Y
1	427.0000	449.6344	-22.83444
2	1530.000	1487.764	42.23645
3	261.0000	238.1656	22.83444
4	1734.000	1615.848	118.1518
5	477.0000	499.8344	-22.83444
6	623.0000	686.3503	-63.35035
7	1005.000	1139.462	-134.4615
8	295.0000	249.4206	45.57944
9	363.0000	466.3627	-103.3627
10	188.0000	48.10974	139.8903
11	164.0000	172.0695	11.93052
12	256.0000	214.9339	41.06611
13	279.0000	317.6356	-38.63558
14	221.0000	257.2100	-36.21002

deteroriation, which in principle increases progressively with age. Maintenance needs essentially affect the amount of money needed to carry out the works. Therefore cost of maitenance is likely to increase with building age. In the present model, there is a positive relationship between age of the building and costs of maintenance so that it may be possible to predict the likely costs of future maintenance costs of a building.

5.4 Physical characteristics

The remaining four factors are essentially surrogates for design decisions. These include windows, walls, room height and number of habitable rooms. The most expensive windows were metal casements with glass louvres, while wooden shutters cost least. The metal casement often rust under Mombasa's climate, while glasses are often vandalised by children and need frequent replacement. There is thus a non-continuous positive relationship showing that windows account for 7.4% of the variation in maitenance. Although grouped together with doors in figures 2 and 3, they account for the greater part of the maintenance costs as well as incidence of workload.

Walls have a negative relationship, implying that it is cheaper to maintain bricks than stone/concrete blocks. There were, however, no houses with stone walling, but several with concrete block walls which are rendered in cement plaster. This combined with wall height may be responsible for the high cost of decoration incurred on walls. Room height is a measure of vertical components and elements of a building. A greater height than is necessary for comfort will increase the quantity of building components and elements that will need maintenance. Room heights in Mombasa varied from 2.4 to 3.0m. Increasing the room height say from 2.6 to 3.0 m. increases the height by 15.4%, and therefore the wall area to be redecorated also increases by similar proportion. It has been suggested that an optimum building size may be determined by the compactness of the building described in terms of wall area/floor area ratio of 1.00. The average room height should not exceed 2.5m. Room height therefore has a positive relationship with cost per room in the form
$Ym = 2.63 + 9.25 X_{13}$.

The number of habitable rooms per unit of accommodation is a measure of the size of accommodation meant for one household. It has been suggested elsewhere by the author that a reasonable size of accommodation for a family in Kenya is three-bedrooms and a sitting room in addition to the necessary sanitary and cooking facilities. This was based on cultural sex differentiation within a family where parents would occupy one bedroom, and each of the group of boys and girls still living with the family would occupy one bedroom each.

When statistical relationships are considered, the cost and number of rooms is given by $Ym = 831.865 - 0.59349 x 46$. This implies that maintenance would fall by 0.59 for every additional room provided overall, however, number of rooms account for 3%

of the change in R^2.

6. Conclusion

This study has attempted to present information on the quantitative aspects of building maintenance by firstly identifying areas of maintenance expenditure, and then proposing a possible model for predicting future maintenance costs. The study, however, recognises that this attempt is far from being conclusive for a number of reasons. Firstly, there is need to extend the investigation into other climatic regions, as well as among different housing authorities, both public and private. There will be further need to determine the non-linear aspects of the relationships. Secondly, the study recognises that maintenance costs cannot be explained on the basis of quantitative aspects only.

The qualitative and non-quantifiable aspects of building maintenance such as management policy, organisation considerations, profitability consideration and environmental criteria are subjects of intensive research in maintenance management. However, we should be bold enough to carry out research in other areas whether predictable or explanatory, because each aspect in its way may lead to better management of the built environment.

References

Bowen, P.A.(May, 1982) Problems in economic-cost modelling, in Quantity Surveyor, pp 83-85.

Bowen, P.A. (February, 1984) Cost modelling: an alternative estimating approach, in Chartered Quantity Surveyor, pp 191-194.

Breston, D.T. (1978) Cost model in Chartered Surveyor, Building and Quantity Surveyors Quarterly, Vol. 5 No.5, pp 56-59.

McCaffer, R. (December, 1975) Some examples of the use of regression analysis as an estimating tool, in Chartered Surveyor, pp 81-86.

Neave, H.R. (1978) Statistics tables for mathematicians and the behavioural and management sciences. George Allen and Unwin, London, pp 44-47.

Holmes, R. et al (July, 1981) Maitenance costs of flat roof. BRE Information Paper No. 1P 11/81.

Skinner, N.P. (1979) Variations in local authority house maintenance expenditure. Building Research Establishment Note N 117/79.

Syagga, P.M. (January, 1979) Maintenance and management of council housing in Housing, Volume 15 No. pp 11-13.

Syagga, P.M. (1979) Management of local authority housing estates in Kenya. M.A. Thesis, University of Nairobi, pp 69-140.

Syagga, P.M. (1985) Impact of building design on maitenance costs of residential housing estates owned by Mombasa Municipal Council Kenya. Ph.D. Thesis, University of Nairobi, pp 270-348.

Part IV
Maintenance, design
and feedback

DESIGN FEEDBACK – SUCCESSES AND FAILURES

CLIVE BRIFFETT MSc(Arch), FRICS, CertEd(FE), MSIB
School of Building and Estate Management, National University of
Singapore

Abstract
Design Feedback is a familiar technique to members of the
building team but is it appropriate, worthwhile or necessary?
Designers and maintainers involved in the collection and use of
feedback must weigh the cost against the benefits. Developers
and owners can adversely affect the time required to implement
it. Property managers and building users often determine the
standard of quality achieved by it.
The need for and nature of design feedback is questioned by these
conflicting objectives.
This paper assesses the validity of design feedback, investigates
the areas of research and methods of education concerned with it
and discusses the practical applications.
Key words: Design, Feedback, Maintenance.

Design feedback is firmly established in the building maintenance
industry and operates as an important mechanism to provide a link
between maintenance problems and design processes. It can take a
variety of forms ranging from the traditional maintenance design
communication to the self generated systems of designers.
Design feedback can only be a valuable and reliable tool however
if there is an incentive to prepare it, an expertise to analyse
it, a system to store it and a readiness to receive it. Experience has shown that these desirable conditions do not always
exist and this paper attempts to assess the validity of design
feedback and to suggest means by which its effectiveness can be
improved.

The need for the system has been clearly established over the
last 20 years with so many building failures occurring that
relate directly or indirectly to design. A large majority of the
defects have been identified as being avoidable and repetitive
and through feedback it is possible to reduce these to a minimum.

In order to lay a foundation for this discussion each group of
professionals and layman involved with or likely to benefit from
design feedback are firstly considered.

Figure 1

Figure 1 illustrates the groups and identifies their sequential relationships in the industry.

Designers

Architects are always of first consideration and unfortunately in much literature on the subject may be defined as the only designers. Perhaps the convenience of having only "one bottom to kick" has created this misconception.

Design work also derives from engineers including structural, mechanical, electrical, and those trained in other specialist services. In many cases the defects found in completed buildings may be affiliated to or caused by work initiated by these professionals.

Building Surveyors are another distinct and expanding group who undertake design duties mainly in the area of renovation, rehabilitation, or restoration works and whilst they claim to be well versed in maintenance problems they are not necessarily expert in the design processes.

Decisions on design matters are also heavily influenced by clients opinions and time, cost, and quality determinants. Quantity surveyors acting as a building cost consultants influence major design decisions and Project and Construction Managers also have a role to play.

216

Constructors

Builders, installers, and fitting out companies often find themselves at both ends of the design feedback operation. On the one hand they may be forced to come up with design solutions and on the other be responsible for remedying defects.

Users

Despite being the layman fraternity this group is important in design feedback. They have the most to gain from it and a lot to lose from the lack of it. The functional and financial consequences of building defects are very problematical for this group. Much can be learnt from users on the origin and symptoms of problems and future design should be geared to meet their needs. It would therefore be unwise to ignore or deride their complaints on the basis of lack of expert knowledge. Buildings which lose resentful users also lose money!

Maintainers

The main responsibility for initiating design feedback lies within this group who may include property managers, building inspectors, estate managers private their consultants, and contractors themselves. There must be an incentive and an expertise available to ensure that design feedback is relevant and comprehensive.

Researchers

A wide selection of groups or individuals operate within public statutory organisations or private specialist consultancies, trade organisations or educational institutions to research into building problems. Detailed investigations, analysis, collection and storage processes are undertaken to produce published results.

Having identified the parties concerned with and affected by design feedback it is appropriate to consider the links between them.

Figure 2 below clearly shows that the traditional direct link from researchers and maintainers to designers is only one of the options. This is an interesting observation as other means of feedback can be just as effective and in some circumstances may be more appropriate.

Figure 2

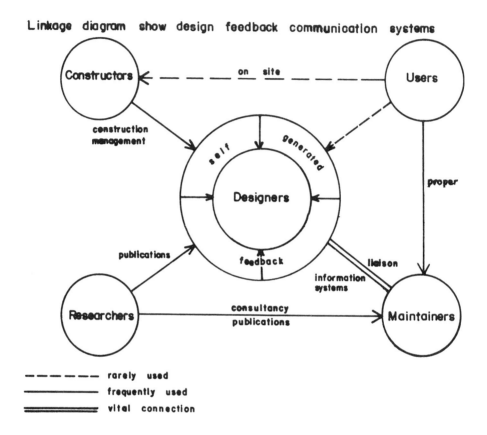

Linkage diagram show design feedback communication systems

rarely used
frequently used
vital connection

In the **designer** group there is an opportunity for self generated feedback for the purpose of upgrading design. This is
particularly useful as it avoids the problems of communication
and liaison between different professionals.

Engineers in the service industry are probably the most effective self learners of design feedback because they do not generally divorce their design skills from direct involvement in
running and maintaining services.

Architects on the other hand are arguably the worst because
standard practice dictates that they sign off once a building is
commissioned and rarely step inside the structure again. There
are of course many exceptions to this rule and the trend for
architects to deal with existing buildings and be increasingly
subject to liabilities for professional negligence has moved the

218

architectural profession a long way from its conceptual design pedestal.

Building surveyors have advantages and opportunities for self feedback which are frequently realised due to their training in and close attention to maintenance work.

In developing countries there is a much greater reliance placed on **constructors** to come up with design solutions due to a "buck passing" situation exercised by architects and property managers. The result is often very unsatisfactory as the lowest tenders are chosen and poor quality work results. Due to the difficulties of establishing legal liabilities inferior work becomes the norm and ironically creates more rectification work for the constructors. Developed countries also experience problems where a loss of craft skills, an increasing distrust between professionals and a continuing division between design and construction processes permit. The construction and project management arrangements now gaining favour and the package deals encompassing professionals within a defined group do provide better opportunities for in house design feedback.

Users are becoming more particular, more demanding, and more able through legal means to get what they want. The complexity of buildings and services and the increasing use of untested technology however have worked against providing full satisfaction. Pressures created by suppliers and manufacturers to market services and facilities under the guise of fashion trends and high tech living styles are additional problems. In a practical sense users cannot directly contribute effectively to design feedback but do provide useful information for maintainers and researchers.

Maintainers have made significant advances in design feedback principally through computer technology and have provided an excellent collection and storage resource which can be easily accessed by interested parties. The problem here lies mainly in the techniques used to identify source causes; the reuseable value of information stored, and the successful transmission of the information to designers. Other speakers will no doubt be covering the computer aspects in more detail.

Researchers have also been working hard at design feedback for some years and BRE started in the field in the 1930's. The problems here have been to present research material which is accurate, easily understood and above all applicable to practice. A considerable amount of feedback has simply been filed away serving only the self fulfillment needs of the researcher and never reaches or makes any impact on designers. William Allen formerly of BRE recently quoted a case in point where sulphate problems in brickwork were fully researched, explained and published in the 1950's but this did very little to prevent reoccurrence of the defect which is still going on today.[1]

This last problem brings us to the main point at issue. How can design feedback be effective in reducing to a minimum the substantial number of defects which have previously been known to occur and are avoidable?

The following comments are presented in response to this question.

Designer expertise and commitment to learning

Architectural education today is still in its infancy as far as
design feedback is concerned. Too much time and emphasis is
placed on conceptual design and throughout the five years of
learning insufficient attention is given to the basics of construction technology, the science of building material performance
and the rudiments of maintenance technology. Architectural gra-
duates therefore arrive in practice with substantial gaps in
their knowledge. Faced with the additional problem of changing
technology there is little time available to keep abreast of the
consequences of poor design. It is vital for the design process
to include a better utilisation of feedback information to assess
performances of structure, components and finishes. Too many
designers are manipulated by client pressures, over influenced by
manufacturers claims and misled by contractors quality controls.
The ability to create satisfactory and workable designs derives
from knowledge and experience and the incentive to keep learning.
These can best be achieved by architectural, engineering, and
other design students spending much more time in practical training during their studies where they may benefit from the experience of other professionals. The most effective learning
results from real experiences as well as academic case studies.

Design/Maintenance Liaison

This method of design feedback has been in vogue for some years
and it is easier to implement for large in house organisations.
The PSA have promoted the concept and opportunities also exist in
property and construction management packages.[2] The contribution
of property managers, maintenance professionals, construction
managers to design processes is potentially enormous.[3] Unfortunately in practise it frequently does not work! The reasons
invariably relate to the professional prejudices and personal
conflicts which occur. To achieve any real success it is necessary to break down these barriers by creating teams of designers
who work for one organisation on a permanent basis. In the past
the lower status of maintenance professionals have operated
against such coordination. Educational institutions have a lot
to answer for in promoting these divisions even if it has only be
done in innocense. Property managers may also derive benefits
from involvement in the design stage where they will acquire an
in depth knowledge of the building under construction and have an
opportunity to prepare a detailed manual for use by maintainers
and occupiers of the completed building.

There are of course circumstances where the future manager of the building cannot be established at the design stage and reliance must therefore be placed on other means of feedback to designers.

Cost Appraisal Techniques

The amount of money spent on repairs and maintenance in relation to new building work now represents one third of total costs. The potential for saving money is therefore enormous and clients are becoming increasingly aware of its significance. Life cycle costing calculations are frequently requested these days in feasibility studies and quantity surveyors are playing an increasingly important role in advising an alternative means of construction. Design feedback in terms of costs have become much more sophisticated with the BMCIS availability of information. In developing countries such techniques are still very much in their infancy and the involvement of speculative developers tend to operate against their use due to the absence of a long term interest in investment. The trend for building economists to provide constructive and worthwhile information is healthy and should be promoted by all professionals who wish clients to obtain good value for money.

Feedback Communication Systems

Given the difficulties of liaison techniques and the long term problems of persuading clients to employ more professionals in the design process we must acknowledge that feedback communication systems are still very important and should be continued.[4] The problems alluded to in the introduction of getting the message across are still very real. The time and effort spent in collecting information is wasted if it eventually finds its way into the office litter bins or is lost in a multitude of computer diskettes. Why does this happen? There are many reasons and it is not possible to come up with solutions to them all. One major element is marketing. If a designer is faced with an array of glossy attractive literature from manufacturers which expertly define the fashionable advantages of using a product there is a tendency for it to be believed. If on the other hand he is presented with a long, wordy and technically involved research analysis which attempts to give an unbiased account of a product, he is likely to become confused and frustrated. Design feedback systems have to be accurate, concise, relevant, and appealingly presentable. In addition they need to be well organised and immediately accessible. If not the limitations of time and lack of incentive will result in non communication. Computerised systems can meet many of these requirements but the production of drawings as well as text is also an important element for successful usage.

221

In conclusion it must be stated that the building industry has now reached a situation in which the technology and innovative styles of management and organisation are able to achieve a much greater success in design feedback. I firmly believe that educational institutions have not done enough to promote team approaches to projects and maintenance work and professional prejudices have profilerated to the detriment of successful interaction and ultimate effectiveness. Design Feedback from practice must be viewed as a necessary and worthwhile concept as laboratory research work has often proved to be misleading and often irrelevant. The systems of feedback are many and in each case there is much room for improvement. In the knowledge that there is the expertise and the effective tools for communication these must be promoted and presented in strict conformance to the needs of the end user. Design feedback can only be successful if the information can be obtained at a reasonable cost, within an acceptable time and to a desired quality. Have'nt we heard that before somewhere?

References

1. Failures are good opportunities for learning. William Allen, Bickerdike Allen Partners CIB 86 Advancing Building Technology.
2. PSA Design/Maintenance Liaison Construction 1981 (36) pp. 29-30.
3. Chartered Institute of Building Maintenance Management - a guide to good practice pp. 62.
4. Maintenance policy programming and information feedback. B.A. Speight Building Maintenance and Preservation E.D. Mills. Pgs. 131-140.

FEEDBACK TO THE DESIGN/MAINTENANCE TEAM

JOHN FAGG
Assistant Education Architect, Inner London Education
Authority

Abstract
There is an awareness in the building team of the value
of feedback to ensure that new building projects benefit
from the experience gained in previous projects.

   Methods of obtaining feedback are outlined and the
difficulties of storing and communicating data are
recognised. Data is available from many sources and the
designers problems in accessing and researching the
information inhibit its use. Proposals are made for
exchanging feedback to widen the use of available data
and procedures for its adoption through standard drawings
and standard specification clauses are advocated.
Key words: Feedback, Constructional Detail, Conceptual
Design, Faults, Information, Failures.

1.   Introduction

A simple definition of feedback might be "Knowledge
acquired from experience during construction in addition
to that arising from problems encountered during building
maintenance and observations of the building in use".

   Feedback occurs in two categories -
      1   Constructional detailing
   and 2   Conceptual design

   Disasters are news and may reach the headlines in the
newspapers or be featured in television news, whether it
is a componemt which has failed to stand up to the rigors
of climate or a design concept which appeared right at
the time but has now been rejected by the users.

   There is evidence that building failures have been
occurring for centuries and the visitor admiring fan
vaulting in one of our cathedrals might not credit that
failures did occur as the craftsmen developed their

223

skills in stone masonary. However, there is equally good
evidence that the feedback from these failures was
effective in establishing the ground rules which are
responsible for such elegance in so many Gothic
buildings. At this distance in time from the event it is
not possible to be sure if feedback was achieved easily
or with considerable difficulty. Although the 'message'
was simple its communication must have presented
problems.

Feedback on conceptual design from observation of
buildings in use is also essential and places great
responsibility on the shoulders of the designer.
Previous personal experience of a building type may be
limited and few examples available for first hand
appraisal. In these circumstances access to reliable
information is essential for the research which precedes
design proposals.

The complexity of modern building makes feedback
vital. It enables the designer to make the right choice
of materials and components with suitable construction
detailing for the project in hand, but it also must be
backed up by efficient supervision.

Good maintenance practice also requires good feedback
and is primarily concerned with the designer but
throughout this paper references to the designer do
embrace both Architect and Building Surveyor professions.

2.   The Case for Feedback

The design of buildings calls for a constant feedback of
experience if technical advances are to be properly
exploited. The designer needs factual information about
the behaviour of materials and coponents; the use and
abuse of finishes and the effectiveness or otherwise of
the detailing.

Sweeping statements have been made about the costs of
remedial works required to new buildings to eliminate
problems which manifest themselves in the first few years
of its life and sometimes before handover. However
inaccurate the estimates of cost may be it must be
acknowledged that most buildings require some input to
remedy defects and provision for such expenditure is
rarely allowed for in the capital cost of a building

The building industry is not isolated from
technological advances and there is no good reason why it
should be. Nevertheless there is need for caution in
accepting too readily the materials and methods which
although pre-tested do not receive major long term tests

until actually built into a building which has a longer life than most other artefacts. Good components can be inaccurately assembled with disasterous results.

The furore and frustration which is generated by major one-off failures is typified by the Ronan Point incident when an explosion resulted in partial structural collapse. It was the subject of exhaustive enquiries, recommendations for remedial work and revised design criteria. Weathertightness of flat roofs is a widespread failure. Much research into the reasons has resulted in recommendations which if correctly interpreted would avoid their repetition but it was salutary to note in a recent report that failures were still frequently occurring due to inadequate detailing.

From the human angle "experience" is the one commodity that comes with involvement in the industry over a long period. For many designers there is a great urge to develop some way of getting access to this experience in a thoroughly professional way to ensure that buildings are built with due regard. A final ceveat is to draw attention to the changing pattern of work in the industry where more designers are tackling the rehabilitation of existing buildings than ever before - feedback in this field is the life blood of success.

Persons handling the maintenance of buildings have a special interest in feedback. Many do so enthusiastically only to find that the designer is preoccupied with other problems and because much feedback information is a series of negatives rather than positives it is not readily received. Another problem is that feedback is frequently unavoidably couched in terms which imply criticism of a designer and attempts to avoid identifying the author may only be superficially effective.

As referred to above some failures are due to the poor execution of the work and it is pointless to hold the designer responsible when the fault lies either in the hands of the tradesman or site supervisors. Some defects have thir origin in the building process itself. Inaccuracies during construction and neglect of good building practice do happen and point to the need for closer supervision of the hour by hour building processes by foremen and trade supervisors. Specifications are sometimes either not understood or ignored on site unless specific points are made about a process. Codes of Practice are all very well but the average craftsman is unlikely to be aware of their finer points and the urge to earn bonus may carry far greater weight.

It is also relevant to point out that feedback systems
are primarily designed to cover the needs of the
professional and essential information about execution is
by-passing the people who need to know. Is there a
simple remedy for this lack of communication with the
practical side of the industry? Surely, it must be given
more consideration than it has received in the past if
the building industry is to have pride in its work.

3. Systems

The ideal feedback system is one which is scientifically
factual based on observation, correct diagnosis and
carefully considered remedies where faults are noted but
which equally draws attention to the features and
solutions which should be repeated because of their
excellence. A recently published BRE Information Paper
(IP 11/82) "Design decision making in architectural
practice" does give an insight into the practical
problems facing a designer, both in fragmentation of the
time spent on projects and the high degree of reliance on
personal experience in design decision-making. Although
information services for the designer have improved
immeasurably over the past 25 years the vast amount of
information which has been accumulated is still difficult
to access principally because it is generated in a
variety of different organisations. Shortage of time is
also a deterrent to the thorough research which is
necessary.

4. Availability

Feedback needs to be at hand when the decision is taken
by the designer. Ideally it should be beside the
designer when he is working on that element of the
building. But before making suggestions as to how best
this might be done it is worthwhile to look at the whole
concept and scope of feedback. That it needs to be
readily available is beyond argument but the nature of
the information and the degree of detail is open to
discussion. There is need for feedback on overall design
concepts but special techniques must be employed to
obtain valid and reliable information. A designer needs
to be fully aware of the effect of design features on
building users. For example, when designing to combat
vandalism the manner in which space is handled may make
supervision of those spaces either practicable or
imparacticable.

Constructional detailing is the area where everyone in
the industry is concerned that feedback should be
effective in eliminating problems but it is certain that

it cannot be achieved without greatly improved communications.

5. Information Gathering

The quality of feedback depends on efficient information gathering and presentation of the results of studying that data in a way which is simple yet comprehensive.

Sources of information do include the whole of the building team but that derived from the experience of the person handling building maintenance is frequently the most practical and relevant. By the very nature of the work most people in the maintenance field are under great pressure and some procedure is necessary if feedback is not to be overlooked. A procedure which has been proved over a number of years is regular reporting by maintenance officers using a pro-forma at the time of the handover for maintenance and then subsequent reports six months and twelve months later with provision for special reports at any time should it be necessary to report a major defect. A system like this has been operated successfully by the GLC/ILEA Architect's Department over a number of years and the PSA have a similar procedure which works well. Most of the information gathered is related mainly to construction methods and details.

Report forms (see over) are stored in a confidential file in alphabetical sequence by the name of the building. Each report is cross referenced under building type - using a CI/SfB classification.

Storage of the information and access to it does present problems. Because of the sensitivity of the subject matter the information has always been considered "Confidential" and circulation has been restricted. Feedback information must be more generally available. Designers are encouraged to consult maintenance staff during the preparation of construction drawings but the effectiveness of this liaison has proved to be variable. An experiment of holding a "Surgery" where designers could discuss matters informally with a Maintenance Officer was abandoned due to the limited use made of the facility. There are other options. A novel idea was for Maintenance Officers to act in a similar way to Building Control Officers in regard to Building Regulations and issue a Maintenance Certificate. It would place undue responsibility on the certifying officer and a team approach to liaison is more likely to succeed.

	CI/SfB: : : :
1. Element:	3. Building Type:

2. Description or annotated sketch or photograph	4.
	  a. Location
	
	  b. Date of Completion
	
	  c. Position or function of item

5. Present state:	
6. Long term effect:	
7. Cause of failure:	
8. Design or construction correction:	
9. Remedial work and cost:	

Building evaluation is much more time consuming but is comprehensive and enables many more of the team to participate. It is best where the client takes part in the study in conjunction with representatives of the design team and maintenance organisation. The composition of the team should take account of the type of building being evaluated and the services involved. An effective use of this method of information gathering has been used for new hospitals. The leader of the team was a doctor (of medicine) who had much practical advice to impart but even more importantly conveyed an infectious enthusiasm for the subject. Based on his experience he advocated the procedures below to ensure a successful outcome. It will be readily understood that hospitals are complex buildings with many services to be integrated. His advice was not to tackle the whole building if a part was likely to yield worthwhile results.

1. First to make a general inspection. The key members of the team meeting the users informally to look around the whole building.

2. Secondly having decided what the evaluation should include develop a plan of action and arrange a preliminary meeting of the whole team so that work is well organised and the time on site is kept to a minimum because a major exercise is always disruptive for the users and their co-operation is essential.

3. Thirdly to prepare check lists to avoid overlooking points. With experience the preparation of these lists becomes an essential part of the preparatory work during stages 1 & 2.

4. Debriefing by the whole team meeting to discuss and agree their findings to generate feedback.

Such a method of building evaluation was adopted by the Education Architect Three primary schools were selected for this purpose with the overall objective of improving the quality of subsequent projects. Each of the buildings selected had been in use for a period of a least 12 months in order to assess how they had stood up to weather and usage. One of the buildings was treated as a pilot study and from this was developed a simple and logical method of conducting the inspection together with check lists and forms for recording the information Appendix A.

This building evaluation exercise identified design improvements which would benefit the users as well as improvements of constructional details to give better

229

performance. Some of the design improvements noted were in the handling of external spaces and landscape. Although individually modest the improvements collectively pointed to better use of the site and its maintenance. Of equal importance was the degree of interest stirred up amongst the designers in the Department who applauded this "Scientific" appraisal of work by colleagues who had already gained their respect. It undoubtedly resulted in better buildings as the findings were published and the evaluation teams were available for consultation. There is a case for a continuing programme of building evaluation but it is labour intensive and a forward programme of new buildings is necessary to justify the expense.

The actions which contributed to its success were as follows:-

1. It was an 'in house' study which had the full support of management.

2. The teams were good communicators and were able to contribute their collective experience to designers undertaking new projects.

3. The teams recognised the distraction generated by their work in the schools and carried out the evaluation swiftly and methodically.

4. The readiness of the building users to participate in discussions and to the pointers they gave to the team.

6. Communication

Everyone concerned with building maintenance has a vested interest in establishing good communications with designers, because defects prevention is a cardinal principal of a sound maintenance policy. It must be admmitted that much of the feedback message falls on deaf ears or is not relevant at the time when it would be invaluable. An appreciation of the problems facing the designer when he is making decisions has been referred to above and an effective communication system must take this into account.

Perhaps the best feedback is that achieved on a person to person basis, and if designer and maintainer meet to discuss projects at key points much can be done informally.

The initial meeting should be at briefing stage when the broad concepts are developed and there is a need for several meetings during the preparation of contract particulars. Site visits during construction are also important so that the maintainer can see at first hand how the building is being put together. It is only by persevering with these meetings that the full benefits can accrue. At the outset there may be reticence to offer advice or on the other hand to seek it. Given experience on one or two projects skill are quickly developed. It is useful for the 'maintainer' to have an aide memoire of frequently recurring problems.

When an organisation uses standard drawings it is important that these should be kept up to date embodying the results of feedback. Much of the resistance of designers to use standard drawings is overcome where they are seen to be outstandingly good. Furthermore, standard specification clauses should be constantly updated from current feedback.

It is sometimes of great value to arrange exhibitions of repeated failures. Most designers grasp visual communications more readily than written descriptions which may be capable of misinterpretation. This method also has the advantage of drawing attention to various aspects of a failure and enabling the designer to concentrate on those aspects which are of particular interest to him and relevant to the project in hand.

Throughout the building industry there is information which ought to be brought together in a comprehensive way so that a designer has a series of Practice Notes which he can refer to during the various stages of a project. Although it may be impractical to produce such a document on a national scale it should with the necessary dedication be possible for large organisations to produce their own. If there was support for such an idea a simple framework for the Notes could be agreed and various participating authorities could exchange feedback.

7.   Conclusion

Better buildings depend on ensuring that what is occurring today, both good and bad, in the current building stock is taken into account by everyone in the building industry so that decisions are made in the light of experience. Feedback will play an ever increasing role if it is reliable and convenient to use.

Bibliography

GLC Detailing for Building Construction : Architectural
Press 1980
BRE Information paper 1P 11/82   Design Decisions making
in Architectural practice
BRE Defect Action Sheets

BUILDING EVALUATION
Technical Appraisal of School Buildings

Main Elements for Checking

1. External works -   Boundary walls and fences
                        Gates
                        Retaining walls and steps
                        Paths
                        Playspaces
                        Roads and car parking
                        Provision for planting and grass

2. External envelope - Roof - Coverings and drainage
                        Walls - Masonary and brickwork
                                Rendering
                                Timber and its coatings
                        Window and louvres
                        Doors
                        Downpipes, etc.

3. Interior   -   Ceilings
                        Light fittings
                        Roof lights
                        Walls
                        Wall coverings and pin-up
                        Glazed screens
                        Sliding folding partitions
                        Provision for curtains
                        WC Cubicles
                        Tiling
                        Flooring and floor coverings
                        Duct and access covers
                        Doors and ironmongery

4. Services   -   Light fittings and switches
                        Heating equipment and pipework
                        Ventilation equipment
                        Fire fighting equipment
                        Fire alarms and broadcast
                        equipment (inc TV)

5. Fittings   -   Sanitary fittings and supplies

                        Built in furniture
                        Storage shelves and racking
                        Chalkboards

THE EVALUATION OF DETERMINANTS IN MAINTENANCE EXPENDITURE ON LOCAL
AUTHORITY DWELLINGS

ROY HOLMES
Department of Surveying, Bristol Polytechnic

Abstract
Although Local Authority dwellings form just under one third of the
national housing stock little is known about the factors that contribute to their maintenance costs. This paper is based on research
into the factors which determine such costs, data covering a period
of between five and ten years was collected from four authorities.
The major factors of dwelling age, height and type, size and construction, labour-force and social issues are discussed. Maintenance
policy is also examined. The paper highlights the need for each
authority to develop policies and strategies based on detailed maintenance feedback.
Key Words Maintenance, Costs, Housing, Local Authority, Coding,
Management, Labour.

1. INTRODUCTION

Over the past fifteen years building maintenance has become a
'growth' area. In terms of the total output for the Construction
Industry the amount spent on maintenance has risen from 28% to 45%.
In the housing sector, during the same period, the percentage of
maintenance expenditure doubled.

There is a surprising lack of useful feedback data on maintenance
costs; little is known about the effects of age and height of dwellings on the cost of repairs. In many cases the maintenance costs for
various house types are not known, variation of costs in housing
areas have not been examined in detail and indiscernible factors e.g.
estate status and type of work-force have not been considered when
preparing maintenance strategies. Maintenance decisions involve a
complex network of human attitudes and behaviour and such factors
must be taken into account and their influence evaluated. A significant improvement in maintenance feedback is required if maintenance
cost trends are to be monitored.

The dramatic rise in maintenance expenditure on Local Authority
dwellings calls for the identification of the major determinants in
such expenditure, so that the whole approach to maintenance management can move from a concept of clerical pragmatism to one of analysis and informed strategy.

2.0 Age factor

2.1 Inter-authority comparison

To consider the effects of age on maintenance costs data were collected from four local authorities of varying size, the data covered a
period of between five and ten years. The costs for repairs were
analysed in broad age bands, namely, inter-war stock (1919 - 1945),
post-war 1 stock (1946 - 1964) and post-war 2 stock (1965+). The
data are shown in Figure 1. At this broad level of analysis the data
confirms that repair costs increase with age; it will be noticed that
three of the four authorities have very similar age/cost patterns for
repairs.

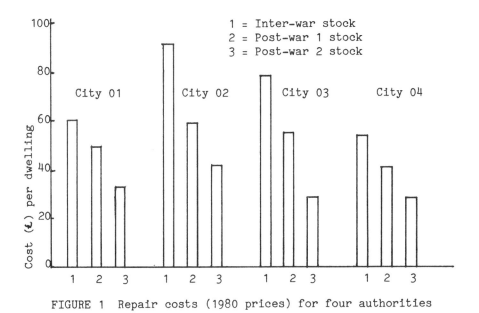

FIGURE 1   Repair costs (1980 prices) for four authorities

Skinner (1981) has shown, see Figure 2, that if one considers the
age/cost trend for a large number of dwellings there is a positive
relationship between age and cost.

Given the fact that there is a correlation between age and maintenance costs it could be argued that maintenance budgets and maintenance strategies could be developed from such age/cost trends.
However, the value of such global trends in maintenance management
must be questioned since maintenance strategies would normally be
based on the 'need' of particular estates or housing areas; broad
age/cost trends can only be used for predicting possible increases in
the overall maintenance budget.

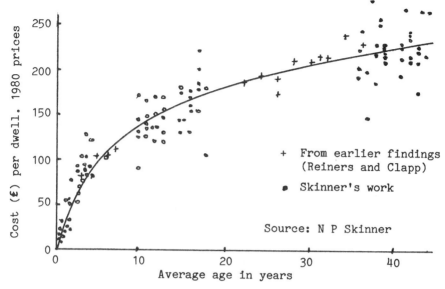

FIGURE 2   Age/Cost relationship for 1-2 storey houses

Furthermore, it will be appreciated that to achieve the age/cost curve in Figure 2 an extremely large sample of maintenance costs, for a large number of authorities, had to be used, therefore the usefulness of such a trend for any particular authority is limited. It was not possible to repeat such a smooth age/cost graph for any of the authorities in the study, even though two of the authorities had a stock in the region of 50,000 dwellings. The age factor, therefore, appears to be important when one considers the total housing stock in an authority, but its influence on costs in specific housing areas was not significant.

In addition to the age factor there are other physical aspects which can offset or even override the age/cost trend. These include type and height of dwellings, size of dwelling and type of construction. These aspects are now considered.

2.2 Type and height of dwellings
Figure 3 shows the cost of repairs and painting for a variety of house types. In particular it will be noticed that sheltered housing is expensive to repair. This is mainly due to the nature of such housing provision, repair requests from the elderly tend to receive prompt attention from the local authority and therefore the cost per dwelling rises more than for normal accommodation. Furthermore, sheltered accommodation usually involves extra services in terms of regular lawn cutting and other external works, which would normally be carried out by the tenant.

The fact that such accommodation is expensive to maintain raises a question concerning the balance of stock; many authorities have a policy of increasing provision for the elderly but it should be noted that such a policy could have a significant effect on the total maintenance bill. Such costs are not age related.

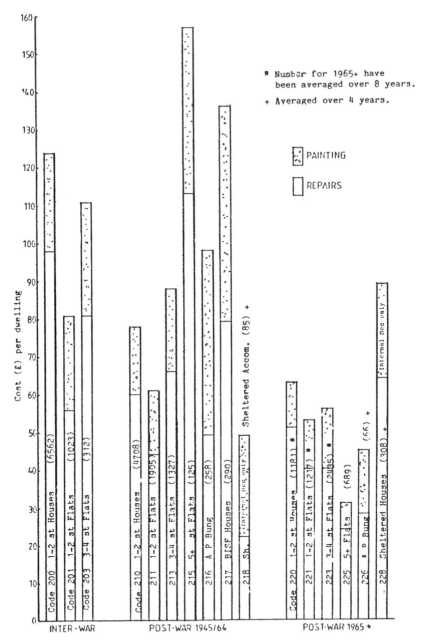

FIGURE 3   Cost variation in maintenance costs for house
types (averaged over eight years — 1980 prices)

The important factor concerning the type of dwelling is the number of
units involved, small numbers of high maintenance-cost dwellings make
little difference to overall cost trends. As the stock pattern
changes, due to sales or new build, it is necessary to monitor the
effects that particular groups of dwellings have on cost trends.

238

From Figure 4 it can be seen that costs correlate with age for the 1-2 storey dwellings, however, if one considers the height factor, say 3-4 storeys, the age factor is less convincing. It can be seen, from this figure, that in City 04 the 3-4 storey post-war 2 dwellings cost more to repair than the post-war 1 stock.

If one considers multi-storey dwellings the height factor is much more important, not because of normal repairs but because such dwellings have a wide variety of special services. Such services are not normally found in low-rise dwellings. The special services include lifts, laundries, communal lighting and caretaking. It was found that repairs to such services increased the normal maintenance costs by a factor of between 1.4 and 2.0.

From these data it can be seen that, irrespective of age, costs vary according to type and height of dwelling. Small numbers of high maintenance-cost dwellings make little difference to the overall cost trend.

2.3 Size of dwelling and construction

Two of the four authorities kept separate records for the cost of maintaining 2 storey flats and 1-2 storey houses, these are shown on Figure 4. The data show that there is a clear distinction in cost per dwelling, flats are much more economical to maintain. As one might expect, lower costs were found for external works, the same was true for all elements with the exception of heating and lighting.

A further analysis, on the cost effects of small dwellings, was carried out by comparing a sample of two-bed houses (53 dwellings) - having a floor area of 716 sq.ft., and a sample of three-bed houses (66 dwellings) - having a floor area of 857 sq.ft. The dwellings were all in one housing area and maintained by the same maintenance team. Data were collected for a period of 14 years from the date built (1967 to 1981). The small houses were cheaper to maintain, however, because the numbers of such houses were low, in terms of the total stock in the housing area, the overall cost effect in the housing area was not significant.

Not only does the size of dwelling have an effect on maintenance costs but so does construction, particularly non-traditional construction; this was investigated. It was not possible to carry out an inter-authority comparison of these dwellings since, with the exception of BISF houses, such dwellings are normally included in the total post-war 1 stock. However, in City 01 large numbers of non-traditional dwellings had been costed separately therefore it was possible to compare their repair costs with costs for traditional dwellings built during the same period. Costs for 11,000 non-traditional dwellings were compared with costs for 3,500 traditional dwellings. Data for these dwellings covered a ten year period, 1970-80. The repair costs were analysed into five repair categories, work to the structure, to structural finishes and fixings (which includes windows and doors), to plumbing, to heating and lighting, and to external works. The details are shown in Figure 5.

It should be stated that the widely publicised structural problems of a number of non-traditional dwellings had not come to light at the time of this study and therefore repairs costs in Figure 5 do not reflect those problems.

239

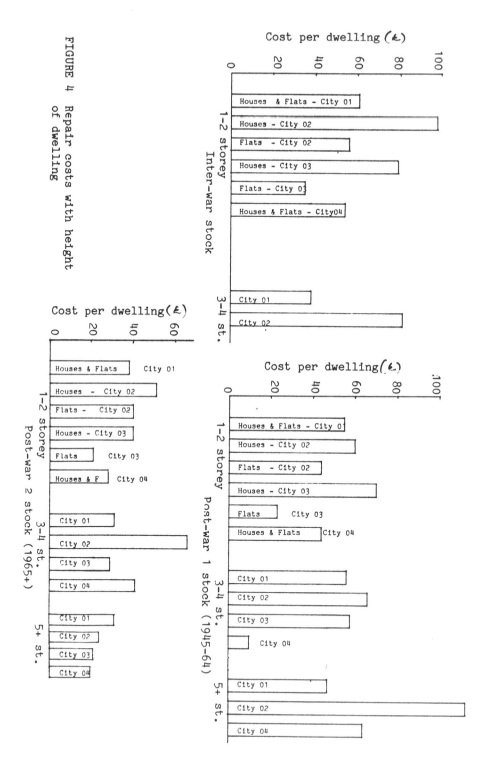

FIGURE 4 Repair costs with height of dwelling

240

It can be seen from Figure 5 that the pattern and range of costs, for traditional and non-traditional dwellings, are very similar. However, some of the non-traditional designs incurred very high repair costs, this confirms that design is more important than age and it follows that if sufficient numbers of such dwellings are owned by an authority the overall effect on the maintenance bill could be significant.

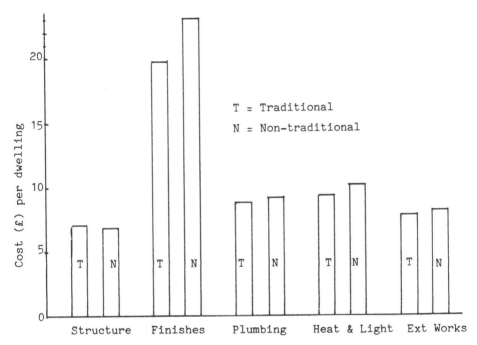

FIGURE 5   Comparison of elemental costs for traditional and non-traditional dwellings (1980 prices)

3.0 Labour factor

3.1 Age, length of service and motivation

The major part of maintenance costs is the labour element. A common perception of maintenance workers is one of elderly workers pursuing a steady job in the latter years of their working life. Such a concept implies high labour costs due to low productivity. To test this concept various aspects of the labour-force were examined. Details from a total of 639 maintenance workers were obtained from the participating authorities.

The mean age of the labour-force was 41 years, with the mean for individual authorities varying between 36 and 46 years, however, 56 per cent of the labour-force were 40 years of age or over. These figures compare well with the figures produced by Jeanes (1966), who

241

found that 58 per cent of operatives in maintenance work were 40 years old or over. Thus the age range for maintenance workers has not changed over the last twenty years. For new construction Phelps Brown (1968) found that only 32 to 40 per cent of the labour-force were over 40 years of age. Clearly, the maintenance labour-force is an older force.

The overall average length of service for the 639 workers was 8.3 years with average varying between authorities from 7.7 to 11 years, somewhat shorter than one might expect if men are motivated by security of work. Holt (1971) outlined the financial and non-financial motivations that draw men into maintenance work and these were tested by means of a questionnaire. Only three factors were found to be very significant, they were:
a) security of job, b) pride in doing work and c) a reasonable wage.

3.2 Productivity
There was a wide range of productivity. If one considers output per man the range is great. Concerning the number of dwellings per man, covered for maintenance, City 01 has a range of 101 to 177 dwellings, per man, and City 04 a range of 172 to 261.

In terms of jobs the average number of repair jobs in City 04 was less than two per dwelling, this was half the number for City 01. It is interesting that two cities having similar stock, both numerically and by age, could have such differences in the amount of work done. A further check against cost per job revealed that the average labour cost in City 01, at 1980 prices, was £6.42 compared with £10.32 in City 04. In addition to the differences discussed above it was found that productivity varied across housing areas, even though similar dwellings were being maintained.

4.0 Social issues and policy

4.1 Social status of housing areas
The data did not support the view that preferential treatment was given to the best housing areas. The data also cast doubt on the suggestion that tenants in low status estates are not diligent in reporting maintenance work, a reason sometimes given for low costs.

To test the findings for high and low status areas it was decided to select one housing area with an average reputation overall but one which also has a mixture of estates in terms of social status. The housing area chosen has three estates and for the purposes of the study the estates are numbered 1 to 3. Estate 2 has the lowest social status in the area, the other estates have a good social status. The data on repair costs covered a twenty year period or, in the case of younger dwellings, the life of the dwellings. When these costs were analysed it was found that estate 2, the estate with the lowest status, cost more to repair than estate 1 even though the latter has much older stock.
Estate 2, with the lowest social status, had the highest number of jobs per dwelling over a twenty year period, a factor that confirms that tenants in such estates do report faults. A great number of the jobs were repairs to windows, mainly glazing work. Clearly, one

might expect that type of repair where there is a large number of children, this was found to be the case.

A further indication that social status affects maintenance costs was found in the cost of relet decoration. Part of estate 2, a sub-estate, could be identified as having the worst social status, on this sub-estate the costs for relet decoration, per dwelling, were twice as high as other dwellings in the area.

When repair costs for large housing areas are considered the effects of low social status on individual estates can be masked. Good estates within a large housing area can offset specific high expenditure from low status estates. Often maintenance feedback is not detailed enough to highlight the problems on particular estates, therefore maintenance strategies may overlook specific maintenance needs.

4.2 Policy

It was found that policy decisions had a great influence on maintenance costs. The response time for repairs, i.e. the amount of time it takes for a workman to attend to a job, is a policy issue. This in turns affects the number of men employed in the DLO or the amount of work put out to contractors in the private sector.

Examples of short-term policy decisions are now given. High costs were found, on one estate, for work on roofs and plastering, on investigation it was discovered that this work was carried out after a policy decision had been made to upgrade the roofs and replace all the windows. On another estate high costs were found for repairs to the structure and external works, after investigation it was discovered that a policy decision had been taken by the Housing Committee, to carry out specific remedial works to the walls and roofs of these houses; the high cost for external works was mainly due to a policy decision to carry out major repair work to fences and gates.

Another aspect of policy must be considered, namely, the amount of discretion given to the work-force. The amount of work done is dependent on the perceptions of the labour involved. Very few authorities pre-inspect all their work, usually the amount of work pre and post-inspected is in the order of 10%. This means that the work-force have to make decisions on the amount of work they do, often the job ticket specifies a general fault which needs clarification when the tradesman visits the dwelling. This amounts to significant discretion which greatly affects costs. An analysis of data for roof repairs revealed that costs could be doubled, for similar jobs, by allowing the labour-force to exercise discretion.

A balance has to be reached, in policy terms, between expenditure and the condition or state of repair of the stock. Furthermore, the status of estates must be considered and the effect of relationships between tenant and housing managers must form part of the decision-making process. Policy decisions were found to influence maintenance costs more than any other factor.

4.3 Maintenance feedback

The authorities in the study did not code work beyond a single digit level therefore, it was not possible, without a great deal of manual work, to ascertain which components were failing. To provide such data it was necessary to extend the code and then to recode the work.

Using the code developed by Holmes and Mellor (1985a), to a level of three digits, data can be extracted which could be extremely valuable in policy making and in the formulation of maintenance strategies. Holmes and Mellor (1985b) demonstrated the versitility of the code on housing and schools to show how feedback can be developed. The system allows the maintenance manager to check the flow of maintenance costs and to build up an accurate picture of pending failures. The system can be easily locked into a property file thus allowing retrieval of information on all dwellings which may have a particular type of component.

5.0 Conclusions

A number of interrelated factors determine maintenance costs and these must be established within each authority before meaningful maintenance strategies and budgets can be prepared.

Authorities should code maintenance work at a level sufficient to identify trends for all the factors discussed. Policy decisions on maintenance should be monitored to assess their effects; the amount of discretion given to the work-force should be evaluated and alternatives should be costed. It may prove to be cost-effective to pre-inspect every maintenance request.

Maintenance strategies should be prepared on an estate basis. This will allow budgets to be prepared according to the needs of the estates and demonstrate to tenants that housing managers are willing to face the problems perceived by the tenants. In every authority tenants were less than happy with the repairs response offered by the management.

Clearly, funds are short and the 'expressed needs' of the tenants, together with the 'perceived needs' of the inspectors, cannot always be met; however, a 'comparative need' assessment, (where the needs of one estate are compared with another), can be applied if the finance is not available to meet the full demand.

References

Skinner, N.P. (1981) House condition, standards and maintenance, Housing Review, July/August, pp 106-109.

Jeans, R.E. (1966) Building Operatives Work, Vol 1, Building Research Station, HMSO, London.

Phelps Brown (1968) Report of the Committee of Inquiry under Professor Phelps Brown in certain matters concerning labour in building and civil engineering. 1968, Cmnd Paper 3714, HMSO, London.

Holt, L. (1971) Motivating maintenance manpower, Proc. 3rd Nat. Building Maintenance Conference, London, pp 129-138.

Holmes, R., Droop, C., and Mellor, P. (1985a) A Coding System for Building Maintenance, CIOB Technical Services, Paper No. 47.

Holmes, R., and Mellor, P. (1985b) Maintenance coding and monitoring: two case studies, CIOB Technical Services, Paper No. 53.

WHERE DOES MAINTENANCE MANAGEMENT BEGIN ?

ir. JOS KOOREN
Building Research Foundation Rotterdam

Abstract
As a result of recent research at the Building Research Foundation two reports are published which have an interest for the management of maintenance, namely:
SBR 103 "The balancing of Building Costs-in-Use against
        investments" and
SBR 127 "From initiative to construction"

The article below explains the importance of a systematic approach to the planning process in order to achieve satisfying results in the field of maintenance-management.
    The first steps on the road of maintenance management depend on decisions by the Principal, or by a project manager appointed by him, on the framing of the management of the project and arranging the project structure. Maintenance management, in the present context, is taken to mean the endeavours undertaken to make maintenance costs manageable. We consider, in this context the integral costs of investments and use, including maintenance costs, since a distinct relationship can be assumed between the quality of investments and the costs-in-use which arise later. Central to this article is the organization of the building process and the influence of this organization on the results of the project, seen from the viewpoint of optimizing investments and costs-in-use in building projects.
Keywords: Maintenance management, project management, Project planning, Information, Building process, Organization, Systems theory.

Contents

1   Introduction
2   Maintenance management as an information problem
3   A model of the building planning process
4   Decision-making and process management
5   Maintenance management in the building process

1 Introduction

It is a well known fact that exploitation and maintenance costs of buildings, during their functional lifetime, amount to 5 to 8 times the investment costs. It is not surprising, therefore, that more and more thought is being given to the relationship between investment costs and the exploitation and maintenance costs incurred later. Both principals and investors are becoming aware that there is a qualitative relationship between investment, exploitation and maintenance costs.

In the present context we consider maintenance management to be the effort involved in controlling exploitation and maintenance costs.

2 Maintenance Management as an Information Problem

There are two problems central to maintenance management:
- the knowledge of exploitation and maintenance costs, and
- the way in which these costs can be controlled.

2.1 Knowledge of exploitation costs

In order to understand exploitation costs we must first find out how these costs originate. It is not news that investment costs and, therefore, to a large extent, the ultimate exploitation costs, are determined largely by the building planning process undertaken, see **Figure 1.**

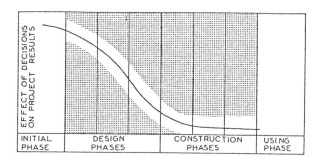

figure 1

We see from the figure that the exploitation costs are determined, especially in the initiative phase and by the planning and design. In the initial phase, the management should, therefore, have available adequate data with which to be able to weigh investments against exploitation costs. Choices must be made, on the basis of this data, between the various alternative possibilities which

246

can influence the exploitation costs.

SBR has developed a method for weighing the investments against costs-in-use (see SBR 103). This, however, is not discussed in the present report. The subject that I am concerned with here is the second aspect of maintenance management:

2.2 The Control of Exploitation and Maintenance Costs

In order to be able to control maintenance costs and other factors, the project must be manageable.

In general the manageability of the building process makes high demands upon information-processing and decision-making.

The project-information should be accurate according to content, quality, location and time. Only then it is possible to provide for effectively control of maintenance costs from the very start of the project.

In order to control the information-processing we need understanding in the way information is produced, transferred and processed.

Also we need to understand how decision-making in the building-process in structured.

Requirements and concepts can be formulated from this understanding, which relate to maintenance management. As a result, maintenance-orientated design becomes one of the objectives of the project, and maintenance management becomes an integral part of the project-management.

SBR has undertaken research over a number of years to increase the understanding of project management and the means by which to make projects more manageable. A system-model, developed by SBR, is related to practice and makes it possible to analyse the consequences of project management, information, information processing and other aspects in the building process in detail. In the present context, however, the model is not a ready made recipe, for example, for maintenance management. It is, however, possible to formulate concepts from the results of the model with which to control the building planning process. These concepts can contribute to an important extent to maintenance management.

3 A Model of the Building Planning Process

A characteristic of the model is that it describes the building process as an information processing system. Elements and boundaries of the system can be selected in relation to the objectives for which the systems approach was chosen. In its most general form the building process seen as the project system is shown in **Figure 2.**

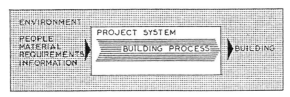

figure 2

247

figure 2
Each building project is a temporary participation between the partners involved which has to be organized afresh for each new project.
In this context we consider the project participants as elements
of the system which develop objective activities within the participation.   In order to do this use has to be made of knowledge,
information, materials and other aids.   These together form the
inputs into the project system from the environment.

In this respect, society is considered to belong to the environment
in which the project is placed, in so far as it, society, affects
the project.
    The basic model, shown in Figure 2, shows a building project
very schematically.   The degree of abstraction of the model can
be decreased by detailing its contents.   The following three aspects
serve to illustrate this:

3.1 Objectives
As a rule, the establishment of a new building is not an objective
in itself; it is a means of housing an organization and the requirements develop within the framework of growth or extension of activities.   For the principal the objective is primarily to improve
the functioning of his organization.   Organization, equipment,
personnel management and other aspects can all benefit as a result.
The building project is, therefore, a sub-project within the larger
entity of the principal's organization.

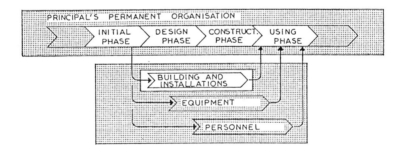

figure 3
The objective of the project system initially, therefore, is not
straight forward but comprises a complex of diverging requirements,
wishes and specifications.   From this initial, barely consistent,
entity specifications must be developed to serve as a basis for
objective building planning.

Traditionally the building project is often shown as a linear succession of programming, design and execution. Often this is incorrect for more complicated projects. We should, rather, see building planning as a development process in which the interaction between programming and design leads to a satisfactory plan for the building works.

3.2 Phasing
The interaction between programming and design results in a variation in the linear form of the planning process which now develops a cyclic character. Objectivity demands that this cycle should not repeat itself indefinitely. To prevent this the process is divided into phases.

0. initial phase
1. development of design alternatives
2. detailing of the selected alternative
3. construction planning
4. construction
5. planning of the using-phase.

figure 4
Phasing is a way of increasing process manageability.
The objectives are firmed-up, step by step, and can, if neces-sary, be adapted without interrupting the process. The results of each phase give the principal, and other (external) judging organizations concerned, clear information about plan development and the progress of the process.

3.2 Project structure
The project structure is related to the participation of the various partners in the building project. Where as the phasing divides the process in time, the functional structure is based on a sub-division of the content of the process itself. The functions within the process relate to the specific contributions which the various participants are deemed to deliver. The main functions in their interrelationship, form together the functional structure of the project system. Each main function is considered as a sub-process. Further differentiation of the main functions comes out in the formation of tasks which are assigned to the various participants.

249

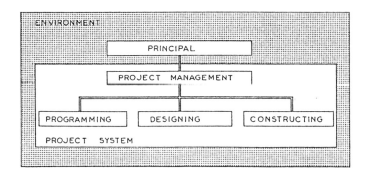

Figure 5, Project structure

4. Decision–making and process management

During the building process decisions have to be taken, of which the number increases in relation to the progress of the project. Planning, activation and decision-making form, in themselves, one process. From the point of view of manageability there should always be a clear understanding of the decision-structure.

The decision-structure is sketched in our model in Figure 6. The decision centres, shown here, have the authority to make decisions, according to the main functions of the process. In practice this authority is subdivided according to the project task structure.

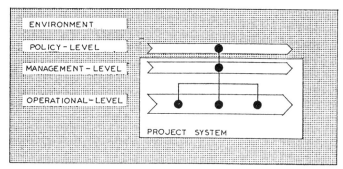

figure 6: Decision structure

The most important decisions, especially at policy level, are taken in the initial phase of the project, these decisions are made by the principal and external authorities concerned with licences and permits. Here careful decision-planning is needed in order to interrupt the process as little as possible. This

250

is primarily the function of the principal, who will generally be assisted by an adviser.

It will be obvious that the starting points, for example, for maximum energy use, maintenance requirements and maintainability should be established already in the initial phase. If decisions are not made in this stage certain choices may be left unnecessarily open which will affect the process in the future.

This process begins with a plan which contains a description of the objectives, the results of the initial phase and a plan of action to achieve this.
The plan of action indicates:
- the task distribution between the various project partners
- their expected contributions to the ultimate results,
- the execution sequence and the planned duration.

At the testing at the end of each phase the results achieved are compared with what was planned. The management process has, therefore, the character of a control loop. In the first phase the emphasis is not yet on the design of a particular building but on the development of alternative design solutions.

The decisions made on the results of the first phase have a decisive influence on the ultimate results of the project. If necessary the project objectives and project structure can be adapted by further detailing in the period between the two phases; specific expertise can be called in, project management strengthened, etc.

In the second and succeeding phases the management process follows, in principle, the same procedures as in the first phase. We see that, because of the far reaching influence of its decisions, the role of management in the initial phase is primarily at policy level. As the building process proceeds the accent falls more and more on the management level of decision and, finally, justifiably, on the operational level.

Information and communication form important aspects in the exercising of the management function in which the awareness of planning, task division and qualitative concepts will demand ever growing consideration.

5. Maintenance Management in the Building Process
The main starting points of the building project, including maintenance aspects, must be established explicitly in the first phase of the project. It has also been shown how, with the help of a system-model the building process can be planned and controlled in agreement with what has been found in practice.

The project-structure is developed in the model from the requirements of a controllable system. Since task division stems from one of the main functions of the process and systematically extends to the operational level, the links can still be traced, and a

251

simple task description achieved.   The controllability of the
process is, in this way, for a large part built into the process.

The information requirements are derived, per phase, from the
main objectives of the project and are determined at the particular
level at which the plan has been worked out.   The planning process
is shown schematically in Figure 7.   The figure indicates the
cycle of programming and design.   The heavy line indicates the
main flow of information (processing).

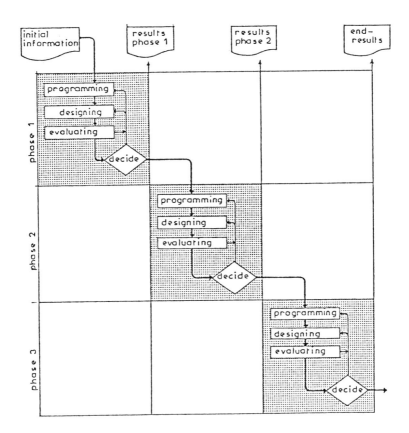

figure 7   flow-chart of the building preparation process
In order to achieve objective and effective maintenance management
the scheme should take into account:
- the value of the initial information available about maintenance
- the way in which this information is processed within one phase
- the decision-making procedure.

252

As mentioned above the process begins with a zero phase in which the process is activated. In this phase there is no logical build up of the process even though this is the phase which is most important for management. In this phase there is, as yet, no functioning system to which the principal can give particular tasks. A number of essential decisions must, however, be taken related to the composition of the project team and the general project policy. Figure 8 illustrates the steps which must be taken in the initiative phase to determine the start conditions for the building planning process.

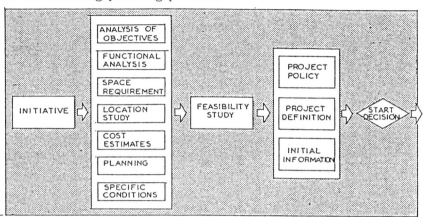

STUDY COMPONENT	REMARKS
Analysis of objectives	– studies of the various types of objectives of the principal's organization.
Functional analysis	– studies of the way in which the objectives can be realized; the people activities, means, etc.
Space requirement	– space requirements estimated in terms of type and quantity, independently of the building for which it will be used.
Location study	– these can vary from investigation of settlement areas and land acquisition to soil investigations and terrain exploitation; land use plans are an important source of information.
Cost estimates	– investment and exploitation costs can be estimated generally from the space requirement and location data.
Planning	– timing can be estimated for the project as a whole. Right data can then be deduced for the building project.
Specific conditions	– analysis of all factors indicated by the analysis of the surrounding which can have a restricting influence on the building project.

Figure 8 Development of the initiative.

In practice the initiative phase generally runs in a less structured and systematic fashion than shown in Figure 8. It is, however, important that the model produces simple start conditions from which an explicit decision can be taken. These start conditions are derived from the start information obtained from the preliminary investigation, project definition and project policy.

The feasibility study examines the various components in relation to their feasibility and forms a basis for the definition of the building project in relation to the overall project. Using the findings of the feasibility study the project objectives can be expressed in concrete terms. This is referred to as the project definition which contains general comments on the main aspects of location, quality, time and costs.

Project policy relates especially to the way in which the object-ives should be realised: organization, decision-making, etc. In practice not much weight is generally attached to this. Often the principal chooses an architect to whom he gives responsibility for both design, and execution of the project policy, not always being fully aware of the consequences. It is obvious that the principal has an important task in the initiative phase of the project and certainly in larger and more complex building works he will appoint experts for this phase. Often an organization expert fills the role of project manager from the start of the building planning process; This can ensure continuity between project initiation and project planning. Often professional prin-cipals appoint their own expertise to this project management role.

Maintenance management should be initiated at the same time that the project definition is being established. Objectives to be aimed at in connection with the future maintenance of the terrain, building, installations and, equipment should also be outlined in this period.

Project policy should then give answers to how these objectives should be achieved and preserved. This can imply that specific expertise in the various areas of technical and cleansing maintenance is retained earlier in the planning phase to advise on the assessment of design alternatives.

A requirement also is that, in this stage, the project management should ensure that adequate information is available to ensure that quality is preserved and that exploitation costs are not exceeded. When we add the main functions in the project structure to the flow chart in Figure 7, a general picture emerges of the information processing within each phase (see Figure 9). In principle information processing in this phase model is comparable for all phases of building planning.

The cyclic process of programming and design is repeatable. Project management has an obvious function here in the preparation of decision making and the preservation of project objectives.

The division of functions which occurs during the distribution

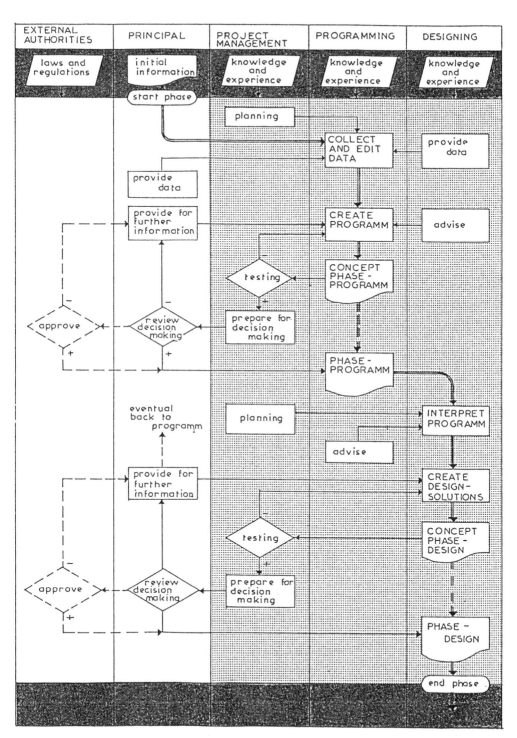

EXTERNAL AUTHORITIES	PRINCIPAL	PROJECT MANAGEMENT	PROGRAMMING	DESIGNING
laws and regulations	initial information	knowledge and experience	knowledge and experience	knowledge and experience

figure 9 Phase model   255

of tasks amongst the partners of the building process sometimes enables several functions to be fulfilled by a single firm or individual. A conscious choice should be made, since the basis for assumptions fulfilling some functions can sometimes be of contradictory importance. In practice the starting points, therefore, for the designs do not always tally with the specifications for maintenance.

It will be obvious that a form of cooperation in project management is according mostly to the requirements of manageability and control as described in the system-model.

THE CLASP BUILDING SYSTEM - DEVELOPMENT AND MAINTENANCE

D.P. LAKIN MBE Dip Arch. RIBA
CLASP Development Group, Nottingham

Abstract
An outline of the situation which led to the design of the system and
the formation of the Consortium is followed by a description of the
CLASP approach to system design and of the benefits of continuing
relationships. Some comments on types of building, their intended
design life and maintenance implications are related to the total
cost-in-use studies now being carried out by some authorities. The
main section of the paper then describes the differing versions of
the CLASP system, drawing attention to maintenance relevant aspects.
Finally the CLASP maintenance experience and the Consortium's
response to today's increasing concern with this aspect of building
is summarized.
Key Words: Consortium, Continuity, Development Group, 5M, JDP,
Mark, Subsidence, System.

1. Introduction

Over the past 30 years, the Consortium of Local Authorities Special
Programme has developed one of the most resilient approaches to
building in the United Kingdom. However, prior to the setting up of
the Consortium in 1957, the Education Act of 1944 had set the scene
for the creation of a new demand for buildings of a different kind
and, immediately following the war an entirely new approach to school
building was first seen in Hertfordshire.

In 1948 the Ministry of Education had set up a Development Group
to study changing educational requirements, their effects on school
buildings, and to develop new building techniques applicable to
school building. A part of this work had resulted in a project at
Belper in Derbyshire, built in 1953/54, which was to form the basis
for the CLASP structural frame. Nottinghamshire saw the start, in
1956, of what became the CLASP system and there has been continuous
development and use of the various versions of the system up to the
present time. The later descriptions of these "Marks" of the system
illustrate how misleading the term CLASP can be, without further
qualification.

CLASP was the first example of a group of public authorities
pooling their resources in a voluntary Consortium to develop and
control a system of construction initially for their own use. Users
of the system are free to invite tenders for construction but the

advice and system documentation provided can help make more professional time available for project design. The Consortium is financed by means of contributions based on a combination of membership fees and a royalty on the contract value. It is controlled by its members and it is that client control of system design, now carried out by the Development Group responsible to the Membership, which ensures that the system continues to be appropriate so that the phrase "the right building, at the right time, at the right cost" remains as true as when it was first coined in the early 1960s.

Whilst its early development was primarily geared to a programme of school building with a mining subsidence emphasis, CLASP performance is now appropriate for most building types apart from housing, heavy industrial, and high-rise developments and its success in minimizing subsidence damage has been fully justified. It has also changed from its original closed system concept with limited aesthetic expression and flexibility to one which allows a wide freedom of expression whilst still maintaining its technical integrity. The system has been used to construct over 3000 buildings in the United Kingdom and overseas, including Hungary, Portugal, France, Italy, Venezuela, Germany and Algeria and was first awarded an Agrement Certificate in 1979.

Over recent years, the interests of the Consortium generally have widened, from an initial prime concern with new build, to encompass the considerable stock of CLASP buildings with component procurement arrangements similarly extended to cover an increasing maintenance requirement. The emphasis given to Maintenance in recent years has been reflected in the setting up of a Maintenance Study Group in 1977 and more recently by an improved representation of that specialist group at the various management levels of the Consortium.

2. The CLASP approach

The design of a building system is never complete but the resources resulting from a Consortium of public authorities working together permit a detailed and systematic approach to the development of components and assemblies which is not possible on a one-off project basis. Equally, the risks of innovation are much greater and for that reason the work of the Development Group is closely monitored by a Steering Group consisting of building professionals, representing the interest of their member authorities, who can bring their collective experience to bear on given problems.

Changing technical, functional and aesthetic requirements of architects, builders and owners, quite apart from statutory changes, make a policy of continuing development work essential. The availability or relative cost of components and assemblies constantly change as do the standards expected by users of their buildings and the British Standards themselves. The main "Mark" changes in CLASP, however, have also been related to changes in the dimensional basis of the system; perhaps the most fundamental being the Mark 5 change from Imperial to Metric measures and its subsequent effect on replacement components with which most concerned with maintenance are only too aware.

However, a change in architectural fashion can also greatly influence the direction of development; an example being the trend from flat to pitch roofs which, whilst often claimed to result solely from maintenance concerns was greatly influenced by the change in architectural fashion to the Neo-Vernacular with its traditional pitch roofs.

The volume of building to which development solutions will be applied is considerable. The involvement of the system users has been maintained strongly at all levels in the Consortium and a system development methodology has generally ensured that innovation has resulted in very few system failures not shared by the industry generally.

Principles of Element or Component Design

Proposal:	Consider need for redesign
Investigation:	Critical assessment of existing
	Assess extent of redesign
	Cost investigation
Design:	Performance specification
	Design decisions in principle
	Detail design/market research
	Mock-up, manufacture and testing
Documentation:	Drawings
	Programme Quotations
	Technical Information
Production:	Fabrication and Quality Control
Feedback:	System defects

An inherent advantage of the public authority Consortium approach is that of continuity in design,construction feedback, and client contact. This makes for steady ongoing improvement of the system design solutions. The Development Group, however, apart from its system design responsibilities, is also concerned with the implications of changes in standards, or liabilities and with giving advice in respect of crisis problems such as asbestos or H.A.C.

One of the most important aspects of continuity is the relationship between initial design and ongoing care represented by the activities of the Maintenance Study Group which bring together the interests of both Consortium members and CLASP building owners generally. Because the membership of this group is not limited to Consortium membership it does, to a large extent, set its own brief and whilst giving an emphasis to CLASP building, it is free to consider subjects outside this narrow remit into the wider field of building maintenance generally. The Consortium may request the Study Group to look at certain areas of common concern and the Group itself, through its representation in the Consortium organisation can advise as appropriate. The Study Group has now for a number of years overcome some of the problems where those responsible for building maintenance have not always been in the same department as that responsible for new building.

CLASP does not lose interest in the completed building when the Final Account is settled and there are examples where necessary remedial work has been carried out as a result of component failure, under the organization of the Development Group some 14 years after the final hand-over of a project.

3. Building   - Types, design life and maintenance

The CLASP building system is used mainly for public amenity buildings although finishes are upgraded to the standards appropriate for prestige buildings on occasion. It is only after some years that valid assessments can be made on whether a building is performing well or not, and this is affected by a number of factors including appropriateness of the design, quality of the building construction, effectiveness of building management and the quality of maintenance it receives.

Whilst CLASP is regarded as a permanent building with a nominal design life of 60 years, certainly this has been influenced by loan repayment periods in the public sector. Temporary and demountable buildings tend to be inconvenient and often expensive but the real problem is that no one seems to want to relinquish a building once they have it.

Many of today's permanent buildings are no longer really suited to the function they are called upon to perform. Changes in fuel costs for heating and lighting since the original design with poor insulation and ineffective servicing controls, coupled with the fact that many older buildings are simply too big for their purpose is leading to a query on building life as an absolute. Do we build too well?

Studies are currently underway in some Local Authorities to investigate the viability of replacing comparatively modern but inappropriate and under-used buildings by more efficient solutions to today's requirements by a new building. Even over very short time scales, the type of the building required can change, perhaps in response to advances in other fields such as mini computers, or resulting from changes in use and life style, imposed standards, user expectations or for reasons of politics or finance.

Total costs-in-use are now subject to increasing scrutiny and most "permanent" buildings include many components with a life span far shorter than the nominal expectation of the building structure. Built-up flat roof finishes are only now beginning to exceed the 10-15 year period, "maintenance free" suspended ceilings deteriorate and whilst the proportion of building cost represented by services continues to increase, services, in common with many other moving parts of buildings, can certainly expect to be replaced or improved within a 30 year period. One of the advantages of dry component construction is that a degree of demountability is inherent, normally permitting some dismantling and component re-use so that upgrading, alteration and extension are that much more easily carried out, with less disturbance, and without the high initial cost normally associated with so-called "demountable" building.

The running costs of buildings cover many aspects and include cleaning requirements, running repairs, vandalism, security and crisis problems apart from basic services costs and the needs of planned maintenance related to the variable durability of the

260

buildings component parts. It has been said that increasing the initial building cost will reduce future maintenance requirements and this appears attractive whilst funds for maintenance seem to be a continuing problem, but if discounted cash-flow techniques are applied, it has been shown to be cheaper in the long run to economise on first costs and spend more on maintenance. More facts appear necessary to establish the right balance.

Accuracy of information is still a problem in relating maintenance costs to buildings. More feed-back is required to those designing new buildings from those who maintain the existing stock. Although far from perfect in the way this is working at present, the relationship of the CLASP Maintenance Study Group to the Central Development Team helps CLASP move in the right direction. This is assisted by the standardization of system building which has the great advantage of reducing the variation between buildings and so provides a better opportunity to assess performance in work, and through feed-back reduce maintenance costs and the likelihood of faults repeating in new buildings.

4. Versions of the CLASP system

The common thread continuing through the CLASP system design is that of a mainly light dry component system with subsidence capability. Although performance requirements have changed related to a wider range of building types, and latterly there has been a move away from the fairly rigid constraints associated with the early days of system building, change has been carried out within the general policy of the Consortium and maintenance characteristics have steadily improved.

Mark 2 (1957-60)
Whilst the initial development took place against the national back-ground of a massive programme of school building - a time of great demand on the industry with its shortages of material and craft labour - the mining subsidence requirements particular to Nottinghamshire were the exciting aspects which led to innovatry so-lutions. It is certainly true to say that although maintenance was not a prime consideration at that time, the minimisation of subsi-dence damage certainly was, and proved durability was a major factor in the selection of materials for use externally.

The corrosion protection of the steel frame components, fabricated from both hot and cold formed steel, was of the pickle dip and stove enamel type specification with galvanizing as an option for external-ly exposed situations only. Roofs were truly flat with low pitches on the assembly hall roofs for reasons of economic beam design, not for requirements of maintenance and the finish. Flat roofs, common for schools over many years, reflected the incompatibility of education planning needs with the disciplines of pitch roofs. Upper floors were of timber construction and the impact sound reducing performance achieved by the use of a foam-backed rubber flooring originating in France which is only now starting to be replaced.

The choice of claddings for the external walls was very much

influenced by traditional materials so that the tile hanging of
Sussex, and the pitch painted shiplap boarding of the East Coast
with the universality of aggregate faced concrete became the three
basic cladding options which carried through for many years.
Good first growth timber was still available for the "all clears"
Columbian pine window frames with their hardwood nosings. Vitreous
enamel with its "Stephens Ink" proved durability was an obvious, and
at the time economic choice for window infills. Internally, with a
then achievable 6 year decoration cycle, the selection of "Bellrock"
partitions, varnished hardwood for screens and doorsets, plasterboard and fibrous plaster for ceilings, all made no claims to low
maintenance.

Maintenance feed-back occurs over a period of time and in 1956
felt flat roofing guarantees were still available with the true
cost of two layer rag base felts still to be revealed. Extension
projects are continuing to reveal surprisingly good performance from
the steel frame protection specification. Vertical tiling has
weathered well, and greatly assisted in the early acceptance of
CLASP because of its familiar appearance, but is deficient in
impact resistance for many school locations. The original idea of a
pitch finish for weather boarding was soon replaced with "Arpax"
the durability claims of which have been substantiated. Boarding was
not preservative treated at that time, but no general schemes of
replacement have yet been required. Painting of windows had been
accepted from the beginning and although assumed repainting cycles
have not generally been maintained, the quality of the timber has
resulted in good continuing performance. Vitreous enamel has performed well and the Swedish espagnolette bolts built in to the casement windows are still performing.

The first ever CLASP project has been undermined on at least seven
separate occasions and the repair cost of the resultant superficial
damage has been minimal with the building continuing in use at all
times.

Marks 3/3B (1960-1962/3-66)
The rapid increase in the size of building programme from some £1 m
in 1957 to approaching £7 m in 1961 pointed to the attractions and
advantages to be obtained from "mass-production". In fact, CLASP has
never generated requirements beyond those of batch production, but it
did lead to one of the most serious mistakes in the life of the
Consortium by emphasing the needs of efficient factory production
at the expense of site assembly. However, the re-design of a
number of components to improve the assembly process and to exploit
the benefits of factory production led to shorter contact periods and
substantial cost reductions.

Pre-fabricated timber roof decks replaced in-situ boarding and the
reduced protection to the external wall by the smaller projecting
eaves resulted from appearance considerations as much as cost
reduction. The roof finish itself, then as now, continues to be a
matter for individual users to determine and reflects strong individual preferences. The change to dry jointed "Paramount" partitioning
made erection far cleaner but involved considerable joinery work. It

was during the course of this version of the system that the mineral fibre tile in a fire-resistant suspension showed itself to be competitive with the previous designs as well as being self finished with consequent ongoing maintenance advantage.

However, the main change in Mark 3 concerned the external wall. A possible range of 3-4000 window types made to project requirements were rationalized into a total range of 50 units. The differing site fixing requirements of aluminium sliding window, ventilating louvre, glass and vitreous enamel inserts were accommodated by a variety of optionals beads which supplemented the basic frame sections. Continuity and strength of these composite windows was achieved by the introduction of plywood stiffeners between the frames with joints then being cloaked with a hardwood bead. The aim of improved factory production was achieved but site fixing problems soon led to the partial factory assembly of storey height composite panels.

Too great a reliance on mastics, too optimistic an assessment of available site skills, a lowered timber quality and the later extended painting cycles, all contributed to a maintenance problem which led to the institution of replacement component arrangements in 1977.

The louvre specified, was an economic design of Australian origin whose performance was so poor and inappropriate for permanent building use in the United Kingdom, that there has been continuing resistance, by the Consortium to a reconsideration of the vastly improved designs available today.

Whilst the basic cladding materials continued to include those of the previous mark, the support was rationalized and all claddings were fixed on similar factory produced frames, with a separate inner lining variation of the internal partitions. Concrete cladding was regarded as a large "tile" measuring 3'4" X 2'0 with overlapping horizontal and recessed drained joints vertically. Weather tests carried out on this panel were very empiric but the design has proved itself in practice. An attempt to improve the impact performance of the vertical hung tiling by the introduction of the "mathematical" tile, traditionally having a brick proportioned thickened face, proved to be no better than the plain tile it was introduced to supplement.

For some time a "5M" residential version of CLASP ran parallel with Mark 3 and had shallower structural zones and a smaller grid with vertical concrete cladding reflecting the greater demand for "hole in wall" domestic windows.

In hindsight the Mark 3 period may be regarded as a period of learning and consolidation. Great improvements were made in terms of the quality of building achieved, the speed at which it could be built and the very considerable economies gained as the result of development work. These all helped the very real social pressures and problems of the time to be met but whilst the problems of flat felt roofs and mastics are not unique to CLASP, the Mark 3 system cannot claim to be an unqualified success in maintenance terms.

Mark 4/4B (1965-69/70-1973)
Mark 4 CLASP reflected the needs of a rapidly escalating annual

programme and for the first time resulted from the single minded
activites of a full-time Development Group. Detailed studies of site
assembly techniques were a part of the development work which also
took account of the fundamental changes which had taken place in the
industry over the previous 10 years. The brief had also been to
include the residential performance requirements previously met by
the "5M" version. The change to a 3'0" structural grid presaged
metrication and the European preferred standard for system building
of 900 mm.

The same basic foundation principles were maintained, but perimeter projections reduced and precast foundation pads introduced
which permitted rapid frame erection, but perimeter paving was a
continued necessity to prevent wash out. Account was taken of BRE
advice at the time on the design of flat roofs without impossibly
complicating the system by providing pitched top chords to flat roof
beams for spans exceeding 12'0", which uniquely achieved falls
over most of a Mark 4 roof. The condensation risk in school roofs is
not generally high and the cold roof concept with insulation at
ceiling level has performed satisfactorily where the design ventilation of the flat roof has been maintained. The Mark 4B plywood roof
decks however have proved somewhat less tolerant than the earlier
boarded decks where appropriate measures of good cross ventilation or
local extraction have not been provided in areas such as kitchens and
changing-rooms especially when coupled with the subsequent insertion
of cavity barriers.

The residential requirement coupled with changes in school design
led to the vertically spanning window and cladding concept of the external walls. The aim of reduced contract periods led to the pre-
finishing of timber windows and the introduction of gasket glazing,
for the first time ever in a timber frame context. This was a major
and bold decision which improved the subsidence performance by reducing the likelihood of glass breakage during mining movement,facili-
tated delivery to site of a pre-finished window including glazing,
and greatly reduced reliance on mastics. Generally, the gasket glazing has proved itself and original concerns on re-glazing due to
unfamiliarity have not proved to be a problem, perhaps because of
general progress in this direction in the industry. It was only
towards the end of the Mark when a general deterioration in standards
of available timber was appreciated that preservative treatment was
introduced. Consequently, whilst the basic design of the window is
vastly superior to that of the design it superseded, less than ideal
painting cycles are now resulting in some reports of rot in frames as
is the case with much painted external joinery of this date.

Continuing development refined the design of window and gasket
sections and resulted in further economies. Vertical concrete cladding joints relied on a convoluted edge profile and baffles and have
resulted in no serious problems. The replacement of some perimeter
steel frame components by cladding units performing a structural
function also achieved further economy.

Internally, Mark 4 saw the introduction of a new partition of
great maintenance significance. The Expanded Metal Company partition
resulted from a Ministry of Education performance enquiry. The

Stelvetite faced steel partition was pre-finished with high abrasion resistance which together with the stove enamelled door frames and screens and the "Minaboard" ceilings now created a CLASP internal environment where, for many years, the only necessary decoration would be that of the door leaves and windows. Similar partition systems available today are about 50% more expensive with but with a far less abrasion resistant surface.

Programme values of about £20m now justified the special design of a compatible range of ironmongery for Mark 4B intended to be of high quality, good design, fabricated in stainless steel, and available at extremely competitive prices. Moving part failures at the user interface are a common cause of dissatisfaction with buildings generally and feed back continues to indicate good performance from this range of ironmongery. A less satisfactory story is that of internal door hinges where the later introduction of a "lift off" facility to improve assembly and reduce damage during construction has resulted in the need for a replacement design, compatible with the steel door frame, which is available as part of the maintenance service.

An impending increase in further education building in 1965 led to a joint Development Project between the Department of Education and Science and the Consortium for the design of a version of the system appropriate for the extended performance required, based on and intended for use in conjunction with Mark 4B. This Mark 4B/JDP version of the system was introduced in 1967 and continued until its performance became largely incorporated in Mark 5.

Undoubtedly Mark 4/4B saw such a significant improvement in the quality of internal spaces as well as their maintenance characteristics that they have not been improved upon substantially since. However, the end of the Mark 4 period was to see two events with far reaching implications for the Consortium and the system design; - Local Government Reorganisation and a spate of arson, particularly frequent in the North East where many buildings were in CLASP construction, culminating in the fire at the Fairfield Old Persons Home, were to greatly influence the design of subsequent versions of the system.

Mark 5 (1972-1984)

Arson directed against public buildings in the early 70s reinforced architects' concern with design in relation to fire and greatly influenced the decision to eliminate combustible materials in Mark 5 wherever possible.

The later Mark 5 versions of CLASP also saw the first response to a change in fashion and in the attitude of designers who were, in turn, perhaps responding to a less silent public. Bricks and tile roofs were added to the CLASP vocabulary. Metrication had made the Mark 4 version obsolete and the opportunity presented by a £30 m programme was taken to optimize factory production, reduce still further site craft labour with a view to speeding construction and set maintenance as a real target for the exterior as well as the inside of CLASP buildings.

The polyester resin fixed foundation pins were introduced and

have given rise to no problems, whilst the change to a zinc rich
protection system for the steel frame with universal galvanizing of
all hollow sections, in addition to those subject to exposure, has
further reduced any possible long term corrosion problems. The
galvanized trapezoidal decking had limited falls like Mark 4 and
received no additional treatment except in potentially humid
locations.

The finish to "flat" roofs continued to be of built-up felt to
project specification with maintenance free histories of these
early high tensile felts now fully justifying the claims made.
Early projects were designed with cold roofs but recommendations
for roof level insulation made in 1975 reduced the need for roof
space ventilation. Pitch roofs were introduced firstly in the form
of mono pitches, and later as an engineered timber trussed rafter
roof designed to support traditional materials and also to perform
the structural function of the alternative flat roof diaphragm.
Upper floor construction was now of pre-cast concrete decks with
subcontract screed and finish.

The external wall element incorporated significant changes with
pre-stressed lighter weight concrete cladding panels, factory made
brick work panels and the plastic coated windows. The Mark 5 window
story indicates how even with the greatest care, innovation involves
risk, but equally how the Consortium approach and its continuing
collaborative arrangements with key suppliers can retrieve potentially serious situations.

The plastic coated timber window nomination resulted from a performance specification enquiry. The window principle had been used
for many years in Germany, mainly in domestic high-rise situations.
CLASP acceptance followed exhaustive checking; the firm obtained
the design rights for the U.K. and went on to found a successful
component industry in England. That stage, however, was not reached
without some early problems which were resolved jointly by the firm,
its suppliers, and a Consortium Study Group set up for the purpose.
Comparatively minor changes between the U.K. and the German application and methods were found to be the problem which was resolved
chemically as well as by extrusion and assembly modifications. The
firm stood by its performance warranty, and defective windows were
replaced. Maintenance problems today mainly relate to impact abuse,
partly caused by the windows apparent similarity to painted timber.
Ironically, whilst it has been said that only the doors need painting
in Mark 5, deterioration in external doors leaves and their hinges is
now leading to the introduction of replacement arrangements.

Having achieved a maintenance free interior demand justified the
introduction of a lower cost partition option with a pin-up or
plaster board face; its use was limited but the need for interior
decoration had been reintroduced.

Mark 5 was in many ways the most thorough and sophisticated
version of CLASP as a prefabricated, self finished and low maintenance building system with a peak annual programme value at 1986
prices, in excess of £100 m. Whilst the introduction of traditionally clad timber supported pitch roofs was a change with major
implications, as was the introduction of brick work panels,appear-

266

ance not maintenance was the prime motivation, and the trend back to traditional materials for visual not maintenance reasons, was to continue into Mark 6.

CLASP 6 (1983--)

The decision to redesign the CLASP system was taken when it had become clear that the large building programmes of the 1970s had passed and that reductions in volume requirements were questioning the design solutions of much of the system. It also took place at a time when architectural fashions and attitudes were becoming less concerned with the economics of the building site or the drawing office than with freedom of design, a return to tradition and an appreciation of the existing building stock. The Consortium took the view, however, that any small upturn in building demand could again lead to the overheating seen during the building boom of the 1970s and it was felt that the continued availability of a public sector controlled building system was therefore vital.

The CLASP 6 design has reduced costs considerably, relies far less on specialist manufacture and has opened up to permit a very large degree of design flexibility whilst maintaining a closed system for use when required. A greater emphasis on improved maintenance performance has been extended to include that of energy conservation.

The construction sequence is an aspect of design which is normally considered by architects. Lessons learnt from Mark 5 have extended this to dismantling procedures related to anticipated maintenance requirements and now ensure that re-roofing at abutment upstands can be carried out independently of the cladding above.

The pitch roof, whilst continuing to support the same finishes, is now fully framed in steel, and although few flat roofs have been built in recent years, the continued provision of a warm roof design with falls, in conjunction with high performance felt, should be far better that earlier CLASP equivalents. Disaffection with the appearance of aggregate faced concrete cladding led to its disappearance as a viable option and with it the pre-fabricated brick work panels. Whilst the design choice open to architects has been widened, the support systems have been standardized and claddings currently include in-situ brickwork and metal siding. The latter, whilst being popular is currently subject to a durability investigation although experience of Hoescht Tedlar faced material indicates continuing good performance over 15 years and the claims made for the "Colourcoat HB 200" look promising. A commercially available GRC panel is currently being considered but has yet to be integrated into the system.

Polyester powder coatings have transformed both the appearance and the maintenance characteristics of aluminium which is now being used for the main framing of windows as well as the opening lights. However, its similar acceptance for ironmongery is already resulting in signs of .wear on door knobs, but perhaps the design life of primary coloured furniture should be less than that of stainless steel.

A brief to reduce initial building costs has led to the inclusion of alternative doorsets and partitions which will require decoration. Whilst their main use is intended to be for residential type building, where for example, wall paper is desirable in any event, the in-

introduction of a low cost, lower performance option carries the risk of inappropriate use with a resulting rise in maintenance costs. As with Mark 5, although the solutions differ, and design options exist, a CLASP 6 building can be designed and built with a very low maintenance requirement; that the techniques and system solutions have changed and that much is now available "off the shelf" is a measure of how the industry as a whole as well as CLASP itself have evolved to meet similar problems.

5. Clasp Maintenance experience

What the Consortium has been trying to do and how system design has met these various targets has been described to put the maintenance aspect of system performance into its Consortium context. It is probably true to say that although considerations of durability and good detailing were an assumed part of the design process, it was not really until Mark 4 that maintenance targets were really set and since that time, maintenance considerations have become more important as maintenance budgets have reduced. The effect on system design may be seen progressively, through ceilings, internal screens and doorsets, partitions, external walls, windows and pitch roofs.

It was in 1976 that the Heriot-Watt University report, produced by the SDD, concluded on the basis of Marks 2, 3 and 4 that the incidence of maintenance in CLASP construction was "no better or no worse" than other forms of construction. Now it is about 15 years since most of the subsequent maintenance related improvements all came together in Mark 5 and early indications are that the reduced maintenance requirements are starting to be reflected in maintenance expenditure figures.

Changes in the CLASP organisation and in the system have always been in response to the needs of the Membership, and many have maintenance implications but no building can be maintenance free, there will be problems, and an approach to building which through its associated maintenance service continues its "after-sales" interest in both old and new buildings as well as providing assistance in the resolution of common problems, can only give reassurance to the building owners and help to those responsible for maintaining them.

Component Standing offer and manufacturing arrangements organized by the Consortium now also include the needs of maintenance and refurbishment and vary from special runs of Imperial sized components to supply and fix arrangements for windows.

References

The story of CLASP Ministry of Education Building Bulletin No.19, HMSO 1961.
CLASP/JDP The Development of a Building System for Higher Education Department of Education and Science, Building Bulletin No 45, HMSO 1970.
Successful Design for Mining Subsidence Architect's Journal 74
Maintenance of CLASP Construction Research Group Report. SDD 1976

MAINTAINING THE SYSTEM OF MAINTENANCE: AN OVERVIEW

PROFESSOR P.E. O'SULLIVAN and C.G. POWELL
Welsh School of Architecture, University of Wales Institute of
Science and Technology

Abstract
An overview is taken of the national system of maintenance, seen in
behavioural terms as an aggregation of roles and interests, held
together by a network of relationships and responsibilities. The
various interests share certain attitudes and beliefs which change
over time. Particular attention is paid to three aspects of the
system, the first being people and policy, in private and public
sector organizations. Here are found contrasting patterns of
responsibility, and scarcity of skills. The second aspect, funding,
notes that the familiar distinction between capital and maintenance
expenditures is weakening. The third aspect, briefing and feedback,
notes the activities and roles of designers and building users and a
need for different approaches to compilation of the brief and use of
best available knowledge. A concluding reconsideration of roles and
responsibilities draws attention to disparity between current, and
desirable, practices. A contrast is drawn between patterns of role
and responsiblity which, on the one hand, would be best for the system
as a whole and, on the other hand, best for the individual interests in
the system. The study concludes that building users would be well
placed to initiate change in the system.
Key words: Maintenance, Responsibility, Role, Personnel, Funding,
Feedback, Briefing.

1. View of the maintenance system

Maintenance of buildings is said to be 'work undertaken in order to
keep or restore every facility....to an acceptable standard' (BS3811).
In the same spirit, this paper is intended to be 'work undertaken in
order to keep or restore' the system which carries out maintenance.
The paper begins by considering the system of maintenance in general
terms.

The view adopted here of the maintenance 'system' is an all-
embracing one which includes the behaviour of those whose interests
and actions impinge on maintenance, formal organizational structures
and processes, and phenomena which sustain operational and theoretical
maintenance activity. Maintenance activity itself is taken to

269

comprise operations and supporting activity carried out on and about buildings from handover to demolition, to sustain them 'to an acceptable standard'.

The vastness of the maintenance system stretches from the extremes of desk-bound manager wrestling with resource allocation problems, to Frod with hammer 'persuading' a recalcitrant stop-cock. To make sense of so large and heterogeneous a system, it will be necessary to take a particular perspective. The system will be observed in terms of an aggregation, or family, of roles and interest groups, of individuals, informal coalitions, departments, and firms. This aggregation is held together by a complicated network of relationships as manifested in responsibilities, obligations, contracts, and exchanges of money, and other rewards such as satisfaction and freedom from censure. Gentlemens' agreements and conspiracies of silence also play their parts. The aggregation as a whole expands, contracts and shifts ground, and interest groups and relationships restlessly multiply, divide and alter. As in all families, there are occasional squabbles and perturbations. Nevertheless, through the flux there is a considerable measure of stability and some unity of purpose. After all, buildings need maintaining and are certain to continue that way. The demand side is on an assured rising trend; a circumstance which merits close examination of the supply side.

People in interest groups in the system - whether casual window cleaners or surveyor overlooking a building stock worth millions - share beliefs and attitudes. Maintenance has its share of orthodoxies and conventional wisdom. Some are stale orthodoxies of yesterday, while others are fresh and destined to be the commonplaces of tomorrow. Some will be mentioned to set the context.

One orthodoxy is that there are at present sharpening contrasts in standards of maintenance in different parts of the national building stock. Among plentiful examples is the contrast between standards prevalent in prosperous southern service industries, and standards in stagnant smokestack industries elsewhere. Again, there is the difference in standards in, say, prestige offices and new up-market retail outlets on the one hand, and buildings for some public transport undertakings, on the other hand. Similarly, there are said to be growing differences between standards generally in private sector and public sector. Then there is contrast between the vigour of the suburban d.i.y. field - if that may be included in the system - and the opposite in decaying inner-city housing. These contrasts demonstrate the breadth of the subject and wealth of variety within it. They also emphasize the rising trend of quality standards, or aspirations, associated with best practice.

The second orthodoxy is that innovation diffusion is as active as ever, or more so. There are straightforward product innovations, such as 'inorganic flexifit thurling grommets' (in RIBA Journal recently). Additionally there are design innovations, in which major products are brought together in a novel manner. Innovation, readers need no reminding, is risk. How much and where are important unknowns,

270

less problematical is that risk from this source is growing rather than declining.

The third orthodoxy is known to experts everywhere and it is that irrationality prevails: buildings are commonly occupied, operated and maintained irrationally. Designers despair that users use things wrongly and heating engineers complain that controls are misused (or not used at all). Note in passing the paradox of the man who prides himself on his supreme skill at the wheel of his car, yet who is ignorant of the position of his living room thermostat.

The fourth orthodoxy is about people responsible for maintenance of large institutional building stocks. A disparity exists there between increasingly sophisticated management and information systems, and what actually happens at operational level. Clever data retrieval and prediction techniques may say what should be done to a building and when. However, we all know that out there on the cold scaffold the picture looks very different; the gulf between management systems and practical operations has never been wider.

The fifth orthodoxy follows this, although not everyone would own up to it. Given the intractable and unpredictable nature of maintenance problems, people understandably find it in their interest to spread risk. They pass on direct accountability, or maintain a prudent distance, like 1914-18 war top brass.

The final orthodoxy (although many remain unstated) is the most self-evident; that much remains to be done before all is well. The way is now clear to examine in more detail a trio of major aspects of the system.

2. Maintenance people and policy

The organizational structures set up by institutions to maintain their building stocks may be characterised as being of two contrasting types. These two represent generalised 'ideal' models of maintenance organizations which make policy, initiate and monitor operations and in some cases also execute the operations. The two models embody characteristics in their purest forms, and in reality many maintenance organizations combine, to some degree, characteristics of both models.

The first model is the private sector organizational model. This is found typically among national companies owning large building stocks such as hotels, catering facilities and retail outlets. Typically, policy-making is carried out centrally, remote from operations on the ground. Responsibility for site activity is pushed down and away by policy-makers and management. Operational aspects are delegated and re-delegated for implementation by contract firms and low-grade site personnel. The view from London headquarters of life in remote provincial plant rooms can be very indistinct. Policy makers being removed from practical issues, are sheltered from the

271

problems and risks of error on site. On site, meanwhile, risks are inevitably run from day-to-day because knowledge is incomplete; causes and consequences are so often imponderable. The efficiency of the model is much helped by competition which is possible at operational level. Maintenance contractors are tested and survive in place according to their capacity to meet requirements at an economic rate. Issues which assume importance because responsibility is pushed down the hierarchy of command are liability, terms of contracts and the scope and quality of operations. In all, the model is successful and perpetuated by leading building owners. Success, however, is short term, rather than long. Successful middle managers are likely to be promoted into other areas of responsibility, far outside maintenance. The field of maintenance is seen in career terms as a stepping stone (or a graveyard). Lower down the hierarchy, among junior management and supervisory grades, good performers are difficult to identify, because effectiveness cannot readily be measured. A satisfactory career structure is missing.

The second model is the public sector organizational model. Approximations to it are in such fields as health care and local authority housing. This model contrasts with the foregoing one in that responsibility is pushed upwards, away from the operational level. Site operations are executed largely or partly by direct labour, managed by a chain of responsibility stretching upwards. The model has potential long-term strengths in offering scope for a satisfactory career structure. Good performers anywhere in the hierarchy may be identified readily and promoted. Unfortunately, it often happens that the organizational hierarchy is under-populated by people of the right calibre. There is an inability to attract and retain sufficiently qualified and motivated personnel, which retards effectiveness.

There are points of note about the two models such as the sharp contrast in the way in which responsibility is pushed up in one case and down in the other. Other points arise from similarities rather than differences between the two models. One point is that both models encourage managerial displacement activities. An example is the elaborate system for collection and manipulation of expensive and sometimes useless data. The aims of such activities are praiseworthy, but their distance from operational realities is to be deplored. Another point of similarity between the two models is the inadequate quality and quantity of maintenance personnel, both blue and white collar, which results. Of those present, many are at the wrong level, relative to ability. The reasons for this may arise from historical accident: maintenance once was a low-profile activity; major buildings once required less attention to fabric and plant (if any); menial labour once was plentiful; and building users once had different attitudes (or none) towards life cycle costs. However, the maintenance system of today and tomorrow cannot be sustained under a legacy of attitudes based on obsolete building form, social order and economics. The issue of inadequate maintenance personnel is connected with missing roles and, worse, fumbled responsibilities. The problem of supply of the well-educated, competent engineers capable of tackling the challenge of maintenance will not easily go away. Here, issues affecting maintenance surely are near some fundamental problems of the national economy. To create an attractive career structure with adequate reward, the field of maintenance must compete more effectively with rival career opportunities for some of the best minds.

3. Funding for maintenance

The second major aspect of the system is funding and the starting point is that there is never enough of it. Infinite building wants always have to compete for all-too-finite means. This affects maintenance as much as anything else about buildings - probably more - although longer term consequences may be temporarily concealed. Conditions of endemic scarcity have encouraged much to be written about optimum distribution of resources through the life cycle of buildings, about best value for money, and so on. Theoretical work notwithstanding, resources in practice seem seldom to be distributed optimally. Initial spending on buildings is commonly too low to contain subsequent maintenance costs so that the building user ends up paying heavy maintenance costs. Plaintive remarks are heard, but when the next new project comes round, expenditure continues to be postponed and cheap-to-build, expensive-to-maintain buildings continue to appear. Recurring expenditure on maintenance, which ensues from low first costs, is used to compensate for initial parsimony. The failures of cheap building are remedied by maintenance; a shift of responsibility has occurred between designers and maintenance staff. Instances of this sort can be multiplied, as when extensive and costly fitting out contracts effectively blur the distinction between first cost and maintenance cost. Some buildings may be, say, five years old before they may be said to be truly 'finished', if ever they are. The overlapping procedures of building completion and maintenance are difficult to distinguish. While some elements in such buildings are brought by phases towards 'completion', other elements - the less substantial and the short lived - may be slipping quietly into decline. Again, another way in which initial and maintenance costs overlap is in connection with high disturbance costs arising from maintenance operations. With many buildings used increasingly intensively, and with less available 'slack' in terms of space and time, disturbance costs figure more prominently with building users. Such disturbance costs may be preferred by users (consciously or not) to high initial costs which, had they been incurred, would have contained or eliminated the costs of disturbance. Here again, responsiblity which might be carried at design stage is picked up later during maintenance.

The familiar distinction between capital and maintenance expenditure is losing clarity and being gradually replaced by an indistinct boundary between the two. Indeed, rather than thinking of a boundary, it may be conceptually helpful to think in terms of a continuum with capital expenditure at one pole and maintenance at the other, and varying degrees of each in between. In the longer term such a merging may help activity funded as maintenance to share some of the close attention and interest which at present attends new construction: the status of maintenance will be enhanced. Meanwhile, the increasingly indistinct boundary between capital and maintenance expenditure confers benefits on some interests in the system. Designers can more easily and legitimately evade responsibility for producing reliable buildings, since heavy early maintenance is regarded as a reasonable way (even a short term financially desirable way) in which to deal with defects. It is preferred to permit defects and to apply remedies, than to prevent defects in the first place. Building users' concern at high capital cost of building is allayed. This is because capital expenditure is contained by implicit acceptance of subsequent high maintenance expenditure, and concealed by the indistinct boundary with maintenance expenditure. Maintenance people can shift part of the responsibility for their crippling workload on to designers, while benefitting in the context of their parent institution from a size- able budget to dispose of as they please. Indistinct boundaries between capital and maintenance expenditures are to the benefit of some interests in their relationships one with another.

4.   Briefing designers to minimise maintenance

The trio of major aspects is completed by briefing for new build and how it is related to subsequent maintenance. The issue is that the often-lamented missing feedback link between operational and mainten- ance experience with existing buildings, and design decisions for new ones, is still missing. Without feedback from live experience, designers are prone to repeating the same old mistakes. And lack of adequate feedback is worsened by the already-noted unrelenting pace of innovation and diffusion. This heightens the need to make use of best available knowledge in the forms of standards, codes and so on, and to do the utmost to bridge the applicability cap. The task here is not to apportion blame for a lamentable state of affairs, or to decide whether the problem is one of lack of useable feedback data or a case of data falling on deaf ears.

It will be more constructive to look further at current and future responsibility for initial briefing. The accepted view is that design professionals are indispensable at this stage, except in the case of the simplest buildings, because available knowledge is incomplete. The professionals' task, willingly accepted, is to take on the problems and attendant risks inherent in working in an area of uncertainty. Building users are happy to delegate responsibility for brief compilation to the professionals who, for their part, are equally happy to grasp the measure of control which arises from the task. As the project progresses the professionals are assumed to proceed according to two simple rules. One is that they will use the best available knowledge in the course of their work. The other is that they will do what they can to limit errors and misjudgements, when faced with novel problems with unforseeable consequences. To abide by the rules it is necessary to seek the opinions of experts in the needs of building users, namely the building users themselves. This is not unreasonable although in the days of small building users who built simply and seldom it was different. Today many users are large and build with complexity and often. The question arises as to how much, and how often, the professionals seek the users' views. The extent to which they do so is a measure of how seriously they regard the rules of using best available knowledge and seeking to limit errors. The professionals possess the outsider's fresh approach to building need which is often very valuable, but it is not the only valid approach. Equally helpful is the users' own assessment of needs, based on intimate, long-standing and up-to-date experience.

Very close attention to users' views is not all that professionals need to bear in mind. There also is close attention to the probable consequences of getting something wrong and, not least, how to design easily-operated and low maintenance buildings. These tasks require a sustained and thoroughgoing research and development-based effort, using best available knowledge. At present there seems little enough incentive to professionals to familiarise with and utilise feedback and other data which would give the most reliable and efficient designs. To sum up this section: users have closest experience of building needs, so they should accept greater responsibility in briefing, rather than awaiting results and complaining afterwards (or worse, altering buildings under construction); design professionals should narrow the applicability gap, since they have closest access to best available knowledge from research and development sources. Thus each interest should act to draw most from their own particular experience, users about themselves and their needs, professionals from research and development.

5. Roles and responsibilities reconsidered

To recapitulate three themes: the system is hampered by lack of the right people in the right places; the distinction between capital expenditure on new build and expenditure on maintenance is becoming blurred; and benefits would follow from users becoming more active in brief compilation together with better professional use of research and development-based knowledge. Definition of roles and responsibilities lie near the roots of these themes.

Interests in the system agree about many of the aims, functions and what should be done for maximum effectiveness of maintenance processes. Yet at the same time, a conspiracy of silence reigns over the system when it comes to taking action to achieve ends agreed to be desirable. For example, maintenance experts generally agree that a policy of preventative maintenance is desirable although it makes little favourable impact on building users. In contrast, a policy of crisis failure repairs makes big impact on users. When nothing goes wrong users give no credit to maintenance people, but when failures are repaired quickly, users are impressed. The point is that maintenance experts believe that preventative maintenance is preferable to crisis repair, but unfortunately it attracts no kudos from the users. Thus experts who know what should be done are tempted to collude among themselves to do something different and inferior, or

275

to connive to do nothing at all. Experts know what would be best for
users, but find it advantageous to conspire in silence to pursue
narrower sectional interests. Some relationships between interests
in the system are analagous to informal trade protection agreements,
and probably almost as undesirable for those on the outside of them.
Each interest behaves as if it had more to gain, or less to lose, by
being acquiescent in the implicit values of the system than by
challenging them.

Who could take a holistic view of the system and resulting service,
to reconsider and re-order roles and relationships of the interests
within it? The key figure is the user, the first link in the causal
chain of building provision, operation and maintenance, and ultimate
source of demand from whom all else follows. The experienced user
interest is a free agent, if necessary able to avoid the hampering
relationships with other interests in the system. The user interest
also is well informed about building needs, able to take an
unprejudiced view based on clear market preferences, and able to lay
down the service required and how it is to be achieved. Users in the
conduct of their businesses are accustomed to decide aims and then
will the means, so they may be expected to approach maintenance in a
similar way. In doing so they would specify requirements for the
complete mechanism of maintenance from programme, contracts and
expenditure, to provision of operational manuals. Returning to the
title of the paper, it is to the user that the maintenance system
should look to find the impetus to maintain itself.

MAINTENANCE OF BITUMINOUS ROOF COVERINGS

ir. R POELS
Building Research Foundation, Rotterdam

Abstract
Research has been made into the conditions of bituminous roof coverings in the Netherlands, especially into the state of maintenance of traditional and modern materials. The data recovered have been compiled into guidelines for a policy of maintenance that is right technically and economically.

Five different kinds of maintenance have been discussed, together with the points of time when they will have to take place. Examples have been given in the inspection forms.

Keywords: Ageing, Carrying out of maintenance, Regularity of maintenance checks, Inspection techniques.

1   Introduction

A study group of the Building Research Foundation has in 1984/1985 collected information with manufacturers of roofing-materials, advisory institutions and maintenance managers in order to find out about the maintenance of bituminous roof coverings. Next, the collected information has been scanned on the essential aspects of maintenance of roofs, and after that remodelled into manageable guide-lines for principals, designers, roofing companies and managers of real estate. These guide-lines together with the results of this research have been put into a report (report no. 144), that appeared in 1986.

This research involves two groups of roofing materials:

1   roof coverings made from 'traditional' roofing materials on the basis of tar or bitumen (roofing felt, asphalt-impregnated felt or asphalt-impregnated fibre-glass);

2   roof coverings made from 'modern' roofing-materials on basis of APP- or SRS-modified bitumen and with an inserted polyester matting.

Until about 1975 bituminous roof coverings in the Netherlands were only made from the materials mentioned under 1. Their maintenance has been carried out through the years by nearly all roofing

277

companies; the techniques of the maintenance are accordingly widely known, they have been assimilated in the guide-lines of the report.

The maintenance of the roof coverings mentioned under 2. have as yet caused no special problems, since they have been introduced some 10 years ago. It has appeared from a large number of inspections of 5 to 12 years old roofs of this type, that the modifications of bitumen of generally have much better resistance against ageing than the traditional blown bitumen. Still, also this material will come eventually to the end of its useful life and steps will possibly have to be taken to extend it, if at least this is best from an economic point of view.

It may be doubtful whether the methods and materials of maintenance that are commonly used for the traditional roof coverings mentioned under 1. can be employed as a matter of course to lengthen the life-cycle of modified bituminous materials in a suitable and economic way. The Building Research Foundation will set up a closer survey into this matter.

An important conclusion which can be drawn from research already conducted, is that in both groups roof coverings, maintenance seems principally determined by the specific characteristics of the top layer of the roofing and the finish that has been applied. That is, as far as defects have to be repaired as a result of deficiencies in design, material or execution.

2 The Necessity of Maintenance

The roof is supposed to protect the building, the activities and the people in it from the climate outside. Therefore it should function well and permanently, which means careful maintenance. Maintenance for bituminous roof coverings as a rule appears necessary for two reasons:

a   the materials employed are subject to ageing.
b   damages   to the roof coverings happen especially as a result of loading by users.
    The largest influence on the ageing phenomenon comes from the outside climate, that together with the climate inside produces a physical-chemical, biological and mechanical effect on the roof covering. The ageing behaviour of the roof covering can be influenced to a considerable extent during the design and execution of the construction, but in the last resort the manager of the building determines the life-cycle of the roof by his policy.

The policy of the manager of the building consists of two components:
1   The technique of maintenance, which includes: making the necessary provisions in order to keep the roof covering in good shape for the whole of the expected life-cycle, without being

obliged to actually renew the roof covering.

2   Planning and estimates of maintenance: the aspects of planning of maintenance which include the economic life-cycle, can only be considered with regard to the specific possibilities of the owner/manager.

Roof covering is never, no more than any other part of the building, absolutely 'free of maintenance'. And it will always be necessary to check on the functioning of the roof covering.

The amount of maintenance that is necessary - the maintenance liability - can be different in each case. For bituminous roof coverings the following factors greatly determine the maintenance liability:
-    the kind of bitumen used in the toplayer;
-    the structure of the roof covering;
-    the kind and quality of the underlayer;
-    the way in which the roof covering is fastened;
-    the craftsmanship with which the roof covering and the connecting and finishing details are designed and executed.

3   Types of maintenance
The customary maintenance can be divided into five types.

Type 1:   Cleansing maintenance
This type of maintenance consists of removing substances, object and overgrowth from the surface of the roofing, that can be detrimental to the waterdrainage, the water-resistance and the durability.

Cleansing maintenance is necessary at the moment the roofing is ready. No specific professional knowledge is required; the owner/manager can do it himself, if necessary, with the instructions from the roofing company.

Dependent on the risk of pollution, cleansing maintenance is necessary one to four times a year.

Type 2:   Inspecting maintenance
This maintenance provides the basis information for maintenance planning and maintenance estimates.

It consists of recording the quality at that moment of the roof covering and notify the measures that should be taken.

See for further information chapter 5.

Inspecting maintenance is just like cleansing maintenance necessary as soon as the roof covering is ready and the frequency is dependent on the likelihood of deficiencies. Inspection should be carried out by persons with adequate professional knowledge, so that it might be noticed in time and effectively whether measures should be taken and which according to the conditions of deficiencies or shortages. The inspector should be able to translate his observations into concrete advice in order to execute the repairs.

Dependent on the risk of damages and/or the existence of other deficiencies, this inspection is necessary once or twice a year. Inspecting maintenance can, of course, take place at the same time as cleansing maintenance.

Type 3: Repairing maintenance
This maintenance consists of repairing (local) damages and deficiencies of the roof covering or the protective finish in order to
guarantee preservation of the water drainage, water resistance
and durability.
    Repairing maintenance should be done by professional roofers,
preferably by the company that fitted the materials.

Type 4: Complementary maintenance
Complementary maintenance which takes place in the so called year
of maintenance, consists of improving parts or layers which have
come to the end of their life-cycle, or of adding materials (an
extra layer) in order to guarantee preservation of water resistance
and durability.
    If an extra layer of material is fitted (strips of brushed
and sprayed substances) it should be certain that the existing
roof covering and the construction underneath is of such quality
that the treatment is justified technically as well as economically.

Type 5: Replacing maintenance
Replacing maintenance is maintenance to the roof that is carried
out when a situation is reached where complementary maintenance,
whether from a technical or an economic point of view would not
produce an acceptable result. This maintenance consists of fitting
new roofing, and there is a choice between:
a   fitting new roofing – with or without an extra insulation
     layer – onto the existing roofing;
b   removal of the existing roofing – if necessary including
     the base and/or the supporting structure – followed by fitting
     a new roofing, with or without an extra insulation layer.

4   Regularity in maintenance checks
Maintenance can only be meaningful when it takes place at the
time when the quality of the roofing is such that there is an
actual technical and economic profit. When the ageing has gone
too far, maintenance of types 3 or 4 will hardly be profitable.
So there should be a careful estimate, when maintenance should
take place and which type of maintenance is relevant.
    The particular time at which and regularity with which maintenance
should be carried out, depend on the technical aspects of the
roof covering, but maintenance of types 4 or 5 also depend on:
–   consideration of secondary nature, which have indirect influence
     on the roof covering, for example, improvement of roof insula-
     tion, alteration of the style of the roof or the use of the
     roof surface, alteration of the destination of the building.
–   the desired level of maintenance, which can be a result of
     financial and/or operational considerations.
The only common factor of all roofs which can be regarded before-
hand as a (reasonable) constant, is the type of material.
    Therefore, in manuals for maintenance, generally tables are
used, in which estimates are given of the life-cycle and of the
regularity with which maintenance (of type 4) will have to be

280

carried out, starting from the type of roof covering. Such an outline should really be readjusted for every specific roof surface.

Report No 144 of the Building Research Foundation, mentioned in the introduction, has for both types of roof coverings, concerned in the research, estimates of the regularity with which maintenance-work has been mentioned as an indication. The owner/manager can use this information as a working-plan to record his maintenance schematically and reserve the necessary budget.

5   Manual for inspectors

As stated in chapter 3, regular cleansing maintenance, but also regular inspecting maintenance of roofing is necessary and the frequency is largely dependent on the likelihood of deficiencies. It is usual that inspections take place at least once every two years. The inspection should preferably be carried out system-atically with the help of a checklist, and specific aspects of details of the roof should be paid special attention.

The observations should be noted down in such a way that they convey a clear picture of the condition of the roof covering.

On account of those observations, actions have to be carried out with the help of a professional roofer, so that the appropriate functioning of the roof is guaranteed.

On pages following of this paper examples are given of inspection forms in the form of checklist, on which observations can be noted down briefly. In the report, it is emphasised that the actual execution of repairs and other revisions of the roof covering should in principle be carried out by professional roofers.

6   Dutch regulations

The Dutch Institute of Normalisation has drafted a few standards for bituminous roof coverings. Guide-lines and requirements are given for inspection methods of bituminous materials in the form of strips and, amongst others, for inflammability and fire-resistance of the roof constructions and roof materials. The roofing companies, united in Vebidak, have published guide-lines and recommended constructions for the execution of steel roofs with thermal insula-tion and bituminous roof covering. The Building Research Foundation has made six reports on flat roofs with bituminous roof covering.

A. INSPECTION FORM FOR ROOFSURFACES - Roofsurface:

Checklist	Evaluation (put a circle)	Remarks
1. general picture	good/reasonable/not good	

2. water drainage	stagnant/not stagnant	
2.1 roof wet for a long time	yes no	
2.2 probable cause	Water-outlets too high/sagging roof/no participations/other waterthresholds	
2.3 indication of place		

3. dirt and overgrowth	none/occasionally/common	
3.1 kind	slime/sand/pulvarised slate/algae/ moss/sedum/other plants	
3.2 indication of place		
4. levelness	good/reasonable/not good	
4.1 probable cause	surface not level/sagging roofsurface/ other	
4.2 indication of place		

5. mineral layer	closed/bare in places/pressed into bitumen/filthy	

6. stripmaterial		
6.1 creases	none/occasionally/common yes/no at seam underlayer flat/sharp open/closed overlap	
6.2 blisters	none/occasionally/common small/large low/high	
6.3 opened blisters	indication of place between layers 1 and 2, 2 and 3 under roofing do/do not contain moisture/water	
6.4 pimples	none/occasionally/common	
6.5 open seams	none/occasionally/common length depth	
6.6 cracks	none/occasionally/common yes/no at seam underlayer indication of place	
6.7 shrinkage	none/occasionally/common length/width overlap (apparent) shifting indication of place	
6.8 bare spots	none/occasionally/common	
bituminous upper . layer	smooth/crackle surface/weathered	
inserted layer	yes/no visible	
6.9 bituminous upper layer	smooth/crackle surface/weathered	

282

B. INSPECTION FORM FOR ROOFDETAILS - Part:

Checklist		Evaluation (put a circle) Remarks
1.	Lining Elevation	(tilting fillet, vertical lining etc.)
1.1	creases	none/occasionally/common
1.2	blisters	none/occasionally/common
1.3	pimples	none/occasionally/common
1.4	open seams	none/occasionally/common
1.5	cracks	none/occasionally/common
1.6	shrinkage	width/length of strip
1.7	bare spots	none/occasionally/common
1.8	bituminous upper layer	smooth/crackle surface/weathered
1.9	sagging	none/occasionally/common
1.10		
2.	Finishing lining	(rooftrim, zinc strip, bottom leads etc
2.1	damage and deformation	none/occasionally/common
2.2	ageing	good/reasonable/bad
2.3	fastening	good/reasonable/not good
2.4		
3.	joining sticking-sheet	(of rainwaterdrainage, dome, ventilation-hood, etc.)
3.1	damage and deformation	none/occasionally/common
3.2	fastening of sheet	good/reasonable/not good
4.	quality of accessory	(roofdome, gravelborder, spherical grid, ventilating pipe, etc.)
4.1	damage and deformation	
5.	quality protective detail	(protective sheet, chimney, pointing still, etc.)
5.1	rain- and/or waterresistance	good/reasonable/not good
6.	other aspects	(for example obstruction, contact surfaces, supports/roof covering)

If necessary, a separate list can be completed for every different part or group of similar parts.

MAINTENANCE CONSIDERATIONS DURING THE DESIGN PROCESS

W A WALLACE
Department of Construction
& Environment Engineering
Bristol Polytechnic

DANNY S S THEN
Department of Building
Heriot-Watt University
Edinburgh

Abstract
This paper reports on some of the findings of a research study carried out at the Department of Building at Heriot-Watt University, that was concerned with the use of information in the architectural decision making process. Various aspects of the design process were considered, with aspects of maintenance and associated variables featuring prominently. The results presented relate to the incidence and use of maintenance or maintenance-related information during the design stage from initial briefing to production information.
Key words: Maintenance and Design, Maintenance Information.

Introduction

The ultimate function of any building is to maximize the benefits to be derived (financial or otherwise) over the life of the building at minimum expenditure (on maintenance, repairs and renovation). Into any completed building, consciously or not, a permanent operating cost is built into the design that lasts over the life of the building. To design with maintenance in mind is not a conspicious practice, yet over the lifespan of the building an owner will meet maintenance and repairs costs equalling twice or three times its initial capital costs. In this direction, therefore, lies a virtually unexplored field in which a potential owner would rightly expect his designers to take a lively and effective interest. Unfortunately, feedback of information from users to designers is a rare occurence.

This paper attempts to throw some light on the use of maintenance information during the design process by architectural practices.

Sample of Building Projects

A complex engineering building design was analysed on a cross-sectional basis over an eighteen month period. An on-going pilot study of a less complex technological building was also carried out. Validation of longitudinal results was provided by the analysis of 14 other designs on a cross-sectional basis. Validation samples ranged from an extremely complex engineering building to simple housing.

285

Research   Method

Design team members were interviewed throughout each design
process.   Where possible, Architects, Quantity Surveyors and
Client Representatives were interviewed.   Design team meetings
were also attended and recorded using shorthand.   In the case of
the longitudinal study, more than 20 meetings were observed.

Each statement was recorded and analysed using Content Analysis.
This technique has been widely used in psychological and
linguistical research over the past twenty years.   Statements are
divided into variable occurance units.   In it's simplest form,
content analysis reveals the frequency of occurance of a selected
word leading onto psychological inferences of the mind state of
the speaker.   For example, if an individual consistently uses a
selected word, it may be assumed that this work features
prominently in the thought processes of that individual.   In
addition, content analysis allows word association concordances
to be calculated.   For example, two words may appear in the same
sentence.   If this happens more often than would be expected by
chance alone,   then it is reasonable to infer a pre-occupation
between the two words in the thought processes of the speakers.

This paper presents results based upon this method of analysis.

Maintenance Information in the Design Process

Results indicated that Design Team Architects referred to
maintenance to an increasing extent as the design processes
continued.   In the early stages, maintenance was relatively
infrequently referred to.   The frequency of references to
maintenance increased appreciably towards the later stages of the
design process.   Figure (1) shows variations in the frequency of
references to maintenance for six design processes.   The results
indicate that this increased frequency effect was more pronounced
in the case of the less complex designs.

Qualitative analysis of interview responses indicated that
Architects began to consider maintenance to a greater extent in
the later stages because the greater detail of design tends to
make the Architects recall maintenance details from previous
designs.   Architects often referred to maintenance aspects when
suggesting or discussing a specific item of equipment or a
specific item of fabric.

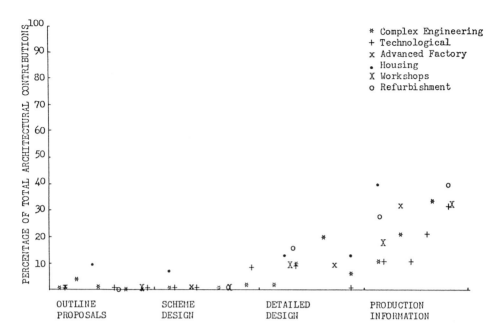

Figure 1 - Variation in Architects References to Maintenance

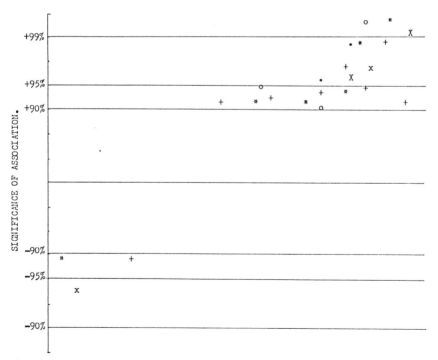

Figure 2 - Significance of Association between Past Experience
and Maintenance
(Only 90% or higher significance levels are shown)

287

Figure 2 shows the significance of association between references to past experience and references to maintenance. These curves indicate that the Design Team Architects were increasingly referring to past experience and maintenance in the same sentence, so that the significance of association between these two variables became appreciably higher than would be expected by chance alone.

More detailed examination of this increasing association revealed that references to maintenance were also significantly associated with references to new design goals. In most designs, various changes are made to the design in the later stages, for example in response to a requirement to reduce costs. Design Team members often suggested new design goals and preferences, and maintenance references became increasingly associated with these in the later stages of the design. An example of this increasing association is shown in Figure 3. These curves show the significance of association between references to maintenance and references to new design goals. The results indicate that in the later stages of the design, new design goals were being increasingly associated with maintenance.

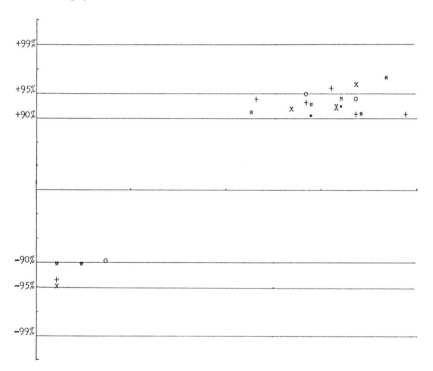

Figure 3 – Significance of Association between New Goals and Maintenance

(Only 90% or higher significance levels are shown)

The curves in Figure 3 also indicate that during the early stages of some of the designs (the more complex ones), there was a significant level of disassociation between references to new goals and maintenance. This suggests that these Architects were deliberately not referring to maintenance aspects in the earlier stages when discussing new design goals. Qualitiative results indicated that this was due to other design 'preoccupations' during those stages. New design goals were largely discussed in terms of cost and aesthetics in the earlier stages of the designs. In the later stages, cost factors were prominent, but the aesthetic factors appeared to be largely replaced by maintenance factors.

Results have provided further details on this increasing cost and maintenance relationship in the later stages of the design. In most of the designs, cost-reductions became necessary in the later stages. Results have also indicated that the Design Team Architects were increasingly referring to maintenance factors in response to cost reduction references. Curves which show this trend are shown in Figure 4.

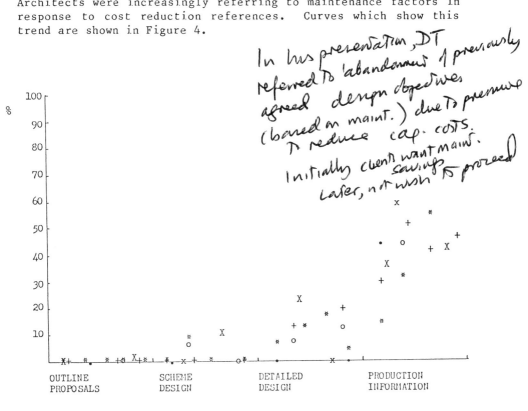

Figure 4 - Percentage of Architect Responses to Cost Reduction Suggestions which contained a Reference to Maintenance

Conclusions

This paper has shown that design team pre-occupation with maintenance factors varies over the course of a design. Results indicate that there is an increasing concern with maintenance towards the later stages of the design process and this pre-occupation relates to costs and practical factors.

The chief instigator or source of maintenance considerations is the architect. Maintenance factors appear to be used by the architect as a defence against potential cost reduction exercises put forward by the client. Architects increasingly refer to maintenance considerations when faced with late stage cost reduction proposals from the client. This tends to be substantiated by references to past experience with increasing reference to specific past designs. Architects defences against late stage cost reduction proposals are often supported/defended by the Quantity Surveyor in the design team.

References

Mackinder, M. and Marvin, H. (1982) Design decision-making in architectural practice. Institute of dvance Architectural Studies, University of York, Research paper 19.

Budd. (1967) Content Analysis of communications. Macmillan.

**Part V
Organisation
of the work**

MANAGEMENT PROCESSES RELATED TO THE MAINTENANCE OF HISTORIC BUILDINGS

R W GRIMSHAW
Department of Civil Engineering
University of Salford

Abstract
The object of this paper is to examine the particular maintenance problems posed by historic buildings and the way these problems are reflected in the management of their maintenance and the arrangements made for financing maintenance. The points made will be related to the current management of the medieval buildings of St John's College, Oxford. The first section will list those elements of the fabric which pose special maintenance problems, the second will look in detail at the management issues and the organisation best suited to meet the needs of historic buildings and the third will examine the problems of making provision for financing maintenance.
Key words: Historic buildings, Maintenance management, Skills, Planning, Budgeting, Building fabric, Planned maintenance, Cost control.

Introduction
Before dealing with detailed issues it is necessary to define exactly what we mean by historic buildings, conservation and maintenance.

Historic buildings are more than just old buildings of architectural importance. They are, as Bernard Fielden describes, "a symbol of our cultural identity and continuity - a part of our heritage", and as such it is generally accepted that they should be maintained for as long as possible and without materially altering the fabric of special architectural features. The maintenance and care of these buildings must, therefore, be viewed in the very long term with the time span to be considered running into hundreds of years.

Conservation is not just maintaining the fabric of the building. It has come to imply both the use of special skills in making repairs and taking protective measures to preserve buildings, and also striking a balance between preservation and economic usage. The latter is an important assumption. In conserving historic buildings, the object is not to preserve them as ancient monuments but as working buildings which have an economic as well as historic value. Realistically, it is only in this way that we can hope to keep these buildings.

The object of maintenance has been defined by John Earl as

293

"Work undertaken in order to keep, restore or improve every facility, ie. every part of a building, its services and surrounds, to a currently accepted standard, and to sustain the utility and value of the facility". The implication of this statement is that it is not the object of maintenance to keep the building in its existing state but up to the "currently accepted standard", implying a continual improvement in the facilities as expectations rise. This can have serious implications for the fabric of historic buildings.

The Fabric
Historic buildings have the same maintenance problems as most buildings but some elements of the fabric pose special maintenance problems which require specialist skills. Although all historic buildings are different in their structure and fabric, certain elements of the buildings of St John's College do illustrate such problems and some of these will be examined briefly.

Stonework
All the medieval buildings of the college were built of limestone largely with Ashlar facing. The original stone, which came from a local quarry, is only moderately durable and particularly prone to sulphate attack. The original quarry is now worked out and finding replacement stone poses problems in terms of both durability and aesthetics. The other problem facing management is the frequency and nature of repairs.

Replacement stone must match the existing as closely as possible but be durable. The latter is increasingly important with the increased levels of atmospheric sulphur dioxide and the choice of a stone which deteriorates rapidly can have a dramatic effect on the life span of stonework and on long term maintenance costs. Therefore, some Bath stones, which may be the closest match in terms of colour and texture are not used but the much more durable Clipsham. This stone provides a reasonable balance between the two criteria.

Patch repair of stonework using mortar mixes and surface treatments are both rejected by St John's management, as likely to cause more rapid deterioration of stonework in the long run and the only repairs to stonework are long term replacement programmes. Frequency is difficult to judge. Too rapid a replacement programme is wasteful of money but leaving the job too long can lead to much more extensive work than necessary. The location of the stonework also affects the rate at which it deteriorates. St John's answer to this problem is a long term rolling programme of stonework repairs over a 30 year span in the course of which all the worst areas of stonework in the college will have been replaced.

Roof Structure

The intricate oak trusses that make up the roof structure of the medieval buildings should last indefinately if they are kept in the right conditions. The main threat to them comes through fungal attack and deathwatch beetle. Fungal attack is prevented by keeping water out of the roof space by paying special attention to coverings, parapets and valley gutters and by making sure the timbers are well ventilated. Simple management measures like clearing the parapets of snow on the morning after a snowfall are also important. Any outbreaks of fungal attack must be spotted quickly and dealt with early.

The most likely source of deathwatch beetle is the timber itself or adjacent timbers. Effective treatments are available but early detection of flight holes beetles is desirable to minimise damage and this places a premium on regular inspection.

Roof Coverings

The original covering of the roofs was by Stonesfield stone slates supplied from a local quarry which is now worked out. The stone slates are of such a distinctive uneven texture that finding a satisfactory replacement is difficult. To use the alternative natural stone slates or welsh slates would alter the external appearance of the buildings dramatically. Second hand Stonesfields are available but there is no steady source of supply and the slates are of variable quality. The solution which has been tried is to use concrete slates faced with stone dust and with an irregular surface, that goes some way to mimic the surface of the original slates. Aesthetically, they are close enough to the appearance of the originals not to alter the external appearance too much but they do not have quite the same character. However, they are the next best thing and more acceptable than any of the alternatives. They have now been used on several buldings.

Leadwork to parapet flashings and valleys is well maintained and any replacement work carried out with 6 or 7lb lead which should have a life span in excess of one hundred years.

Stone Ornamentation

The statuary and other ornamental stonework deteriorate more rapidly than the stone facework because of greater exposure and the fact that they have more surface areas to trap and hold water. They are by nature made of softer stone. Little can be done to protect the stone and, at St John's, maintenance has consisted of recording details by photograph and replacement when detailing becomes worn.

Recent developments in preservatives such as "Brethane" developed by BRE may provide a means of protecting such delicate stone in the long term but this has still to be proved.

Doors

Doors pose a particular maintenance problem for two reasons. The first is the heavy wear and tear they receive from occupants and the second is the need to upgrade them to provide adequate fire resistance. The first problem can only be contained by making prompt repairs and ensuring that all ironmongery is sturdy.

The second problem is more serious and the upgrading of doors to half-hour fire resistance has proved expensive and time consuming. In general, the doors and frames are made of oak and the doors are panelled. The main problem comes in upgrading the panels whilst maintaining the original appearance. It is not aesthetically acceptable to replace the panels and impossible to take them out and split them to form a sandwich construction. Therefore, the only way of upgrading the doors has been to add fire resisting panels to the back, sacrificing the appearance of the back of the door but leaving the front, facing out into the corridor, intact.

Panelling

The introduction of central heating has had a dramatic effect on all internal joinery and panelling in particular. The effect has been to dry out the timber rapidly which has lead to warping and cracking. As most of the panelling is constructed of thin oak sheets, repairs are difficult and detract more from the appearance than the cracks themselves. At present the cracks are tolerated but in rooms which have timberwork of particular importance, like the Hall and Chapel, then heating has been kept to background levels.

The installation of modern services inevitably disturbs existing finishes and even after installation adequate access is necessary. The planning of services has been done, where possible, to minimise disruption and the work has been carried out to the highest quality to try to avoid the damage that could be caused by leakage. Frost protection is practised, especially in roof spaces.

Plasterwork

Decorative fibrous plasterwork is an important part of the interior decoration of some of the buildings. The main threats to its integrity are dampness and vibration. The latter is difficult to control but the former, which may come from penetration, rising damp or condensation, can be controlled by good maintenance and the control of the internal environment.

Management

The above last section gives some indication of the special problems facing the maintenance manager in dealing with these buildings, and from this and the definations given in the introduction three main management problems become clear. The first relates to standards and the quality of work. As these buildings are an important part of our heritage, the standard of maintenance work expected is high.

The second relates to time. As these buildings are to be kept indefinately, maintenance must be viewed and planned on a much longer time span and this places a premium on sound forward planning.

The third problem is the craft and management skills needed to carry out adequate repair and conservation work.

Standards of maintenance

The interior and exterior have different requirements. The exterior should be maintained so that its aesthetic qualities and special architectural features are in a condition where they can be enjoyed by all. In other words the exterior must be kept as close as possible to the original. This means that the major elements must be renewed at the point when they have deteriorated to such an extent, that these qualities have been lost.

The interior must also keep any special features intact but it must also be of an acceptable standard to its users in terms of comfort and the facilities provided. The acceptable standard changes over time and poses special management problems. For example, the majority of the buildings at St John's house undergraduates. Twenty years ago there would have been no expectation that such rooms would be centrally heated. At present central heating is now considered the norm and modern heating systems have been installed in spite of the disruption caused, the greater risk of damage caused by burst pipes and the effect the much drier air has on the interior fittings. Changing standards mean a constant balancing between the needs of the user and the needs of the fabric.

The change of standard which has perhaps given the greatest problem is that of fire precautions especially in respect of installing detection and warning systems and the upgrading of doors.

Time and planning

The indefinate life span of these buildings places a premium on forward planning and the programming of work. This proposition is based on two assumptions; the first is that without adequate planning the maintenance of buildings will deteriorate more rapidly and the second is that good planning reduces long term maintenance costs. The extra time dimension increases the temptation to put work off because of short term expedients, especially as budgets are worked out annually. It is hard to argue that putting off the restoration of stonework or a re-roofing programme for one or even five years will create any long term damage. But the cumulative effect of such decisions can lead to expensive crisis maintenance on the grand scale.

The work, then, must be broken down into various categories not according to importance but according to timing. The three categories suggested by Reginald Lee of short, medium and long term programmes is wholly appropriate to planning the maintenance work of historic buildings. According to Fielden inspections should "record visual defects factually, in order to diagnose the causes of decay and propose an effective cure that involves the minimum of intervention". Such inspections have three main aims: the first is to spot defects which require immediate atten-

297

tion; the second is to record the condition of elements in order to plan maintenance works or alter existing plans; and the third is to monitor the effectiveness of repair and maintenance work.

At St John's one third of the buildings are inspected annually and a written report made to the estates committee. In recent years a concerted effort has been made to reduce the length of this report and only record details of those areas which require attention or where past work has not been carried out correctly. It has been felt that reports which are too long may not be efficient in conveying information to policy decision makers.

From the report the maintenance strategy is formulated. The work suggested by the report falls into the five categories suggested by Fielden. These are immediate work, urgent work, necessary work, desirable work and items to be kept under observation. This has an immediate effect on the planning of short and medium term work.

At St John's, the short and medium term routine cyclical maintenance has been organised into a computerised planned maintenance system, which has now been in operation for over 12 years. The computer produces work dockets each month which are handed to the Clerk of Works. Each docket comprises a specific task the frequency of which is either weekly, monthly, quarterly or annually. The docket lists the work to be done, its location and the operative to carry out the task. Originally it had a complicated grid reference scheme for location but this has been dropped in favour of location names which are familiar to the workmen. When the job is completed the tradesman returns the initialled docket to the CoW, making comments on the work, its frequency and other works which may need to be done. This feedback is an important part of the system and enables the planning strategy to be refined. If the docket is not reported back to the computer as being completed then a reminder is sent to the CoW. However, the system can only work if the CoW has sufficient DEL labour available to carry out the works. The systems is reviewed annually, with particular attention being given to the frequency of tasks and over the years it has been simplified and consolidated.

The planned maintenance system also helps in the planning of the long term major repair items because the information on the condition of the elements of the fabric is being fed back to the management at all times. These major items of repair and restoration are planned on an individual basis as far in advance as possible, as part of a rolling programme. The time spans involved can be as much as 30 years. Re-roofing, stonework restoration, chimney repairs and the upgrading of services are all dealt with on this basis with the plan being reviewed periodically. Many of these jobs have a long preparation and lead-in time, especially if they involve planning consents.

Skills

With historic buildings the conventional management decisions as to the choice between directly employed labour (DEL) and contract labour is complicated by the need to have available tradesmen

298

with specific skills. It is generally accepted that skilled trades-men in certain tradional crafts are becoming scarce as the modern construction industry neither requires such skills in volume nor rewards them. Therefore, finding tradesmen with such skills can be difficult but employing them through contract expensive. A decision must therefore be made as to which skills should be employed directly, if available, and which should be left to be provided by specialist contractors.

Although they are fortunate at present in having in their employment some fine craftsmen, the management at St John's find the future situation worrying. Many of the tradesmen are nearing retirement and training young craftsmen to take their place is difficult. The low wages which are paid in maintenance work, because of low productivity, means that once youngsters are fully trained they can earn much more money on building sites and in a high cost area like Oxford, few can resist the temptation. There is therefore a real danger that the specialist skills needed for conservation, which can best be learnt from skilled craftsmen, will die out altogether.

St John's have a large DEL organisation employing some 30 operatives which means a wide range of skills can be employed. However, this high staffing level can only be maintained because DEL is also used on the Colleges large urban estate in Oxford.

In terms of specialist skills, St John's employs plasterers, a joiner/cabinet maker, a bricklayer, a plumber skilled in leadwork, and two masons. The factors involved in deciding to employ two masons illustrates the general problem in deciding who to employ.

There are many stone buildings in Oxford and only two large firms involved in stonework. Because the colleges and university want most major work to be carried out during the summer, the cost of stonework is high and getting the work done when you want it is difficult. Some major schemes have to wait several years before commencement. The college therefore took the decision to employ first one then two masons. Two are necessary in order to take on large restoration tasks and the Library Front, where an entire stone elevation has been renewed, is the first major piece of restoration undertaken by them, with pleasing results and low costs. However, care must be taken to programme their work in order to fully utilise their skills and the effect of losing one mason in the middle of a major restoration would be difficult. However, if they can keep their masons, the college can plan further major restoration works with confidence.

The employment of too many specialised tradesmen can, however, conflict with the need for flexibility necessary to make a small DEL force work effeciently.

Specific skills like the restoration of statuary and decorative stonework are brought in from outside and large jobs in college, which do not require high levels of skill, are let to contract to prevent the DEL becoming bogged down in large scale works, preventing them from carrying out routine planned maintenance work.

299

Organisation

The line of authority at St John's goes from the Governing Body, via the Domestic Committee and the Bursar, to the Assistant Bursar who is the effective manager of the maintenance organisation. Under him is a Clerk of Works and the operatives. None of the operatives have a formal managerial function, as might happen with a trades foreman, but the older senior tradesmen do take that role unofficially. The Assistant Bursar also has under him a building surveyor who deals with planning, preparing schemes both for contract and DEL and project management.

The organisation is then very light on management numbers, especially when it is considered that it has to deal with contract works and works outside the college and it relies on the goodwill of the tradesmen to operate the planned maintenance system efficiently. However, because the management structure is so simple, decision making is not held up because of bureaucracy and the official lines of command are very clear. The planned maintenance programme helps in this, enabling the management structure to operate efficiently as does the forward planning of large schemes.

Cost Control

Although it is not the intention of this paper to go into accountancy practice, some indication of the problems associated with financing of the maintenance of historic buildings is necessary.

The basis of good financial control is an efficient cost control system, accurate estimating, realistic annual budgets and the setting aside of adequate sums for long term restoration. It is in this respect that many maintenance organisations run into problems.

Once a maintenance strategy and programme have been worked out, it must be accurately costed. The costing falls into two sections: firstly the routine day-to-day maintenance, which should be costed into an annual maintenance budget including DEL costs, plant and materials allowances, management and administration costs, contract costs and a contingency sum; secondly the costing of specific long term maintenance schemes.

Where accurate records of past expenditure are kept, the preparation of adequate annual maintenance budgets is not difficult. Labour costs are known and the ratio of labour costs to materials costs, which is usually constant, can be determined from past records. The level of contingency necessary can also be judged from past experience, but it must be of a sufficient size to allow the management to act quickly and flexibly in an emergency. With historic buildings this contingency is likely to be higher than with other buildings. If contractors are used for routine maintenance instead of DEL, then the negotiation of an annual charge for scheduled maintenance would help budgeting.

Whereas the assessment may be easy, getting the money out of an organisation which may not see maintenance as a priority, may be more difficult. The maintenance management should keep a high profile and be prepared to spell out the dire consequences of inadequate maintenance budgets.

The management at St John's, whilst taking care to assess annual budgets properly, to ensure an adequate supply of funds, also take great care to ensure that current budgets are strictly controlled. This makes sure that potential overspends are spotted quickly and corrective action taken. To do this the annual budgets for the fabric maintenance are split down into various cost heads each of one is given a separate account and separate code. All the invoices, for materials plant and outside contractors, and all the labour returns are coded and checked to ensure that they are being posted to the correct head. Printouts from the computer are then given each month for each head, so that individual postings can be checked and spending compared with projected spending. This tight budgetary control ensures that maintenance costs are kept in check, large overspends do not occur and realistic budgets are prepared. Only a well-organised and computerised accounting system allows this to be done without imposing too great an administrative burden.

Long term projects are more difficult to cost in two ways. The first is because repairs to old buildings are high risk, in that it is difficult to anticipate what problems will be found when the structure is opened up. Proper informed inspection can reduce the risk and large contingency sums in contracts are always desirable but difficult to assess. At St John's 10% is used wherever possible, but if tenders are in excess of estimates then the contingency sum can be the first to go.

Good planning in terms of flexible programming, negotiated rather than tendered contracts and sound project management all help to reduce costs.

The second problem is time and the long time scales which may be involved. Assessing the cost of repairs to be carried out in 20 or 30 years time and persuading an organisation to start setting aside sums for such works is difficult. Even if costs can be accurately estimated, the use of standard discounting to arrive at a present value to be set aside gives very speculative figures which almost certainly will not give the organisation the right amount of money to spend at the time. In the face of this problem, some organisations seem to ignore the current provision in the hope that they will somehow have enough money in the future. The frequent appeals to the public for money for repairs may indicate that this hope is not always well founded.

All that can be said is that making some provision for future works is better than making none, however inaccurate. It may also be expediant to set aside an annual sum for major repairs and allow unspent monies to be carried forward each year. It is better to be overprovided than to have to resort to desperate public appeals when repairs reach a crisis point.

However, planned preventative maintenance should reduce the scale and cost of long term major works, by the constant monitoring of condition, to spot major problems early and to be able to estimate rates of decay. It is essential to be able to assess condition in order to be able to anticipate work.

Good planning also enables schemes to be brought forward systematically, to spread out capital spending and enable it to be planned.

This should prevent a large number of "crisis" schemes appearing.

Conclusions

The purpose of this paper has been to isolate the main theses in the management of the maintenance of historic buildings, which make this task different from that of other maintenance areas. The conclusion will try to summarise these themes.

Historic buildings have been defined as buildings which will be kept indefinately, with the original fabric kept as intact as possible, but as working buildings with an economic value. In this latter respect they require continual upgrading to keep up to modern standards.

The upkeep of the same elements of the fabric presents particular problems, in terms of the craft skills necessary to maintain them and the choice of materials for replacement. This requires a careful approach by the management, if the original character of the building is going to be maintained.

The organisation of the management poses problems in three areas. The need to maintain the building in economic usage means that the upgrading of the interior facilities, to keep up to modern standards, can conflict with the needs of the fabric. The long time scale over which repair works should be considered, emphasises the need for good planning and estimating techniques. Planned preventative maintenance and regular inspections, can aid in reducing long term renewal cycles and in helping them to be planned properly.

The skilled craftsmen needed to carry out some of the work of repair and renewal, are, in some instances hard to find, and poses the question of whether to employ direct or employ via contract

Effective cost control relies on realistic budgeting, the control of spending to prevent budget deficits and accurate estimating to allow sufficient funds to set aside for future major works. Employers need to be told of the consequences of not spending enough on maintenance and the value of having an efficient planned maintenance system to reduce long term costs.

If an organisation faced with the management of historic buildings care to solve these problems, then the future of the fabric of the building should be secure.

References

Bowyer, J (1980) Vernacular Building Conservation. Architectural Press

Earl, J. (1977) Conservation: The Maintenance of Older Buildings, in Building Conversion and Rehabilitation (ed. T.A.Markus) Butterworth

Fielden, Sir B.M. (1982) Conservation of Historic Buildings. Butterworth

Lee, R. (1981) Building Maintenance Management. Granda

Speight, B.A. (1977) Maintenance Policy, Programming and Feedback, in Building Conversion and Rehabilitation (ed. T.A. Markus) Butterworth

THE USE OF DIRECT LABOUR IN LOCAL AUTHORITY MAINTENANCE CONTRACTS

JOHN G. LOWE
Department of Building, Heriot-Watt University, Edinburgh

Abstract
The vast majority of local authorities in the U.K. maintain some form of direct labour organisation (DLO) to carry out construction works on behalf of the council. A large proportion of those direct labour organisations confine their activities to the maintenance and repair of existing buildings. The paper is aimed at evaluating the costs and benefits to the local authority and to the community at large of the use of direct labour for local authority maintenance projects rather than using contractors. The paper commences with a discussion of the economic background and the reasons why many local authorities built up their direct labour organisation. The paper then considers the impact of those reforms introduced in 1980 by the Local Government Planning and Land Act in so far as it affects the operation of direct labour organisations undertaking maintenance contracts. The circumstances when the interests perceived by the council are likely to conflict with the interests of the community at large are then identified and analysed. The paper concludes with a discussion of the appropriate mode of control for direct labour undertaking maintenance contracts and the extent to which the existing legislation meets up to those requirements.
Key words: Direct labour organisations, Local authorities, Central government, Maintenance contracts.

1. Introduction

1.1 Outline
The United Kingdom has a significant proportion of construction works carried out by the direct labour sector. Direct labour, in this context, is defined as production by construction staff and operatives directly employed by the client organisation rather than by letting the works to a contractor. While there are a few examples of private sector companies establishing direct labour organisations, the majority are to be found within the local authority sector and the bulk of this work is in the field of maintenance and repair.

This paper is concerned with an evaluation of the decision to use direct labour for local authority maintenance works from the point of view of the local authority and the community at large. It must be stressed that this does not relate to the balance between the private and the public sectors of the economy but with the mode of provision of public sector works.

1.2 Justifications for the use of direct labour
A number of reasons have be put forward as to why direct labour has proved so much more popular with the local government sector than for the private sector. These can be grouped into two categories:- those which will lead to a direct financial or neo-financial advantage for the client: "economic factors", and those concerned with wider socio-political or economic issues: "ideological factors".

The "economic factors" apply in circumstances where action may be necessary to correct a missallocation of resources due to the exist-ance of externalities. It is also argued that a D.L.O. has greater flexibility for carrying out the type of work faced by a local gov-ernment client including such areas as emergency repairs and will acquire particular skills in repetitive tasks such as planned main-tenance of council housing with tenants "in situ". There are also tactical advantages for a client with a DLO, in that it may be used to act as a check on tenders from outside contractors. Equally it will always be available to undertake work at a reasonable price during periods of high demand. It can even be used to complete a contract abandoned by an insolvent contractor. Finally it is asserted that a DLO can deliver higher quality work with consequential savings in life cycle costs.

The "ideological factors" relate to such areas as safety-at-work, apprentice training, decasualisation, equal opportunities, local emp-loyment, and unionisation. While these may be legitimate points of concern to a local authority they are clearly unrelated to the direct financial situation of the local authority as building client.

1.3 The growth of direct labour
The growth of direct labour in the local authority sector stemmed from a mixture of the above factors - ideology tempered with economic pragmatism. It was also consistent with general local authority practice in terms of delivery of service. The use of direct labour, until recently, has been virtually universal in such areas as refuse collection, street cleansing, and grass cutting. Thus it argued that building works, in particular maintenance, ought to be carried out by local government employees in line with other municipal services.

However a major incentive for the expansion of the use of direct labour occurred in the early 1970s when the Heath administration launched a construction led economic boom. As a result, local author-ities found it increasingly difficult to let contracts when there was much more profitable speculative work available. This problem was compounded by the very tight cost yardsticks applied to much of their work. Thus, to avoid a repetition of this problem, many local author-ities responded by building up their own DLO so as to provide an "in-house" capability to undertake mundane but essential tasks. As the boom collapsed and the world economy was plunged into recession following the oil price increases in the aftermath of the Arab-Israeli war, so the contractual sector became keen to undertake local authority contracts. Because many local authorities had adopted a policy of expanding the use of direct labour and being faced with a shortfall in work gave preference to a DLO and thus effectively shut out the contractual sector, this lead to a major political campaign by the construction firms culminating in legislation to control the use of direct labour by local authorities.

2. Legislative action

2.1 Criticisms of direct labour
Direct labour has recently been subjected to a good deal of criticism throughout the local government sector. This was originally applied primarily to construction but this has been widened to other areas such as refuse collection and street cleaning. Such criticisms are generally based on the assumption that since direct labour will be to some extent isolated from the forces of competition, it will be "expensive, wasteful, inefficient, and inadequate" as well as being "vastly overstaffed, subject to ruinous restrictive practices by their labour force and top heavy with unnecessary layers of bureaucracy" (Forsyth, 1980).

It is argued that there is little logic in the traditional divide between work carried out by direct labour and that contracted out and that inertia, political dogma, and restrictive practices are the sole reasons for such public provision.

The other criticism which can be levelled at direct labour is that the relatively stable employment structure for local government staff is inappropriate for construction work given the instability of demand. This will be particularly pertinent given that DLOs face restrictions on who they can undertake work for. Thus while the workload is subject to fluctuations outside the control of the local authority because of changing spending policies by central government, the workforce will be variable only to a limited extent.

The main thrust of the policy advocated by the critics of direct labour is the letting of all such services on a contractual basis. This will not necessarily exclude direct labour but will oblige it to compete for all work with outside contractors. There is within much of the literature an implicit assumption that under such circumstances, the vast majority of DLOs would be too inefficient to compete with the contractual sector.

2.2 Background to the 1980 Act of Parliament
The above pressure from the construction lobby along with some criticism from the local government accountancy institution – C.I.P.F.A. – lead to the legislative action contained in Part III of the 1980 Local Government Planning and Land Act. These provisions can be split into two categories:

i) Accountancy reforms designed to make all DLOs financially autonomous from the parent authority and to enforce the use of competitive tender for a proportion of the DLO workload.

ii) Reserve powers at the discretion of the Secretary of State to shut down or curtail the activities of a DLO failing to meet a target rate of return on capital invested.

2.3 Accountancy reforms

These provisions in the Act were intended to ensure that the full costs of DLO operations could be identified by requiring the publication of audited accounts separated from those of the parent authority. In addition, DLOs were required to tender for a significant proportion of all projects. These provisions had the effect of transforming all DLOs operating as "service departments" to a "trading department" basis.

2.4 Reserve powers

The Act stipulates that the accounts of a DLO have to be divided into categories, on each of which it is expected make a criterion rate of return (5%) on capital invested. The Secretary of State is empowered to prevent a DLO undertaking work in any category where is has failed to achieve this rate of return.

3. The use of direct labour

3.1 Direct labour workload

The vast majority of local authorities in the U.K. maintain some sort of DLO. The figures for 1981 indicated that 517 out of 522 local authorities employ direct labour - one English Metropolitan County and four Scottish Districts being the exceptions, as illustrated in Table 1 below.

Table 1. Local authorities a direct labour organisation (1981).

Type of authority	Number of authorities	Number with a DLO
England and Wales		
Greater London Council	1	1
Metropolitan Counties	6	5
Non-metropolitan Counties	47	47
London boroughs (incl. City)	33	33
Metropolitan Districts	36	36
Non-metropolitan Districts	334	334
All England and Wales	457	456
Scotland		
Regional Councils	9	9
Island Councils	3	3
District Councils	53	49
All Scotland	65	61
Great Britain	522	517

Source: Hillebrandt (1984)

Direct labour has traditionally proved much more popular for maintenance and repair work that for new building or for refurbishment
contracts. The proportion of maintenance and repair of total direct
labour output has been rising in recent years from 76% in 1970 to
nearly 90% in 1981 (Hillebrandt, 1984). This movement is not surprising given the decline in local authority new work projects.

3.2 Political implications

In an analysis of a sample of 65 DLOs for the period immediately
prior to the implementation of the legislation, all were involved in
maintenance work while only about half undertook new building or
refurbishment contracts (Lowe, 1985). Since the sample included a
broad sprectrum of local authorities types - metropolitan and non-
metropolitan, urban and rural, north and south, Labour and
Conservative controlled - this would appear to be line with the
national statistics and to confirm that direct labour had broad
appeal across the political and geographical spectrum in the case of
repair and maintenance work.

The analysis did confirm that the Labour controlled authorities
appeared to allot proportionately more maintenance work to a DLO than
did other authorities. This is not unexpected given that many of the
factors argued as a justification for the use of direct labour would
have little, if any, appeal to a Conservative authority. The economic
factors would be expected to have attractions for all local authorities while the "ideological" factors would be of more concern to a
left wing authority. On the other hand, authority type and geography
appear to have no bearing on the scale of DLO operations for
maintenance work (Lowe, 1985).

3.3 Impact of the legislation

Since the terms of the legislation have been implemented, it would
appear that the impact has been somewhat limited in that few DLOs
have failed to meet the criterion rate of return or have been closed
down voluntarily. This may be partially due to the reorganisation of
many DLOs on a much sounder basis than was the situation prior to the
legislation. It may also be taken to indicate that many of the DLOs
were nothing like as bad of the critics suggested.

Despite the above points it remains likely that the survival of
the direct labour sector virtually intact is a consequence of
political will on the part of the local authorities. The widespread
use of direct labour prior to the legislation indicates that it
served a purpose - actual or perceived - for the parent authority,
and that most would endeavor to protect a DLO from what would be seen
as undue central government interference.

This could be accomplished in a number of ways by a determined
local authority. On method might be to employ "creative accountancy"
in the calculation of depreciation provisions and valuation of the
capital stock. Equally negotiated contracts could be let to a DLO on
very favourable terms or competitive contracts could be loaded in
favour of the DLO by excluding strong local firms from the shortlist.
Finally, a DLO could win a contract by submitting a low bid but then
boost income by submitting a series of claims to a sympathetic

client. Unless any of the above were applied in so blatant a way as to attract the attention of the District Auditor, there would appear to be no way of preventing such abuse.

4. Analysis

4.1 Evaluation

If direct labour is analysed specifically from the viewpoint of maintenance and repair work, it would appear to indicate that the traditional predominance of this over new work is no accident. Firstly most of the economic advantages of using direct labour such a flexibility in small scale or emergency projects apply more strongly to maintenance and repair than to new work. While this has, to some extent, been undermined by the enforced switch to the "trading department" mode of organisation following the 1980 Act, it still has some validity. Equally the degree of competition is likely to be less keen for non-programmed maintenance contracts particularly housing projects with tenants "in situ". Thus, in the case of maintenance and repair work, not only are the advantages of direct labour more apparent but the disadvantages are less marked.

A good example of this concerns the instability of workload in construction - this will certainly be less apparent in the case of repair and maintenance that for new work. Since much of the former is financed out of current expenditure rather than capital it will be more within the control of the local authority less at the mercy of changing central governmental policy. Thus a local authority would be able to plan its maintenance programmes and recruit an appropriate workforce and be sure of getting the work completed. Thus a major disadvantage of direct labour does not apply in this case.

The suitability of direct labour for maintenance and repair work appears to have been recognised in the drafting of the legislation in that the provisions for contracts to be obtained by competitive tender are less onerous than those applied in the case of new work - thus much higher proportion of maintenance work can be let to a DLO by negotiated contract than will apply for new work.

4.2 Conclusions

While it can be argued that many of the objections to the use of direct labour do certainly apply to maintenance and repair work, they certainly have more validity in the case of new work. This is reflected in the emphasis of most DLOs either exclusively or at least primarily concerned with maintenance and repair.

It can also be argued that most local authorities seem convinced of the suitability of direct labour for such tasks and will continue to use it to a lesser or greater extent no matter what legislation is passed by central government. It is likely that, as a consequence of the legislation, if anything the proportion of new work carried out by direct labour will fall but that repair and maintenance direct labour operations will be more likely to be protected. Any local authority wishing to do this can utilise any of the wide range of measures outlined above.

Thus it can be postulated that the approach adopted by the
government in drafting the 1980 Act failed to appreciate this
position and that the legislation was the weaker because of this.
Thus the Act may have been more effective if its emphasis had been
more oriented towards the identification and disclosure of the
financial status of a DLO and the impact of the use of direct labour
on the local authority's expenditure on construction, rather than on
central control of local government policies.

Notwithstanding the above, the main thrust of the legislation in
establishing DLOs as financially autonomous organisations and the
provisions for a representative and significant proportion of work to
be gained by competitive tender would appear to be a positive measure
which has gone some way to improving the overall efficiency of most
DLOs. If the legislation, by taking into account the issues raised
above, had succeeded in win the support of the local authorities then
it would have been all the better for it.

References

Forsyth, Michael (1980) Reservicing Britain. Adam Smith Institute,
    London.
Hillebrandt, Patricia M. (1984) Analysis of the British Construction
    Industry. Macmillan, London.
Lowe, John G. (1983) Control of direct labour - a critical review,
    Construction Papers 2(2) pp 53-60.
Lowe, John G. (1985) Local authority direct labour organisations -
    an investigation into the impact of political control on the
    nature and volume of their output, paper presented at Seminar at
    the School of Surveying, Newcastle-upon-Tyne Polytechnic, 14th
    November.

EASING THE CONFLICTING DEMANDS WHEN ARRANGING MAINTENANCE CONTRACTS

MARION WEATHERHEAD
Department of Building Economics, South Bank Polytechnic.

Abstract
The conflicting demands of many small jobs, precise contract law
requirements and limited management resources make the management of
maintenance very difficult. These are areas that need to be tackled
if maintenance management is to be more efficient. Three very different methods of easing the conflicts are considered - the special
maintenance contracts, information technology and the possible
rationalisation of the maintenance process as illustrated by the
recent developments in building rehabilitation.
Key words: Maintenance Management, Contracts, Contract Law,
Information Technology, Building Rehabilitation.

1.   Introduction

Building maintenance management is a headache. There is a constant
conflict between many small jobs, individually of little value, and
hence not warranting too much expensive management input, and an
expenditure for many organisations that adds up to many millions of
pounds each year.
    I want to focus on one aspect of maintenance management - the
arranging of the execution of a wide variety of small repairs by
contractors. Whilst the sheer number of small jobs is one difficulty
the precise requirements of contract law is another. Arguments could
be made for streamlining contract law, but accepting that little
change is likely in the near future, I have concentrated on ways
building maintenance managers can improve their operations within the
existing legal framework.
    This paper looks at three very different ways in which action has
and can be taken. Firstly, the development of contract types specifically for maintenance that have rationalised the administration and
documentation. Secondly, the use of information technology to bring
together the many requests for work, to prepare contract documentation and to monitor contract progress and expenditure. Finally, the
possibilities of 'rolling-up' accrued maintenance to modernise the
building using one major contract and hence reducing the need for
piecemeal maintenance in the future.
    To expand up on the difficulties facing the building maintenance

311

manager I shall start by considering the peculiarities of maintenance management particularly with reference to contract law.

2.   The peculiarities of building maintenance

Maintenance and repair work account for 45% of the output of the
construction industry. In terms of construction industry output
building maintenance work had a total value of nearly £13,000m in
1985 (Housing and Construction Statistics, June 1986). Building
rehabilitation works are not defined separately in the statistics.
Works of alteration and improvement are included in the above totals
whereas those for non-housing works are included with the 'New Works'
statistics and are not included above. Consequently the total value
of works to existing buildings will be well over £13,000m.
    Works of maintenance and repair range from replacing a tap washer
to the refurbishment of the Palm House at Kew Gardens. The problems
they pose for the building maintenance manager are equally diverse.
    A large number of the jobs cannot be pre-planned. No-one knows
when a football is going to go through a window or when a freak wind
will blow a roof away. The only certainty is that such occurrences
will arise and that the total value will probably be about the same
each year. The volume of small jobbing repairs varies from organisation to organisation but on average 44% of the money spent on local
authority housing repair works related to jobbing repairs rather
than planned works (Audit Commission, Nov. 1986).
    Maintenance work has another feature which distinguishes it from
new work and that is that the 'building site' is frequently occupied.
Occupants whether residents or commercial tenants, do not like disturbance particularly for works such as rewiring or fire precautions.
    Whilst the building maintenance manager can work at achieving a
good relationship with the occupiers and owners of buildings, once
work starts in a building the relationship is dominated by a third
party - the contractor and the workforce. The lines of communications can rapidly become very complex.
    The difficulties of these relationships are recognised at law.
The contractual relationship is a legal relationship. There is a
formalised system for sorting out many of the difficulties that
arise. However it is not a redress that comes cheaply. To turn to
the Courts or arbitration is expensive; although legal fees may
eventually be paid by the other party. Less tangible are the time
and the stress which can rarely be adequately compensated by the
payment of damages, even if these are forthcoming.
    To avoid disputed contracts, to keep away from the Courts and to
concentrate resources on the maintenance of buildings is an important
aspect of the management of maintenance. To do this means that care
needs to be taken to ensure that all relationships with contractors
are clearly within the requirements of contract law and that the
terms and conditions of the contracts are satisfactory to the
building maintenance manager.
    The requirements of contract law are precise and stem from Common

312

Law. Hence for the most part the requirements are not in statutes but have been set down through the decisions of the Courts. There are three main legal requirements to make a contract. They are the offer, the acceptance and the valuable consideration. All three are needed to make a contract. Normally various terms and conditions are included to define the roles of each party and these cannot be changed later unless both parties agree.

It is essential for planned maintenance management that contracts are created when required and that they contain the desired terms and conditions. Attempts to speed up the system by issuing 'letters of intent' can result in a contract with no agreed terms or conditions. Likewise accepting quotations from contractors can result in the acceptance of very unsatisfactory conditions included in the 'small print' on the reverse of the quotation.

Most contracts do not have to be recorded in writing. It is normally done as a source of evidence. It also acts as an aide-memoire. For both of these uses it is essential that the conditions are unambiguous.

It is the offer, the acceptance and the consideration that need to be recorded in writing. For a building maintenance manager it is easiest to arrange contractual policy for small works so that the other party always makes the offer which can then be accepted; in this way just the offer (including the consideration) and the acceptance become the contract documents. An ideal that is often hard to achieve.

To be very careful about each contract can be almost impossible when hundreds of small contracts are being arranged each week. If not impossible, then it is expensive in the use of professional, managerial and administrative staff.

3.   Contracts for maintenance

The building maintenance manager has to operate in this environment and marry quite precise legal requirements to a situation of building works which are often small, unplanned and of little value.

These aspects have been recognised particularly by the managers of government and local authority estates for years. The result has been the development of contracting systems aimed at easing the burden (Lee, 1981). Term contracts being a notable example. The conditions of the contract are agreed and then the individual jobs are carried out as and when needed during the term of the contract. Payment being arranged either in relation to the labour and materials involved as in a daywork term contract or by the more controlled means of quantifying the work using a schedule of rates as in a measured term contract. Although in some local authority areas it has been found that non-measured dayworks and variations exceeds 50% of the work in measured term contracts (Audit Commission, Nov 1986).

Neither method is ideal,the contractor with many small jobs (although jobs may be as large as £30,000) is not able to develop priorities for the various works in hand which may not suit the building maintenance manager or the occupants. Supervision can be difficult;

313

the incentive to finish off minor items of low value is not great.

Nevertheless, these contract forms do save the building maintenance manager's staff from the time consuming chore of entering into
a completely new contract for each job. In doing this it greatly
reduces the risk of numerous small slipshod contracts. However, the
supervision costs for the daywork contract and the quantity survey-
or's fees for the measured term contract can offset some or all the
advantages.

Another contract especially for maintenance work is the fixed
price maintenance contract developed by the Property Services Agency
of the Department of the Environment. In this instance the contract-
or agrees to keep an estate in good repair for a fixed period of
time. All requests for repair work are then channelled direct to the
contractor who carries out the work. It is in the contractor's
interest to do preventive work and hence avoid expensive failures
(Lee, 1981).

The recent Audit Commission report 'Improving Council House Maintenance' (Nov 1986) found that one-off jobbing repairs contracts can
cost up to 50% more than when the same job is carried out as part of
a maintenance programme. It was suggested in the report that schedules of rates contracts should be adopted as a means of reducing the
number of small jobbing repairs and suggested the production of
a schedule suitable for small local authorities.

4.   Information Technology

With the developments in information technology and the introduction
of computers into building maintenance management it has been possible to rationalise further the arrangements for contracting maintenance work.

The first moves in this direction were presented in Pettitt's report on 'Computer Aids to Housing Maintenance Management' in 1981.
This thesis based on work at Peterborough showed that the use of
computers as an aid to better management of building maintenance
should be developed in this country.

Crawley Borough Council is one local authority that has taken up
the challenge with its'Repairs and DLO System' (1985). Although
conceived to handle all types of repairs and clients, development
resources restricted its introduction to housing repairs. For these
buildings it is now possible to bring up on the screen or as a print
out any property with full status details including the situation
with regard to proposed or completed works plus the state of any
works in progress. Repairs clerks add new requests as they arise and
direct them to a surveyor for inspection if necessary. The surveyor
is told of the requests in regular print-outs and urgent ones are
printed immediately.

When ready the requests can, via the computer, be printed out as
orders to the term contractors. Progress and payments are then recorded and monitored through the computer.

Various other reports are possible, so that programmed and cyclic
maintenance records are available; as are details on service charges,

details of properties converted to aid disabled tenants and a facility register of central heating installations, for example.

The system is aiming to cut through the difficulties of economically managing many small repairs. Through one management tool the handling of many items of information has been systemised making it possible to bring together those, and only those, relevant to the decision to be made. Once operational the regular inputs will be less disportionate to the cost of the works than can be the case without the advantages of information technology.

5. Accumulated Maintenance

The nature of work to existing buildings is currently undergoing a major change. In recent years many reports, such as the National Economic Development Office's 'Investment in the Public Sector Built Infrastructure' (1985) and the Greater London Council's 'London Decaying Infrastructure - The Way Ahead'(1985), have highlighted the increasing backlog of infrastructure maintenance including building maintenance. The Audit Commission's report 'Managing the Crisis in Council Housing (1986) found that 85% of council houses were in need of repair and that there is a repairs backlog of around £20 billion.

In a time of recession cut backs are frequently made to maintenance budgets which, with the high level of resources needed to carry out works (NEDO 1978) plus heavy demands on management as shown above, quickly result in a substantial decline in the condition of buildings.

Failure to carry out routine maintenance soon leads to substantial decay. The high cost of these repairs reduces further the money available for routine maintenance. In this way a vicious circle of constant decline builds up at a far faster rate than the original cut back in maintenance might suggest.

6. Building Rehabilitation

Coupled with this rise in outstanding maintenance had been a shift to building rehabilitation which has been defined as '...the process of returning property to a state of utility through repair or alteration which makes possible efficient contemporary use...'

This shift has been the result of a variety of changes in the provision of the built environment. Moore (1980) has shown it in terms of housing rehabilitation as a reaction to the comprehensive redevelopments of the 1960's. The move to high technology has been accompanied by the rehabilitation of aesthetically pleasing and attractively located redundant mills and warehouses (Symes, 1984 and Weatherhead, 1985) to house the new manufacturing processes. The shift also includes the rehabilitation of blocks of flats and offices built during the 1960's. The work is proving to be an economical way of providing floorspace to modern requirements.

Low land values in the inner cities and other depressed areas plus the incentive of government grants have helped this process. Regeneration of some of these areas has followed with an accompanying increase in land values. Rehabilitation has still continued without the same inducements. Elsewhere buildings that were thought to be too expensive to rehabilitate are now back in use. Schemes such as Conran Roche's Butler's Wharf are well in hand without grants or other government finance. The processes involved in rehabilitation are changing. The architectural historian's conservation approach is giving way as the buildings now attracting the building industry include many of little or no architectural merit.

Today building rehabilitation has been rationalised; piecemeal repairs are becoming a thing of the past and instead whole components are replaced. The building is treated like the washing machine; instead of a skilled mechanic spending time repairing a motor the old one is replaced by a new motor assembly quickly bolted in place. In terms of building it means that a carpenter or joiner is no longer needed to repair a window frame and instead a semi-skilled operative will replace it with a new factory made component. This componentisation is moving much building work from the difficult conditions of the site to the protected environment of the factory floor where it is possible to benefit from continuous production.

The example of windows is a simple one that can also illustrate the way that rehabilitation can be used to upgrade buildings to meet modern standards, as frequently the replacement windows offer greater thermal insulation by doubleglazing and draught-sealing.

The rationalisation of the rehabilitation process is more complicated than the simple replacement of components. Technical and production developments are changing the approach to many aspects of building rehabilitation. For instance, the use of plasterboard to dryline walls with fixing methods that will increase sound insulation, incorporate thermal insulation and vapour barriers and give greater fire protection; off-site production of kitchen units; a constant stream of developments for upgrading roofs whether flat or pitched; the use of the Westwood system for installing a load-bearing beam in a restricted location; the use of high technology to monitor the services and improve control of the building; these and many other developments have helped to make rehabilitation an economically attractive proposition.

Building rehabilitation can wind-up what would be a series of small contracts over a number of years into an economically managed programme of work under one contract. The work can be pre-planned, much can be carried out by specialist contractors who by concentrating on a limited service offer highly competitive prices. Empty buildings made redundant by changes in industrial methods are readily available, as are post-war buildings that fail to meet modern demands.

Contractual methods have varied with use being made of managed contracts, design and build, lump-sum and it has also attracted speculative builders, for instance, Barratt's rehabilitation of Gun Wharf in Wapping, London. It is important that care is taken over specification of materials, components and workmanship. With the use of semi-skilled sub-contractors it is essential that the specifier understands the existing construction and the requirements of the new component to be installed into the existing building. There is often less freedom than in new construction and the component may need to be adapted. The possibilities for faults due to lack of skill, care, knowledge or dexterity by operatives are probably more likely when semi-skilled operatives are inserting their components into an existing building than when working on new build where Bonshor and Harrison (1982) have already highlighted problems in traditional housing.

The use of rehabilitation to overcome accumulated maintenance will only work if the work carried out is of sufficient quality to give many years of service. Harrison (1985) commented on the interim results of a research project studying common faults in housing rehabilitation saying that it is rare for an initial survey to be carried out in sufficient 'degree of detail that it will identify the needs of the building as a basis for rehabilitation and ad hoc decisions are frequently necessary as the work proceeds'.

Currently use is being made of the post modernist style in rehabilitating unsatisfactory buildings as at Lee Valley, Hackney. Often many decorative extras are added to the building when improving the design. These may well require higher maintenance commitments than the previous unadorned structure.

Costs-in-use calculations are important in these circumstances. The calculations should compare the figures for the building as it stands with those for the building after rehabilitation. A cost benefit analysis may be needed to take account of the social benefits not reflected in an economic analysis.

Much of the building rehabilitation that has taken place to date has been linked with a change in ownership of the property. A new owner seeing possibilities in a structure that were not apparent or did not interest the previous owner. If a building is to be sold or leased after rehabilitation costs-in-use will be less significant.

As financial restraint results in further deterioration of the built estate, the advantages of comprehensive rehabilitation with its ensuing componentisation and modernisation as opposed to piece-meal traditional repairs will have much to offer the building maintenance manager. The rolling-up of many small, expensive to manage, contracts into ones large enough to rationalise management as well as building methods will help ease the conflicts facing the building maintenance manager.

7.   Conclusion

The management of building maintenance is not easy. To carry out the task effectively requires that the conflict of many small jobs needing to meet precise, time consuming, legal requirements whilst using expensive management resources needs to be eased.

The special contracts for maintenance were a contribution of previous years although the Audit Commission (Nov. 1986) has shown there is scope to expand their use. The introduction of information technology has opened up ways of improving the systemisation of maintenance management.

317

Yet another way forward may be to concentrate maintenance and modernisation works into one contract to enable the benefits of a rationalised approach to be reaped. The use of low maintenance materials and components, plus energy saving measures could bring reductions in occupancy costs in future years. Whilst by no means a panacea for the difficulties of building maintenance management, the rationalisation that has taken place in the building rehabilitation process may have much to offer the building maintenance manager.

8.   Bibliography

Audit Commission, Improving Council House Maintenance, HMSO, Nov 1986

Audit Commission, Managing the Crisis in Council Housing, HMSO, March 1986

Bonshor, R.B., & Harrison, H.W., Quality in Traditional Housing Vol. 1: an Investigation into Faults and their Avoidance, Building Research Establishment Report, HMSO, 1982.

Crawley Borough Council, Repairs & DLO System: System Specification, Crawley Borough Council, 1985.

GLC (Greater London Council), London's Decaying Infrastructure - The Way Ahead, Summary of Report by Planning Policy Study Group, 1985.

Harrison, H.W., Common Faults in Housing Rehabilitation in Housing Review, Vol. 34, No. 5, Sept/Oct. 1985, pp179-180.

Housing and Construction Statistics, Department of the Environment, June Quarter Part 2, HMSO, 1986.

Lee, R., Building Maintenance Management, 2nd Ed., Granada, 1981.

Moore, R., Reconditioning the Slums: The Development and Role of Housing Rehabilitation, Planning Studies No.7, Polytechnic of Central London, 1980.

NEDO (National Economic Development Office), How flexible is Construction?, HMSO, 1978.

NEDO (National Economic Development Office), Investment in the Public Sector Built Infrastructure, NEDO, 1985.

Pettit, R., Computer Aids to Housing Maintenance Management, HMSO 1981

Symes, M., Case Studies of Architecture for Industry in Brandon, P.S. & Powell, J.A., Quality and Profit in Building Design, E. & F.N. Spon 1984, pp275-288.

Weatherhead, P.K., Thoroughly Modern Mill in Building, Vol. CCXLVIII No. 24, 14 June 1985, pp44-45.

Part VI
Economic factors

INCREASING MAINTENANCE NEEDS ON LIMITED BUDGETS.   A
TECHNIQUE TO ASSIST THE BUILDING MANAGER IN DECISION
MAKING

JOHN BARGH, A.R.I.C.S.
Department of Property Services, Cumbria County Council

Abstract
Cumbria County Council's annual maintenance allocation
falls substantially short of that recommended by national
advice.   It is unlikely that an increase in the maintenance fund will be forthcoming, therefore, a strategy
must be evolved to make effective use of the available
finance.   Under scrutiny is the concept of disposal
of surplus buildings and in particular shedding buildings
which are nearing the end of their life or approaching
major maintenance expenditure.   The Authority have undertaken the task of assessing the disposal based on condition and impending maintenance expenditure with the
aid of a study involving carrying out building condition
surveys, making assumptions as to the likelihood of
element failure and estimating element life cycles.
The life cycles are related to reliability theory and
represented graphically to aid in decisions which may
have to be made about the future of the buildings.
Key words: Breakdown maintenance, Bath tub curve, Residual value profile, Effectiveness, Building deteriology.
Effectiveness curve, Centralised maintenance fund.

1.   Introduction

Cumbria County Council in common with other authorities
has a large and diverse building stock.   This ranges
from traditional stone built properties to system builds
and modern forms.   The Council has some 1,200 properties
consisting of about 2,500 buildings.   The total floor
area is about 868,000 square metres.   In 1977 various
maintenance allocations were consolidated into a Centralised Maintenance Fund which operates to this day to
meet the cost of maintenance work.   Site observations
indicate clearly a deterioration of the stock and although
the Centralised Maintenance Fund has been increased
annually it has not been sufficient to cope with the
demand.   The RICS assessed a figure of 1% to 2% of the
value of the national building stock as a reasonable

321

annual maintenance commitment. The Audit Commission
have accepted this range with 1.8% as the target figure.
Recently Cumbria's maintenance fund allocation was only
0.8% and the likelihood of an increase sufficient to
curb the deterioration is slim. In order to aleviate
this the authority is considering disposal of buildings in the hope that their limited funds will provide
effective maintenance of the remaining stock.
   This paper describes the study which is limited to
the education building stock only, accounting for 38%
of the total number of properties but 72% of the floor
area.

2. Causes of Decay

Information is available within the authority which
gives an indication of the overall condition of the
stock.
   The pre World War 1 buildings, whilst substantially
built of durable materials are now showing signs of
decay simply through age.
   The inter war buildings are still essentially traditional and account for only a small proportion of the
stock. These are not yet suffering major defects.
   The post war stock 1945 - 1965 is basically traditional but some innovations have been included. The
shortage of labour and materials after the war has led
to a lower standard of building and defects are beginning
to show.
   Since 1965 two kinds of buildings have emerged.
The system built lightweight structures and a recent
return to traditional building. The former type uses
many short life materials and together with poor detailing is producing the highest continuous demand on funds.
Frequently complete facades and roofs have to be replaced.
With the latter it is too early to comment with certainty
on its performance.

3. Criteria for Disposal

If a building is surplus to requirements then there
are good grounds for disposal. However, if the building
is in good condition it may be better to keep it and
shed the equivalent in poor accommodation or exchange
it with another department.
   The authority is looking more closely at condition
as being a major factor in determining the future of
a building. There is condition data available and a
general awareness of the performance of different types
of property. However, it is important to be able to
predict more accurately when major expenditure could

occur so that decisions can be taken well in advance. The study under consideration is to analyse a building's maintenance needs over a period. The point prior to the greatest maintenance expenditure is when questions should be asked as to its future. These should include:

(a) Can it be disposed of if its use is on the de-cline?

(b) How does the cost of repairs equate to the cost of a new building?

(c) If it is an ageing structure are major repairs going to recur at a greater frequency?

4. The Study

4.1 Sets

The first leg of the study requires collection of site survey information. To facilitate this the stock is divided into sets. It is important to do this because a type of building will perform in a particular manner and will display different life expectancies and problems compared with other types. This division of the types into sets is required for the site survey and for relating the study to the whole stock as will be seen later. The criteria which decides the sets is:

(a) Period of construction.
(b) Materials used.
(c) Methods of construction.
(d) Style.

The main sets are:

(a) A1 Traditional   Pre 1918
(b) A2 Traditional   1918 - 1945
(c) A3 Traditional   1945 - 1965
(d) A4 Traditional   1965 - 1985
(e) B Moderne   1945 - 1975
(f) C System   1965 - 1980

The dates generally embrace major building programmes within the county. The classification of buildings into sets is carried out with the aid of photographs, plans and condition data.

4.2 The Survey

The type of survey undertaken is dependant upon whether an individual building or group of buildings is to be assessed since the study can be used for either. If the future of a single building is in question then all the elements which are likely to be costly to maintain should be examined. This should include expensive 'one

323

off' items which may occur in the future such as structural cracking. The remainder of this paper should then be followed to conclusion.

The study will, however, concentrate on buildings in sets where it is desired to know the cumulative effect that the maintenance of these sets has on future commitments. Sample buildings from each set are taken for analysis. A more accurate overall picture can be gained as samples of each increase. To reduce survey time, the five elements which consume the most money are analysed. These are the structural frame; external wall and roof finishes; heating and electrical installations. Historically they have accounted for 75% of maintenance fund expenditure and if maintained will keep the buildings upright, weathertight, heated and lit.

The method of survey could follow that assigned to any structural survey but two points should be borne in mind when viewing the condition:

(1) The surveyor will need to look at each element and make an assessment as to its remaining life. Here building deteriology concepts should be employed since orientation of building; proximity to the coast; location of industrial plants emitting pollutants; chemical reaction with adjoining materials; characteristics of materials and many other factors will affect the life and the surveyor will need to be aware of these when making his judgement. For instance, reinforced concrete buildings along coastal regions could be more susceptible to chloride attack than those in inland sheltered regions. Chloride deposits from sea spray coming in contact with the concrete will only exacerbate any existing corrosion resulting in premature failure.

(2) Elements can often be kept going by day-to-day breakdown maintenance even though the time for major refurbishment has passed. The judgement applied in the study is that the end of an elements life is not when the first wear out characteristics appear but when they appear at such a frequency as to make it more economical to replace. This judgement should be made by the surveyor when deciding the remaining life bearing in mind that the purpose of breakdown maintenance is not to finance major repairs.

4.3 Life Cycles
Having decided on the remaining life of the five elements the next step is to determine life cycles, i.e. the frequency with which these elements come up for major repair or replacement. There are various sources. The NBA Construction Consultants have produced a booklet giving some cycles. The Agrement Board produce information and there is local information.

324

The way in which local life cycles are collected
is by looking back in property records to see when elements were previously refurbished and taking the time
between this and their next anticipated refurbishment.
For example it was established that an asphalt roof
covering on a concrete structural roof had lasted about
33 years at two properties inspected. Victorian schools
are just coming up for their first major work to the
slate roof which means these roofs are lasting in excess
of 100 years.

4.4 Reliability Theory

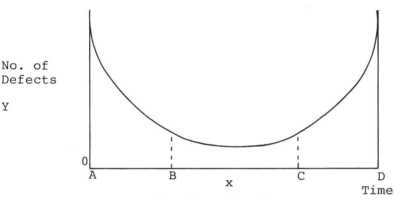

Fig. 1 Bath Tub Curve

The bath tub curve is well known. It can portray how
buildings perform in terms of numbers of defects over
time. A new building often has initial teething troubles
at A and in terms of defects the level is high. The
period between A and B is the 'burn in' as defects fall
and between B and C the building is running at optimum
level. From C to D defects increase as it wears out.
   Although the number of defects is high at A, an element's effectiveness should still be high as it is a
newly commissioned building still required for its purpose
and the element should substantially perform its function.
Between A and B defects fall towards the optimum performance, therefore, effectiveness will remain relatively
unchanged. Towards the end of C the number of defects
are starting to rise depicting signs of wearing out
accompanied by a reduction in effectiveness. For example
if windows start to decay they will not be fully effective in keeping out the weather. By the time D is reached
the element is worn out. The effectiveness will have
reached its lowest before D as a degree of breakdown
maintenance will have been employed to keep the element
going up to D.

Consider the graph in Figure 2 having horizontal
(x) and vertical (y) axes. Time can be represented
on the x axis and on this is plotted the ascertained
life cycles. The time should be of adequate length
for the cycles to be repeated as they will occur again
each time an element is replaced. To produce a shape
depicting the behaviour of the elements as they deteriorate some measure of failure is required and this
is plotted on the y axis. The measure of failure is
taken as percentage residual value or effectiveness
in terms of use and not money. From the comparison
with the bath tub curve the shape as shown in Figure
2 can be produced and is called the Effectiveness curve.
    When an element is wearing out it is desirable to
be in a position to make decisions about it before high
demands on maintenance are made particularly if it is
an expensive item. It is considered that 25% effectiveness should be the level at which to take these decisions
and is represented by a horizontal line taken from the
y axis. The element in Figure 2 has fallen below 25%
effectiveness at point A and if decisions are not taken
then by the time point B is reached maintenance expenditure will be very high. This is wasteful if the building is surplus to requirements. In effect the time
between A and B gives the manager time to make his mind
up. The longer the period between B to R the more breakdown maintenance will be incurred, therefore, this flat
portion of the curve should be as short as possible.
    No data is available to fix the parameters of the
curve but it is thought to be representative of the
behaviour one might expect. A formula has been developed
to produce the curve.

$$Y\% = \left(\frac{1}{2} + \sum_{N=1}^{N=\infty} \frac{N \, \text{Sin} \, (2\pi N \frac{x}{p})}{(2N-1)(2N+1)} \right) \times 100\%$$

Where X = No of years from start of analysis.
      P = Life cycle in years.
      N = Counter.
      Y = Percentage effectiveness.

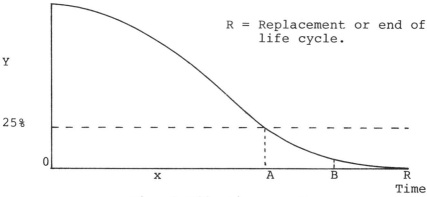

100% Effectiveness

R = Replacement or end of
life cycle.

Y

25%

0

x   A   B   R

Time

Fig. 2 Effectiveness Curve

4.5 The Future of the Stock

The theory leading up to making decisions about the
future of the buildings is explained with reference
to Figure 3. The curve previously defined represents
the time to failure cycle of an element. Here five
elements belonging to a building chosen from a set will
have different life spans but their curves will be the
same. Figure 3 shows these elements combined. Time
is expressed on the horizontal axis and begins with
1986 i.e. the time of survey. One element is already
into its cycle. Others have just begun because they
were recently replaced. Where a cycle ends another
begins with 100% effectiveness. If the theory is run
through a computer it can calculate the number of elements falling below 25% effectiveness in each year.
This is represented by the rows of asterisks below the
x axis and is called the Residual Value Profile. If
read vertically, in the 57th year four elements fall
below 25%. This peak occurs again commencing at year
68. In year 57 the maximum number of elements are on
the decline which represents the greatest impending
maintenance demand and is when one ought to be thinking
about the future of the building. If enough buildings
from the same set are surveyed, analysed and the Residual
Value Profiles added graphically it is possible to assess
the performance of a particular set and make predictions as to future maintenance demands.

In Figure 4 samples from several sets are analysed
and the profiles added by computer to give a graphical
representation of the total maintenance demand for that
proportion of the stock. Here the profiles have been
augmented by an analysis of past repairs to give a more
complete picture. From this it is clear that:

327

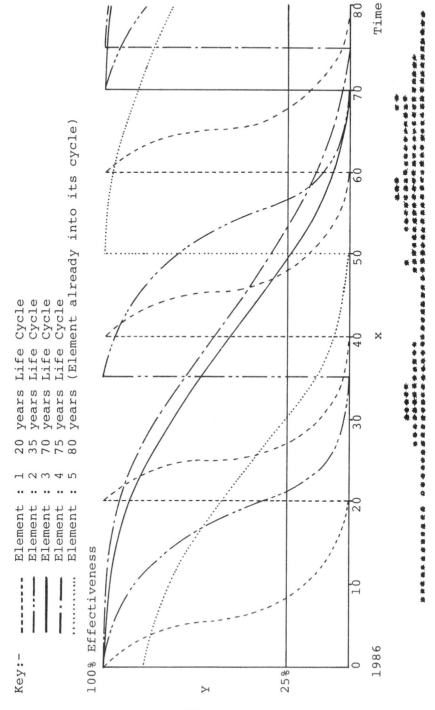

Fig. 3 Combination of Effectiveness Curves analysed over 80 years with Residual
Value Profile

Key:-

Element : 1   20 years Life Cycle
Element : 2   35 years Life Cycle
Element : 3   70 years Life Cycle
Element : 4   75 years Life Cycle
Element : 5   80 years (Element already into its cycle)

100% Effectiveness

Y

25%

1986

0   10   20   30   40   50   60   70   80

x

Time

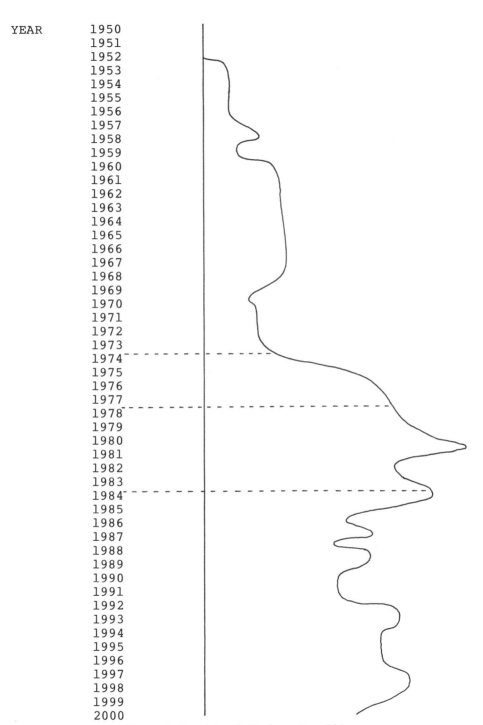

YEAR 1950 1951 1952 1953 1954 1955 1956 1957 1958 1959 1960 1961 1962 1963 1964 1965 1966 1967 1968 1969 1970 1971 1972 1973 1974 1975 1976 1977 1978 1979 1980 1981 1982 1983 1984 1985 1986 1987 1988 1989 1990 1991 1992 1993 1994 1995 1996 1997 1998 1999 2000

Fig. 4 Residual Value Profiles

(a)   There was a large increase in demand between 1950 and 1974.
(b)   There is a peak about 1978 to 1984 resulting in a high demand for finance.
(c)   There will be a continuing demand until 2000 at a rate between recent and post war levels.

5.   Summary

Cumbria County Council are responsible for the mainten-ance of a large building stock and with the likelihood of their maintenance allocation not increasing at a sufficient rate are looking at disposal as a means to reduce demand on funds.   Considering the education build-ing stock the general condition and performance of ele-ments is known.   The authority have agreed to consider condition as a significant criterion for disposal. A study has been devised whereby the building stock is split into sets.   Individual buildings from the sets are surveyed, analysed in terms of life cycles and sub-jected to reliability theory resulting in a graphical shape.   This shape can be used in several combinations to yield a variety of predictions.
The building manager must always try and be one step ahead of events particularly when funds are limited. This paper describes a study which not only helps in the making of decisions about the future of the stock but also reinforces the knowledge of the stock as a whole.

References

DoE R. & D. Bulletin (1969) Building Maintenance Report of Committee.
NBA Construction Consultants (1985) Maintenance cycles and life expectancies of building components and materials.

<u>The Maintenance of Public Housing Assets   -   S.S.H.A.</u>

<u>Practice and Developments</u>

A.E. Colston B.A., A.R.I.A.S.

Technical Maintenance Manager
Scottish Special Housing Association

1.0   <u>Introduction</u>

        Housing maintenance is a much abused term, with a variety of
        meanings, for different people.   In using the words, Asset
        Maintenance I hope to convey a much wider concept of the task
        involved and at the same time describe methods of operation
        from which, the Association gains substantial benefits.

1.1   The classic management approach to any problem is to first
        state the objective.   In housing maintenance this is hardly
        ever done, or at best, the aim is confused, lost sight of or
        plain wrong.   Allow me to define the objective as we see it,
        and the reasons why it should be so.

1.2   Public housing in this country represents an enormous asset,
        funded since the first world war by huge amounts of tax
        payers' money.   The replacement value of the Associations'
        83,000 houses alone, stands at £3 bn approximately.   Almost
        half of that stock was built between 1950 and 1960.   If it
        were allowed to fail over a ten year period we would be faced
        with replacement costs, at current prices, in the region of
        £150m per year for ten years.   Our present annual cash limit
        is a little over one third of that sum.   Quite clearly that
        cannot be allowed to happen and we can only contemplate the
        gradual replacement of sections of the stock.

2.0   <u>Objective</u>

        Therefore the prime objective must be to <u>maximise the lettable</u>
        <u>life of housing stocks</u>.   This applies whether the stock
        numbers 2000 or 200,000.   In doing so one attempts not only
        to satisfy the existing tenant, but to ensure the possibility
        of futive tenancies.   As stated, the objective may sound
        relatively innoquous, but when the implications are
        understood, they dictate a very different concept of housing
        maintenance.

2.1   In common with most housing authorities, the majority of the
        Associations' stock, almost 75% in our case, can be classed as
        traditionally built.   It has a life of at least 100 years and
        in some cases much longer.   In that context we have been
        forced to consider maintenance practices which will provide
        for whole life care over long time scales.   Longer than

individual careers or even human life spans.   Our target
became the 100 year house.   Thus not only do suitable
practices have to be developed, but we must ensure the
continuity of intent is maintained over these same time
scales.

2.2   At first sight, this may seem unrealistic, in the face of a
government policy to transfer as much public housing as
possible, to private ownership.   The political rights and
wrongs of such an issue have no bearing on this paper.
Nevertheless housing will still wear out regardless of
ownership.   In fact many who administer housing grants to the
private owner, argue that to transfer sections, of that stock
to one of the lowest income groups in the market, will in the
long run cost more to support than it would in public
ownership.   It is clear however, that whatever the change in
levels of public stock within that 100 year time scale there
will remain a substantial section of public housing which has
to be maintained.   That cannot be accomplished successfully,
on the basis that it might be sold at some future date, and
therefore the problem remains.

3.0   Maintenance Definitions

It became apparent to us some years ago, that against that
background, response maintenance by itself was wholly
incapable of answering that problem.   In the mid sixties we
began to consider what other alternatives were available.   At
that time there seemed to be three broad categories of
maintenance.

1) Running Maintenance, 2) Response or Jobbing Maintenance,
3) Planned Maintenance.

They are perhaps familiar descriptions now, but are often used
to mean different things.   It may help to clarify our meaning
of these terms by defining their chief characteristics.

3.1   Running Maintenance

We define as the work required to help operational mechanical
plant, lifts, ventilation equipment, pumped water services
etc., which require regular servicing and inspection over
short periods of time, during the whole life of the property.
Grass cutting and weeding of landscaped areas is another
example.   This type of maintenance is often thought of as
planned maintenance, but because of the short time scales and
the few elements affected, is distinct from Planned
Maintenance as we know it.

3.2   Response/Jobbing Maintenance

There are the day to day repairs, emergency responses, and
relet repairs that Landlords must provide.   It is an
essential service whose efficiency has a big effect upon the
tenants perception of the whole housing service.   Perhaps
because of that, jobbing is very often misdirected.   For
these types of repair are high cost one off items, which
however efficiently they are organised and controlled cannot
derive the benefit of scale that other methods produce.
Moreover it is an entirely after the event reaction which
tells you very little about the stock and is almost impossible
to predict what future level of repairs might be required.
There are methods of organising cyclical jobbing repairs, to
reduce high one off costs and computer systems to give better
management control, which I am sure this audience is well
aquainted with.   We are convinced the largest benefit to be
gained in this area, is to limit the amounts and type of
jobbing work to emergency repairs which arise between planned
maintenance cycles and where possible the repair is made
sufficient to hold it until the next round of contract work,
can effect a permanent low cost solution.

3.3   Planned Maintenance

Because the inherent nature of jobbing, work could not by
itself achieve this long life objective.   The Association
introduced some fifteen years ago, a system of Planned
Maintenance.   In that time changes and developments have been
made.   I don't propose to describe the system in detail here,
for it is reasonably well known and a full description exists
in our handbook "Maintenance Planning - the long term care of
Housing Stock".   But suffice to say, it is based on a five
year cycle, where 1/5 of the stock is comprehensively
inspected each year.   The work subsequently identified, is
planned around the painting cycle which is a key element in
the system.   Our experience after three complete cycles,
shows that the major advantages we believed could be gained
have in fact been achieved, namely -

1)   The provision of an accurate description of the stock.

2)   An accurate statement of maintenance need and firm
      control of budgets.

3)   The cost benefits of large scale competitive contracts.

4)   In being preventative as well as corrective the life of
      the property is increased.

Perhaps more than any other maintenance method it does require
and encourage, reliable systems of storing and retrieving

information. Information systems which describe the stock, as built, what has been done to it since, its present condition and what the future requirement is likely to be. The Associations second paper discusses this aspect in greater detail.

4.0   An Integrated Approach

In accepting the individual advantages and disadvantages of these three maintenance systems, it is clear that if our prime objective is to be achieved, it is not a case of one system being better than another, but the integration of all three, managed and controlled within the particular limits of each system. For example the full advantages will not be gained from planned maintenance if jobbing is allowed free reign. The latter will absorb money that could have achieved twice as much under planned maintenance. One has to accept that there are "horses for courses". But in how many authorities do you know, where jobbing repairs are controlled by one department, refurbishment by another and planned maintenance by some other group. The chances of achieving an integrated approach under these conditions is almost nil.

4.1   Working towards that Prime Objective, not only does maintenance require a comprehensive and long sighted approach, but the staffing structures which support them also require a similar re-think. A few years ago my own organisation was forced to change its structure from a departmental one, based on single disciplines, to a multi-discipline team structure. it is not perfect, by any means, but we are now in a much better position to operate a comprehensive approach to our existing stock.

5.0   The Reason for Further Development

Although considerable benefits were gained from planned maintenance as described, for our stock was in far better condition than it might have been without such a system, two new factors accelerated the need for further development.

First, the majority of our stock was nearly forty years old. Although we anticipated an increase in component replacement costs, we could not be sure of the amount or timing of these increases.

Secondly, it became clear some five years ago. government subsidies would decrease substantially and this policy would continue. Therefore we required a clear idea of the future maintenance demand both in the short and long term. As we already knew our funds were insufficient to cover all of the identified work, we had to devise a system of priorities, that enabled the direction of available funds to the most important areas, which at the same time protected the prime objective of maximising lettable life.

6.0   Assessing the Stock

Our first thought was to obtain an overview of the stock and relate long term demand to various categories and age bands. Obviously our five year cycle of inspections did not look far enough ahead.   So each housing development, that is the group of houses provided by the original construction contract, was assessed in terms of work required over the next ten years, for fifteen major elements of the internal and external fabric.   Each development was identified by construction type, age band and regional location, in order to analyse variations in the pattern of need.   Identified work was costed and computed.   To this sum was added, the estimated level of jobbing repairs, the programmed expenditure for modernisation and improvement works and conversions for special needs.   We finally arrived at a relatively crude estimate of need to keep the stock in a lettable condition over the next ten years. (Figure 1).   Of course the total staggered everybody, but could not be faulted, even by the Scottish Development Department, because nobody had a better way of doing it.

7.0   Profiles

Encouraged by our own audacity, we decided to develop a method of examining all components in a development over a 100 year time scale.   This became known as a technical or condition profile.   It operates in tandem with a Management Profile which measures a developments performance, aiming to highlight those areas which are below standard in terms of lettability, vandalism, ability to meet current accommodation requirements and the tenants perception's of elements of the housing fabric.   (Figure 2).   Further work is required on this profile before it is fully operational and for that reason this paper concentrates on the Technical Profile.   Profiling can be defined as a means of revealing the true condition and status of housing groups, so that once there essential nature is understood, their effective management is also ensured.

8.0   Technical Profile

Figure 3 shows a typical profile.   These were manually produced originally, but this example was created by a CAD machine.   We need 1500 approx. of these profiles to cover our total stock, the production and updating of that quantity can only be handled by machine.   But where smaller numbers are involved it is quite feasible to cope manually.

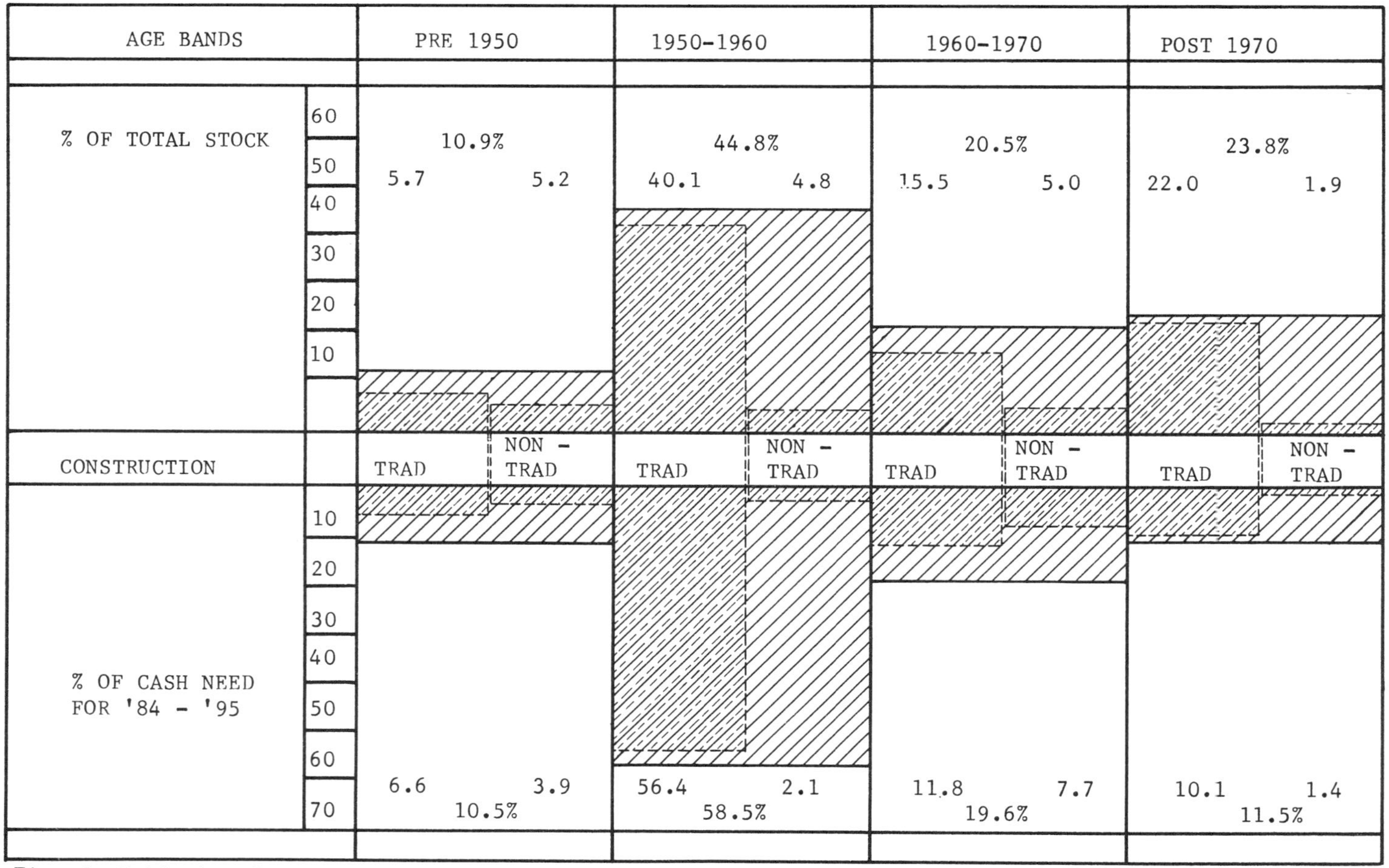

AGE BANDS	PRE 1950	1950–1960	1960–1970	POST 1970
% OF TOTAL STOCK	10.9% (5.7, 5.2)	44.8% (40.1, 4.8)	20.5% (15.5, 5.0)	23.8% (22.0, 1.9)
CONSTRUCTION	TRAD / NON-TRAD	TRAD / NON-TRAD	TRAD / NON-TRAD	TRAD / NON-TRAD
% OF CASH NEED FOR '84 – '95	10.5% (6.6, 3.9)	58.5% (56.4, 2.1)	19.6% (11.8, 7.7)	11.5% (10.1, 1.4)

Fig. 1 Estimate of need to keep stock in lettable condition for ne t ten years

Fig. 2   SSHA MANAGEMENT SCHEME PROFILE

SCHEME IDENTIFICATION   SCHEME DESCRIPTION

REGIONAL OFFICE _____ REGIONAL COUNCIL _____ PROGRAMME _____
AREA OFFICE/FACTOR _____ DISTRICT COUNCIL _____ NO. DWELLINGS _____
                                              ORIG. BUILT
SCHEME CODE _____ B.I. AREA _____ YEAR(S) BUILT _____
SCHEME CODE _____ PM INSPECTION _____ CONSTRUCT.TYPE _____
CONTACT CODE _____ DATE ASSESSED _____ HEATING TYPE _____

STOCK PROFILE

HOUSE TYPE	CURRENT STOCK (APT SIZES)								SOLD STOCK (APT SIZES)							
	1	2	3	4	5	6	7	TOT	1	2	3	4	5	6	7	TOT
C DETACHED																
O SEMI-DETACHED																
T TERRACED																
A FLATS/MAISON.																
G MULTICS																
E TOTAL																

(COTTAGES)

ESTATE MANAGEMENT PROFILE

INFORMATION   COMMENTS

WAITING LISTS: RELETS:
               (from   to)

1. DEMAND	TRANSFER LIST: LONG VOIDS:
2. AREARS	NO. IN ARREARS:AV. ARREAR: (per tenant in arrears
3. HOUSING BEN.	STD. CASES: CERT. CASES:
4. OCCUPANCY	
5. AGE PROFILE	
6. VANDALISM	

SCHEME APPRAISAL

CODINGS 0 - Not Applicable   3 - Problem Exists (High Priority)
         1 - No Known Problem   4 - Request by Tenants for Upgrad.
         2 - Problem Exists (Low Priority).

INTERNAL FITTINGS/FABRIC   EXTERNAL WORKS   FACILITIES
WINDOWS/DOORS _____   CAR PARKING _____   SHOPS _____
HEATING/INSULATION _____   BIN STORAGE _____   SCHOOLS _____
SOUND INSULATION _____   DRYING FACILITIES _____ HEALTH CENTRE/DR. _____
SANITARY WARE _____   DOOR ENTRY SYSTEM _____ PLAY FACILITIES _____
KITCHEN FITTINGS _____   FENCING/PATHS _____   COMMUNITY CENTRE _____

337

Fig. 3 Typical technical profile

SHEET					NOS.	
					ESTATE	
					DEVPT.	
					PLACE	

LOCATION			MATERIALS		FORM	CONSTRUCTION
CODE	ELEMENT	COMPENENT	AS BUILT	CURRENT		SOLD
	WALL	DPC	BIT FELT	BIT FELT		
	BELOW	EXT.CLAD	PTD FCG	PTD FCG		
	WALL	EXT.CLAD	RENDER	RENDER		
	ABOVE	COPE	BK CAVY	BK CAVY		
	G.F.L.	CAV.TIE				
		CAVITY	U/F INS	U/F INS		
		INT.CLAD	P/BD	P/BD		
	WALL	EXT.CLAD	RENDER	RENDER		
	CHY	COPE	BRICK	BRICK		
		COPE	CONC	CONC		
	WDWS.	EXT.FIN	GLOSS	GLOSS		
		FRAME	T. CAST	T. CAST		
		W/STRIP	NIL	NIL		
	DOORS	EXT.FIN	GLOSS	GLOSS		
		FRAME (F)	T. GL.PAN	T.GL.PAN		
		FRAME(R)	T. GL.PAN	T.GL.PAN		
		W/STRIP	NI	NIL		

EXTERNAL   FABRIC

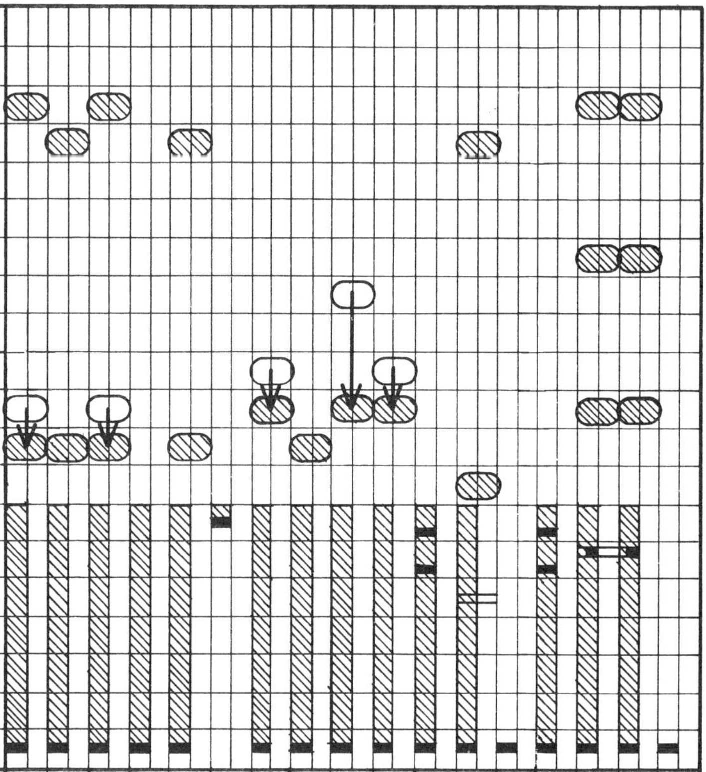

338

The top section contains locational and broad descriptive information, so arranged that by coding, selection by categories, from numbers of Profiles, is possible. On the left hand side are elements of Fabric description with further description of elements and materials. These are grouped into External Fabric, Internal Fittings, Internal Fabric and External Works. Each component is related to a 100 year time scale, divided into five year bands representing our cycle of Planned Maintenance inspections. The history of work is shown against each component in the year that it occurred. A complete change of component is signalled by moving from the top half of the component live to the bottom half with solid black infill. Partial replacement is shown by open infill, brief descriptions of changes are writtin in.

The end of a components life is indicated by a circle. This information is drawn from a list of average component lives compiled from a publication by NBA Consultants and knowledge of component performance within the organisation. The work required at that point in time is then estimated. From this it is possible to construct a model of future costs for the life of a development, for development groups or the total stock. For programming and budgeting purposes work required for the next five to ten years has to be more accurately predicted. Thus for work likely to occur within that period, the end of component life is verified or adjusted for each development through the routine Planned Maintenance inspections. This allows programmes to be completed with confidence and also increases the accuracy of the list of average lives.

To ensure scarce finance is effectively used work identified within the next 5 or 10 years is given a priority from an agreed scale - Figure 4. The appropriate priority is entered in the priority column.

Moving to the right of the profile the next two columns offer an enlarged time scale for the next 10 years. Allowing technical officers to indicate in which year the work should be executed. Because he has a total picture of future work for that development, he can plan for the most effective sequence of work. Once programmed the work can be costed.

For costing April '85 is used as a base date. The degree of change from that date is derived from the B.I.C.S. indices of prices. A series of unit prices is built up to which factors are applied eg the number of houses in a development or the average number windows per house. Thus different estimators can price and costs can be related over long periods of time. The estimated cost is then entered in the top half of the component line, while the cost of completed work is entered subsequently in the bottom half. Allowing a check to be kept on the volume of identified work against that completed.

339

Fig. 4 Priority scale

PRIORITY	CATEGORY	TYPE
1]	PAINTER MAINTENANCE	(PAINTER CONTRACTS (PRE PAINTER REPAIRS
1]	PUBLIC SAFETY	DANGER WITHIN 5 YEARS
2]	STATUTORY REPAIRS	WEATHER PENETRATION WITHIN 5 YEARS
3]	PUBLIC SAFETY	DANGER AFTER 5 YEARS
4]	STATUTORY REPAIR	WEATHER PENETRATION AFTER 5 YEARS
5]	FABRIC REPAIR	END OF COMPONENT LIFE
6]	FABRIC REPAIR	PREVENTS END OF COMPONENT LIFE
7]	INTERNAL IMPROVEMENT	THERMAL UPGRADE
8]	INTERNAL IMPROVEMENT	INTERNAL ALTERATIONS
9]	EXTERNAL WORKS	END OF COMPONENT LIFE
10]	EXTERNAL WORKS	PREVENTATIVE REPAIR
11]	EXTERNAL WORKS	LANDSCAPE UPGRADE

340

The condition column indicates the amount of life left in a
component as a percentage of its existing life.   Key
components can be selected to produce an average condition for
a single delevelopment.   Thus developments can be compared by
condition and over the years it is possible to relate changes
in condition to money invested.

It can be seen that the Technical Profile works at two levels
1) Enabling operating groups to prepare detail priority based
programmes for the next ten years.   2) A development life
cost cycle can be plotted, and these cycles amalgamated to
give long term cost predictions for groups of stock or total
stocks.   This data is particularly useful in bidding for
future funding levels.

9.0   Prioritising Demand

The methods of applying priority to work within individual
profiles has already been outlined.   When determining
priority between different developments another level of
priority is required.   The next paragraph outlines the
reasoning behind this higher level of priority.

The rationale behind Profiling, seeks to identify and give
value to need on a common basis.   That need has to be
compared between sections of the stock or across the whole
stock.   Value is measured by the return obtainable from a
proposed investment.   Return is conditioned by the remaining
life of the house or development.   Life is affected by the
physical condition of the fabric and the forseeable demand for
that house or group of houses.   It is important therefore
that assessments are made on both the condition and demand
factors which influence life.   Hence the requirement for both
Technical and Management Profiles.   If we recall the
objective "to maximise potential life" then within the content
of the existing stock that means the remaining potential life.
Part of the process of obtaining best value from investment in
the stock means that solutions for component replacement
should not have a life significantly greater than that of a
developments main structure.   Ideally they should all die at
the same time.   Therefore if we begin by defining a
developments structure by long, medium and short lives, eg

1)   Traditional brick cavity wall - 100+ years = long

2)   Traditional timber frame - upto 60 years = medium

3)   P.C. come frame with additives - upto 45 years = short.

Then re-sort them using original construction dates into
groups of long, medium and short potential remaining lives.
We then have a basis to alott inter development priorities.

341

Fig. 5 Analysis and presentation of budget sheets for a regional group of stock

		1L	4m	5L	5m	5s	6L	6m	7L	7m	8L	8m	9L	9m	9s	1CL	10m	11Lm
RUNNING TOTALS		76·8		214·9	321·0		1287·6	1319·2			1684·6		1734·6			1928·1		
PRIORITY CATEGORY / FUTURE DEVL LIFE		1L	4m	5L	5m	5s	6L	6m	7L	7m	8L	8m	9L	9m	9s	1CL	10m	11Lm
YEAR 6 PAINTERWORK		76·8																
EXTERNAL FABRIC				98·7	106·1		437·3	31·6										
WALL OPENINGS				36·3			292·3											
HEATING											72·3							
INSULATION						YEAR 6 SPEND					YEAR 6 C/F							
ELECTRICAL				3·1														
KITCHEN BATH & PLUMBING							37·0				193·1							
COMMON AREAS																		
EXTERNAL WORKS																133·5		
① COSTS IDENTIFIED FOR YEAR		76·8		138·1	106·1		766·6	31·6			265·4					133·5		
② WORK N.T.U. IN PREVIOUS YEAR							200·0				100·0		50·0			60·0		
③ IDENTIFIED TOTALS ①+②		76·8		138·1	106·1		966·6	31·6			365·4		50·0			193·5		
④ TOTALS WITHIN TARGET SPEND		76·8		138·1	106·1		747·0	31·6										
⑤ BAL N.T.U. & C.F. TO NEXT YEAR ③-④							219·0				365·4		50·0			193·5		

342

Because the remaining life is the citeria and a seventy year
old traditional development is in the same group as a recently
built timber frame development, then the same priority is
attached to them and the degree of their solution can also be
the same.   Similarly different solutions and costs can be
applied for component replacments in short and long life
stock.   The aim being to obtain the best return or best value
from available money.

10.   Analysing Demand

Using this logic a spread sheet was constructed on a VAX
Rainbow micro using Lotus software to analyse and present
budget sheets for a regional group of stock, completed from
individual Profiles (Figure 5).   Categories of work are
arranged on the left hand side, with priority along the top
ranging from 1 Long to 11 Short.   Also on the left, the spend
year with the 10 year cycle is indicated along with the area
from which the cost originates.   Costs for each work
category are sorted into their correct priority column and a
running total from left to right shown in the top column.
Thus a line can be drawn to meet a budget total and work to
right of that line carried forward to next year.   At the
bottom of that sheet totals are computed for 1) work
identified for that year 2) work not taken up from the
previous year 3) work within the Targetspend4) and the balance
to be carried forward to next year.

As individual costs are coded by the probable year of spend
the component affected and also by any of the location data at
the top of the profile, it is quite feasable not only to trace
the spend back to its source but also calculate for example
the total window replacement programme for the whole stock
over the next ten years.   More significantly there is a
constant check on the amount identified, the amount spent, and
the amount carried forward.   This in turn can be compared
with the changing condition of the stock.

11.0   Formulation of Investment Policies

The ability to formulate such priority based programmes is
clearly advantageous, but there is a further significant
benefit.   Operating from a knowledge of the peaks and troughs
of total demand investment policies can be constructed from
available finance, which secures the future of the most
valuable sections of the stock.   Allowing alternative
strategies to be devised for these sections which either
cannot be funded or do not warrant it.   This in turn
clarifies the arguments for funding levels and spells out the
consequences of funding below levels of need.   Moreover it
will increasingly bring into question our present systems of
housing finance.   The system of borrowing capital money for

the provision of new houses, over 60 years, doesn't recognise
that many times that amount will be required to fund component
replacement costs forty years after the original construction
and twenty years before the first loan is cleared.   As a
result a spiral of debt is created where debt charges can, as
in the Association's case, equal annual revenue or
substantially exceed it.   When our present cushion of house
sales income disappears, as it surely will, new rules for
capital funding will be required if the stock is to survive.
This area of housing economics is a fertile and yet
uncultivated area for research.   Academics please note!

13.   Other Applications

The system as described was developed to meet the particular
problems of managing housing assets.   But I am sure you will
see the connections that exist in the management of different
types of asset.   Whether it be schools, commercial buildings
or industrial plant, the principles of detail knowledge of the
stock, the need to know the timing and levels of future costs
in order to manage todays problem, are common to any
facilities manager.   What will change are the objectives and
time scales which arise from the character of the property
concerned.

14.0   Summary

This paper seeks to describe recent developments in the
Association's maintenance practice.   If any advances have
been made it is not because we are blessed with unusual levels
of financial or human resources (that is far from being so)
but rather we had after prolonged debate a very clear idea of
our prime objective, which allowed us to achieve a measure of
continuity of intent, and that in turn has shaped our
management structure and our practice.   Should this paper
have any message to other organisations with similar
responsibilities it is, that your objective must be clearly
reasoned and frequently tested in order to sustain the
developments of flexible practices necessary to maintain stock
over such long time scales.   Without that, wrong directions
will be taken, resources wasted and good practices will not be
maintained against the swings of fashion.   I hope that in
stating our objective yours may also be clarified.

FORECASTING HOUSING QUALITY DEVELOPMENT AND FUTURE MAINTENANCE
DEMAND/FUNCTIONAL DESIGN OF THE MODEL

CEES DERTH   AKB, Rotterdam *)
TON   DAMEN   Bouwcentrum Rotterdam **)

Introduction
In most developed countries new building is decreasing and the main
activity of the building industry is moving towards the existing
stock. There are lots of problems in the existing housingstock: many
dwellings of bad quality and increasing maintenance arrears.

These problems tend to be come worse as more maintenance is needed
when the housing stock is aging.

For policy-making it is therefore important to have the possibility
to prognose the quality-development of the housing stock by different
levels of maintenance-efforts.

The model, described in this paper, aims to satisfy this need.

Key words: Housing-quality, maintenance-demand, existing housingstock, forcasting model.

Model-describtion

The housingstock is specified as follows:
- age of the dwelling (8 cohorts are distinguished);
- one- and more-family houses;
- ownership (social tenancy, private tenancy, owner-occupied).

In total 48 cells (= housing categories) are distinguished.

For each housing-category the structure of the concerning sub-population is described on the basis of ± 50 buildingcomponents. Each
component can exist of different materials (as an average 5 materials
per component). A sub-population is described with ± 250 elements or
component/material-combination.

*)   AKB = Consultants for quantitative modelling and decision-making
**) Since February 1987: Damen, Gorter, van Rooy b.v.
                         Maintenance-research and Consultancy,
                         Rotterdam

For each element the corresponding quantity in the specific sub-population is given as an average per dwelling (p.e. 0.3 p. Hardwood frontdoor). The respective quantities are taken from the Housing Condition Survey results.

Per element the relevant maintenance-activities are specified. Each activity must be done once or with a certain frequency (= maintenance -cyclus) during the life-time of the element (p.e. painting every 6th year; replacement every 40th year). Acitivities and cycli are the results of seperate empirical and analytical research.

The costs of the maintenance-activities are calculated by multiplication of quantity and cost/unit. The cyclus states when these costs will be needed. By addition of the cost of all elements, the maintenance-cost of that sub-population is derived. The cost can - if wanted - be specified according to main group (e.g. floors, roofs, facades, etc.) and maintenance-category (e.g. running maintenance, structural maintenance, etc.). These costs are called the basic-maintenance costs (KOH).

The basic maintenance costs can be predicted for the future in the way described. These costs however are not equal to the needed maintenance-effort. Therefore the cost must be corrected for a number of influences:
- the existing maintenance-arrears (AOH);
- the reduction of the maintenance-arrears by modernisation-works (improvement);
- the reduction of the maintenance-arrears by demolishing of dwellings;
- the changing number of dwellings per sub-population by demolishment and new building (for the youngest cohort).

In the following paragraphs the calculation of the basis maintenance costs and the necessary corrections are described.

Calculation basic maintenance costs per dwelling

Calculate for each dwelling category, main group and maintenance category $H(i,j)$ ($i = -5, \ldots, 5$; $j = 1, \ldots, 24$).

$H(i,j)$ = basic maintenance costs per dwelling for which the cycle commences the $i.5$th year after construction of the dwelling with a frequency of j years if $j < 5$ and a frequency of $(j-4).5$ years if $j \geqslant 5$.

Per element/activity the costs in the year of execution is the quantity of the element occurring in the respective dwelling multiplied by the applicable unit price or norm.

Allowance is made for the possibility that a particular activity must take place c_1 years after the construction year, and that the activity must thereafter take place every c_2 years ($c_1 \neq c_2$).

346

It is also possible that the respective maintenance norm is k_1 guilders the first time and k_2 ($k_1 \neq k_2$) guilders the second and subsequent times. In such cases one speaks of a non-recurrent cycle (c_1 and k_1) and a recurrent cycle (c_2 and k_2).

The possible cycle durations (for both the non-recurrent and the recurrent cycles) are in years):
1, 2, 3, 4, 5, 10, 15, ... 90, 95, 100
with corresponding cycle numbers:
1, 2, 3, 4, 5, 6,............ 22, 23, 24.

When the user specifies a cycle duration which is not permitted, this is rounded off to the nearest permitted cycle duration.

$H(i,j)$ is calculated without taking into account a possible difference in the maintenance norm (k) between the non-recurrent and the recurrent cycle.
There are 24 cycles to be distinguished (numbered 1,..., 24), with non-recurrent cycle duration $c_1 j$ (j = cycle number) and recurrent cycle duration $c_2 j$.
For all dwellings a "fictive construction year" is now defined per cycle duration: actual construction year + c_1 - c_2.

On the basis of the fictive construction year corresponding to the actual construction year 0, (c_1 - c_2), it can be now be established in general that the activity (activities) pertaining to the cycles with non-recurrent duration c_1 and recurrent duration c_2 will take place for the first time after c_2 years and must thereafter be repeated every c_2 years. From this it follows that for a given cycle duration, the respective indices i and j may be calculated as follows

- i
$$5 i = c_1 - c_2$$

$$i = \frac{c_1 - c_2}{5}$$

- j = c_2 if $c_2 < 5$

$= \frac{c_2}{5} + 4$ if $c_2 \geq 5$

$H(i,J)$ must now be augmented by the maintenance norms multiplied by the quantities of the respective activities.

Summarising
$h(s)$ = the quantity to which s must be applied
$c_1(s)$ = the non-recurrent cycle duration pertaining to activity s
$k_1(s)$ = the maintenance norm pertaining to the non-recurrent cycle of activity s
$c_2(s)$ = the recurrent cycle duration pertaining to activity s

347

$k_2(s)$ = maintenance norm corresponding to the recurrent cycle of activity s

(1)   Initialise $H(i,j) = 0$ for $i = -5, \ldots, 5$
$$j = 1, \ldots, 24$$

(2)   Suppose there have been S activities defined in total. Now put for $s = 1, \ldots, S$:

$$i: = \frac{c_1(s) - c_2(o)}{5}$$

$$j: = c_2(s) \text{ as } c_2(s) < 5$$

$$j: = \frac{c2(s)}{5} + 4 \text{ as } c_2(s) \geq 5$$

$$H(i,j): = H(i,j) + h(s).K_2(s).$$

However, a mistake has been made:in the calculation of the costs with respect to the non-recurrent cycle, the maintenance norms for the recurrent cycle have been taken ($k_2(s)$ instead of $k_1(s)$). This is corrected by means of $E(j)$.
For $s = i, \ldots, S$:

$$j: = c_1(s) \qquad \text{if } c_1(s) < 5$$

$$j: = \frac{c_1(s)}{5} + 4 \qquad \text{if } c_1(s) \geq 5$$

$$E(j) : E(j) + k_1(s) - k_2(s)) h(s)$$

$E(j)$ is thus the correction factor which must be applied in the year j after the actual construction year if $j < 5$, and in the year $(j - 4)5$ after the actual construction year if $j \geq 5$.

If we knew for certain that all the maintenance activities always took place in the year in which they were expected to take place, and never outside that year, then the maintenance costs per dwelling, per dwelling category, per main group, per maintenance category in year k (k > 1985) could be determined as follows.
Let T_0 be the construction year of the dwelling in question.
Then the costs expressed in recurrent maintenance cycles are defined by means of the matrix $h(,)$.

$H(i,j)$ can be taken as the costs which occur as from the fictive year of construction with cycle duration number j as a result of activities which have a non-recurrent cycle duration c_1 and a recurrent cycle duration c_2, thus $c_1 - c_2 = 5i$.
The fictive construction year for $H(i,j)$ for the actual construction year T_0 is thus equal to $T_0 + 1.5$. Year k is thus $k - (T_0 + 5i)$ years after the fictive construction year. The costs in this year (expressed in recurrent cycles) are thus:

$$\sum_{i=-5}^{5} \sum_{j \in J_1} H(i,j)$$

$$J_1 = \left\{ j \in IN \mid 0 < K - (T_0 + 5i) \right.$$
$$\text{and}$$
$$\ell \cdot j = K - (T_0 + 5i)$$
$$\text{for } \ell \in IN \backslash \{0\}$$
$$\text{and}$$
$$j < 5)$$
$$\text{or}$$
$$j = \frac{\dfrac{K - (T_0 + 5i)}{5} + 4}{\ell}$$
$$\left. \ell \in IN \backslash \{0\} \ , \ j \geq 5) \right\}$$

This means in effect that J_1 contains only those cycle numbers which correspond to a cycle duration of which the number of years after the fictive construction year is a multiple.

A correction must now be made should in year k maintenance activities have been planned within the framework of non-recurrent cycles. Based on the actual construction year, the correction amounts to
$$\sum_{j \in J_2} E(j)$$

$$J_2 = \left\{ j \in IN \mid (0 < k - T_0 < 5 \right.$$
$$\text{and } j = k - T_0)$$
$$\text{or}$$
$$(\quad k - T_0 \geq 5$$
$$\text{and } j = \frac{k - T_0}{5} + 4 \ )$$

The basic maintenance costs in year k, for actual construction year T_0, are thus:

$$\sum_{i=-5}^{5} \sum_{j \in J_1} H(i,j) \quad + \sum_{j \in J_2} E(j)$$

J_1 and J_2 defined as above.

In the above no allowance has been made for the fact that the date upon which a maintenance activity must be carried out, is not fixed in advance, but that each activity in each year has a given chance of occurring.

349

Now define:

VKE(j, m)   as the chance that the activities corresponding to a
             non-recurrent cycle with cycle duration number j take
             place in year m after the actual construction year.

VDK(j, m)   as the chance that the activities corresponding to a
             recurrent cycle with cycle duration number j take place
             in year m after the fictive construction year.

(The calculation of VKE and VKD will be discussed later).

Then the costs to be expected in year k for a dwelling constructed
in the year T_0 can be calculated as follows:
KOH   (dwelling   main   maint.)
       (cat.,   group,   cat, k)

$$= \sum_{j=1}^{24} E(j).VKE(j, k - T_0)$$

$$+ \sum_{i=-5}^{5} \sum_{j=1}^{24} H(i,j).VDK(j, k - T_0 - 5i)$$

 whereby:
$k - T_0 > 0$
$k - T_0 - 5i > 0$
must apply.

Calculation influence maintenance in arrears on normative maintenance
requirement

The user of the model specifies for each dwelling category, main
group and maintenance category the average maintenance in arrears per
dwelling in guilders.
In addition for each cycle duration, construction year class combination, the fraction is indicated of the amount of arrears relating
thereto.

As soon as there are (parts of) activities which relate to (parts
of) elements which have accrued arrears of maintenance, these (parts
of) activities are no longer reckoned under normal maintenance.
(The greater the arrears of maintenance, the smaller the normative
maintenance requirement). No allowance therefore has been taken in
the calculation of the KOH and the number of dwellings to which KOH
refers. AOH() is now calculated in such a manner that it is a
reasonable approximation of that part of the maintenance costs which
has been wrongly included in KOH.WV.

w = dwelling category (sub-population)
b = construction year class (cohort)
ℓ = main group
m = maintenance category.

350

AF(b,j)   fraction of the amount of arrears relating to activities with recurrent cycle number j.

AF()   is calculated for each main group and maintenance category.
               The default value for

$$AF(b,j) = \frac{H(5,j)}{\sum\limits_{i=1}^{24} H(5,i)}$$

B(k,ℓ,m)   = amount of arrears in 1985

AW(w,ℓ,m,j): = B(w,ℓ,m) AF(b,j)
               = arrears per dwelling with respect to maintenance cycles with recurrent cycle number j.

AOH(w,ℓ,m,k):= WV(K). $\sum\limits_{j=1}^{24}$ AW(w,ℓ,m,j)
               . VDK(j,k-F)

WV(w)   = $\neq$ dwellings in dwelling category W

F   = the fictive construction year corresponding to the middle construction year of construction year class b.

The specified amounts of arrears B(,,) are not constant over the years. The arrears can change in 3 ways:

1) Improvement effort
2) Demolition of dwellings with arrears
3) Maintenance effort divergent from the normative maintenance requirement.

For soft ware-technical reasons, the above will not be taken into account until in the final report.
The influence of the original arrears (AOH) and that of the 3 above-mentioned factors is initially calculated separately.
B(,,) is thus not explicitly adjusted.

Calculation influence improvement effort on normative maintenance requirement

The user may, in addition to the maintenance effort, state an improvement effort. This is done by specifying:

VF(b,j)   j = 1, ..., 24
  = Fraction of the improvement amount (for dwelling category with corresponding construction year class b) in respect of activities with cycle number j.
    VF(,) is specified for each main group and maintenance category.

351

The default value for VF(,) = AF(,)

JV = year in which the improvement takes place (JV > 1985)

AVW(w,JV)   = number in JV of dwellings to be improved in dwelling
                  category w

C(w,ℓ,m,JV)   = improvement amount per dwelling in year JV in dwelling
                  category w, main group and maintenance category m.

It will be obvious that, when an improvement effort has taken place,
this effort causes in all the subsequent years an increase in the
normative maintenance requirement. The extent to which this occurs
depends upon the chance factor with which regular maintenance to the
improved elements takes place and the extent to which the improved
elements have been improved (fraction multiplied by improvement
amount). This gives the following formula:

VOH (dwelling   main   mainten.
      (category,   group,   category, k)

$$= \sum_{JV=1986}^{k} AVW(w,JV)$$

$$. \sum_{j=1}^{24} VF(b,j) \ C(w,\ell,m,JV) \ VDK(j, \ k - F)$$

= The effect on the normative maintenance in year k of the
improvement efforts carried out from 1986 up to and including
k.

Calculation influence demolition on normative maintenance

The demolition of dwellings influences the normative maintenance
requirement in two ways:

- the number of dwellings by which the normative maintenance
  requirement per dwelling (KOH) is multiplied, decreases each year
  by the number of dwellings demolished in that year.

- The number of demolished dwellings which had accrued arrears of
  maintenance has now been worked up in AOH. Thus, as soon as the
  dwellings have been demolished, AOH must be corrected (reduced)
  for that portion of the arrears which has ceased to exist due to
  the demolition of the dwellings.
  This correction does not take place, however, via AOH, but by
  calculating this portion of the "maintenance costs in AOH" (SOH),
  and augmenting thereby the normative maintenance requirement.

352

VA(b,j) = fraction of the amount of arrears (for dwelling category w, corresponding to construction year class b) with respect to activities with cycle number j for corresponding main group and maintenance category j = 1, ..., 24

Default : VA(b,j) = AF(b,j)

JA = year of demolition, JA ≥ 1986

AAW(w,JA) = number of dwellings from dwelling category w to be demolished in year JA

D(w,ℓ,m,JA)= amount of arrears with respect to demolition in year JA, dwelling category w, main group ℓ, maintenance category m.

Default:

$$D(w,\ell,m,JA) = \frac{B(w,\ell,m)}{\sum_{\ell,m} B(w,\ell,m)} \cdot \sum_{\ell,m} D(w,\ell,m,JA)$$

The expected effect upon the maintenance costs:

SOH (dwelling   main   mainten.   )
    (category,   group,   category,   k)

$$= \sum_{JA = 1986}^{k} AAW(w,JA) \cdot \sum_{j=1}^{24} VA(b,j)D(w,\ell,m,JA).$$

VDK(j, k-F)

= The correction on AOH in the year k to be made on account of the demolition from 1986 up to and including k.

Given the above, it is possible to calculate the total normative maintenance requirement in the year k. In order to simplify the notation we introduce a few more variables:

FRW(w,j) = the fraction of the dwellings file in dwelling category w, falling in year j of the corresponding construction year class

n(w) = the number of construction years of which construction year class corresponding to dwelling category w consists

SAW(w,k) = $\sum_{j=1986}^{k} AAW(w,j)$

= total of the number of dwellings from dwelling category w, demolished from 1986 up to and including k.

353

$$\text{TKOH}(w,\ell,m,k) = \sum_{j=1}^{n(w)} \text{FRW}(w,j) \ (wv(w) - \text{SAW}(w,k))$$

$$\text{KOH}(w,\ell,m,k + n(w) - j)$$

$$- \text{AOH}(w,\ell,m,k)$$
$$+ \text{VOH}(w,\ell,m,k)$$
$$+ \text{SOH}(w,\ell,m,k)$$

Total normative requirement in the year k: $\sum\limits_{w,\ell,m}$ TKOH(w,ℓ,m,k)

The model offers the user 2 options in respect of specification of the maintenance efforts (the improvement effort is not connected with this).

1) Maintenance effort is taken for each year as being equal to the normative maintenance requirement (TKOH)
2) The maintenance effort for the years 1986 up to 2010 can be stated by the user, whereby the difference between the requirement and the effort in each year is regarded as a change in the arrears situation.
   The precise manner in which a maintenance effort diverging from the normative maintenance requirement is worked up, is described in appendix 1.

Appendix 1

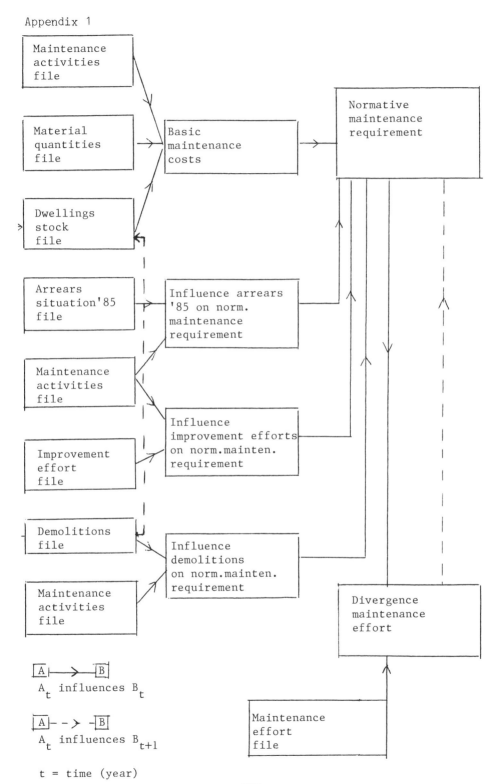

A⌷⟶B
A_t influences B_t

A⌷- - >-B
A_t influences B_{t+1}

t = time (year)

HOME OWNERSHIP AND THE MANAGEMENT OF MAINTENANCE

PETER MALPASS, DAVID GARNETT and SHEILA MACKINTOSH
Department of Surveying, Bristol Polytechnic

Abstract
This paper, which is based on an empirical study of owner occupation
in a low income district of Bristol, argues the case for developing a
research programme which focuses on the notion of 'the owner occupier
as housing manager'. It suggests that there is a research gap
resulting from the fact maintenance research has tended to ignore
problems relating to private home ownership whilst social science
research on home ownership has tended to ignore questions of
maintenance. Much current research into owner occupation has concentrated on problems relating to access to the tenure. With the
continuing growth of owner occupation it is increasingly important to
broaden the debate to include questions about housing in use.
Housing is an important and complex commodity and as the emphasis for
maintaining, repairing and improving it shifts to those who own and
occupy it, there is a real need to develop a better understanding of
the financial and non-financial resources available to different
types of household and the maintenance management strategies adopted
within and between different income groups.
Key words: Owner occupation, The home owner as housing manager,
Finacial resources, Non-financial resources, Maintenance strategies.

Home ownership now accounts for more than three fifths of all housing
in Britain, and expenditure by owner occupiers on repair, maintenance
and improvement probably exceeds £9 billion annually.[1] Despite the
huge sums and the importance of this activity, for the building
industry and the community at large as well as for owner occupiers,
there is very little information on how home owners make decisions
about what work to do to their houses, how they pay for it and how
they carry it out. The English House Condition Survey 1981[2] (EHCS)
and similar local studies[3] provide a picture of the kinds of jobs
that are carried out and the amount of disrepair remaining, but they
give virtually no insight into the decision making processes that lie
behind maintenance activity and inactivity.

The management of maintenance and refurbishment by home owners has
been neglected as a research issue for quite understandable reasons.
The management of property maintenance in general has been perceived
as a specialised technical activity and research in this area has
tended to concentrate on issues such as coding, costing and computer-

357

isation.[4] The focus of research in housing maintenance has naturally been on the public rented sector, in which much of the work has concentrated on how best to manage the maintenance of a large stock of dwellings. Studies in the local authority sector have been aided by a good data base, something which is not available in the owner occupied sector. Against this background it is easy to see that the problems faced by individual home owners, each responsible for just one dwelling, have not been recognised as managerial issues, nor have they been seen as requiring the application of scarce research resources. Maintenance research has, therefore, tended to ignore home ownership.

At the same time, social science research on home ownership has tended to ignore maintenance. This is partly due to the definition of maintenance as 'technical' and therefore not within the frame of reference of social science research. It is also partly a reflection of the widespread public perception of home ownership as inherently desirable and superior to other forms of tenure - a perception which has been assiduously cultivated through the housing policies of successive governments for many years. The thrust of policy has been to expand home ownership, and in this context the focus of research has tended to be on questions of access and mortgage finance, to the exclusion of maintenance and other aspects of housing in use.

However, as it has grown, owner occupation has changed in character, undermining the established assumptions about guaranteed superior standards, and making it more important to examine the whole area of maintenance and its management. A number of trends can be identified. First, the growth of owner occupation, which has accelerated sharply in the 1980s, has drawn in more and more low income purchasers, while at the same time there has been an increase in the numbers of long term elderly owners, many of whom live on low incomes. Second, owner occupation has been spreading more thoroughly into pre-1919 inner urban areas where low house prices have attracted low income, marginal purchasers. Third, a shift in housing policy, dating back to the late 1960s, has led to an extended life for older housing areas as redevelopment has given way to rehabilitation, placing individual owners in the forefront of decisions on improvement and investment. This has been reinforced more recently by clear signals from the government that, "The primary responsibility for maintaining and improving private property rests with the owners."[5] And fourth, there is growing evidence of a gathering problem of disrepair in the owner occupied sector. Whereas in the past private rented housing was regarded as the tenure in which problems of poor quality were concentrated, it is now the case that the majority of dwellings in disrepair are in owner occupation. The 1981 English House Condition Survey estimated that more than half a million owner occupied dwellings required expenditure on repairs exceeding £7,000.[6] It was also confirmed that defects were heavily concentrated in the pre-1919 stock, particularly terraced property with a low rateable value.[7]

Taken together these factors point towards the inner city as an interesting and important setting for research on the changing nature of home ownership. Some valuable research was carried out in the 1970s and early 1980s to examine the working of this part of the

housing market.[8]   However, major unexplored areas remain and our
research on the management of maintenance by owner occupiers has
begun to address a set of issues that previous researchers have
neglected.   The distinctive feature of the research on which this
paper is based is its focus on housing in use and on the owner
occupier as a proprietor with the authority and responsibility to
maintain and repair the house.   Home ownership in inner city areas
puts low income people into a position where they are individually
responsible for managing the maintenance and improvement of houses
which, due to their age and original construction, now generally
require substantial attention on a continuing basis.   The changes
which have brought low income people into home ownership in run down
areas have made it more important than ever to study maintenance
activity.
A key issue in research on the maintenance of older inner city
housing is clearly the availability of financial resources - can low
income home owners afford to carry out the work that their houses
require?   The EHCS looked at finance and found that the people in the
poorest stock generally had the lowest incomes and that only 10%
could finance remedial work from current savings.   Evidence from
local studies such as our own confirm these findings.   In our
research in the Lower Easton area of Bristol we interviewed 179 home
owners in small two and three bedroomed pre-1919 terraced houses.[9]   We
found that in this inner city neighbourhood, which had been
identified by the Bristol House Condition Survey (1982) as an area
with some of the poorest quality housing in the city, 45% of our
respondents had disposable household incomes of less than £100 per
week (in April 1986).   In addition only 20% admitted to having
savings of more than £1,000, and most had no savings at all.   Not
surprisingly, therefore, the high cost of maintenance and refurbishment was identified as the main disadvantage of home ownership, and
half of those who were either not planning to carry out work or who
were postponing work on recognised defects gave lack of money as the
reason.   Shortage of funds may help to explain why 84% had not
commissioned an independent structural survey before buying their
house, despite the obvious risks that this involved in an area like
Lower Easton where the houses are old and subject to subsidence as
well as disrepair.
However, finance is not the only resource issue that needs to be
considered.   The EHCS contains a section on resources which refers
solely to finance, but it is necessary to go further in order to
explain why some houses are well maintained while others nearby are
not.   Finance is obviously important, but it is not in itself sufficient to explain variations in house condition.   In our research, by
concentrating on the idea of the management of maintenance and refurbishment and by developing the notion of the home owner as housing
manager, we have been able to open up a much wider and richer
perspective.   The idea that home owners can be seen as housing
managers is one of the key conceptual insights to emerge from our
research so far.   Amongst other things it draws attention to the need
to look at the whole range of relevant resources.   These include:

1. Time
2. Knowledge
3. Skills
4. Contacts
5. Enthusiasm
6. Confidence
7. Resilience

This list could be altered and extended, and an issue for further research is the clarification of the resources that are a) most important to home owners, and b) most readily available in the existing population of owners. It is important to recognise that home owners are required to make complex and difficult decisions for which they are not necessarily well equipped.

The precise configuration of resources available will vary from owner to owner, in the sense that individuals will have more of some resources and less of others, and the total amount of resources will vary. Thus variations in the quality and quantity of maintenance work carried out will reflect different patterns of available resources. It is important to recognise in this context that two of the most important resources, time and finance, are contingent upon other factors within the household. In other words, the amounts of time and money that can be devoted to maintenance will reflect the total amounts of these resources available to the household, and the other demands made on them. There is a clear opportunity cost here: money spent on the house is money that is not available for expenditure on, for instance, holidays, and time devoted to the house is time not spent with children or friends.

The ways in which resources are combined and used will reflect the particular pattern and amount of resources available to each household, but a useful way of thinking about the management of maintenance is to look at the resource implications of different maintenance strategies, defined in terms of labour inputs. It is possible to start with a simple classification:

1. Paid labour
2. Unpaid labour
3. Do-it-yourself labour

Each of these categories may be sub-divided (e.g. paid labour may be either in the formal or in the black economy), and any particular job may involve any combination of labour inputs.

The resources required in each maintenance strategy will vary. Thus the use of paid labour depends upon the availablity of sufficient finance, but it also requires expenditure in time in finding and choosing a builder. Two additional resources that are valuable here are knowledge of the problem to be remedied and how to tackle it, and good contacts in the building services industry. In our research in Easton we found that home owners had a very poor understanding of housing defects. As already mentioned 84% had not had a structural survey of the dwelling. In addition in our analysis we discovered that when individual owners' perceptions of housing defects were compared to a surveyors assessment 81% recognised fewer

problems than the surveyor.   However, Easton is an area which has a
predominantly skilled manual employment pattern and home owners have
many contacts with people in the buiding trade.   Seventy percent of
households had used paid labour and in 23% of cases they had used a
firm in which a friend or relative was employed.   In total 75% of
households had chosen builders or contractors through some sort of
personal contact or recommendation.   In 21% of cases people had used
the informal rather than the formal economy.   We would suggest that
in areas like Easton trade contacts may compensate somewhat for lack
of knowledge and low incomes and it may well be that home owners in
areas further up-market may have more difficulty in organising paid
labour.

Unpaid labour places less emphasis on finance and more on contacts.
In this approach the home owner draws on the resources of friends,
neighbours or relatives who have expertise in particular fields of
work.   Such services may be received as a gift or may involve some
form of 'payment' which may or may not take the form of reciprocal
assistance with house maintenance.   In the Easton survey 39% of
households had used unpaid labour, particularly for improvement work
such as: rewiring, improvements to the kitchen and bathroom and
replacement of doors and windows.

Do-it-yourself maintenance again draws heavily on the time, knowledge and skills of the home owner.   In Easton 80% of households did
at least some DIY work and 45% did a considerable amount.   Generally
this involved only minor repair work though a certain amount of major
repairs and improvements were carried out to internal fixtures and
finishes.

At this point two questions arise: The first relates to the way
owners are free to choose one approach rather than another, and how
far their choices are determined by available resources.   The second
relates to how the quality and quantity of non-financial resources,
such as time, skills, knowledge and contacts, determines the
effectiveness of the way money is spent on maintaining and improving
the house.

With respect to the first question whilst some people have
sufficient resources to choose a particular maintenance strategy
(based on a personal preference or a judgement of what will deliver
the best results), others are constrained into adopting an approach
which does not reflect their preferences and may result in a lower
standard of work.   For some people this means opting for DIY, even
though they have limited time, skills and enthusiasm.   For others,
especially the elderly, it might mean that they are forced into using
(cheap) paid labour even though they cannot really afford it.

With respect to the second question it is clear that efficient
decisions about maintenance and improvement are not so much a matter
of how much money a home owner has available to spend but how their
non-financial resources enable them to spend it in a cost effective
way.   Our research shows that people with similar financial resources
and similar maintenance and improvement problems have taken very
different approaches to dealing with these problems and some have
been significantly more effective than others.   This underlines the
point that it is the non-financial resources that determine the
capacity of the owner to make efficient use of his or her financial

resources. Despite the crucial effect of these non-financial resources there has been little research into their nature.

It was argued earlier that a combination of factors had created an interest in low income inner city home ownership, and that argument still holds. However, a focus on home owners as the managers of maintenance points to the need for a wider frame of reference, embracing the whole range of housing market positions. The notion of the managerial role of home owners has a liberating effect on housing analysis because it shifts attention away from particular groups and specific areas towards a new set of questions about how home owners in general carry out their management duties. At present there is no systematic evidence available on how housing maintenance is managed by home owners as a group. It is widely assumed (especially for policy purposes) that home owners take good care of their houses, but there is a dearth of understanding of the processes involved, the resources deployed and the owners' perceptions of their role in maintenance management.

It can no longer be assumed that 'access' is the only important policy issue associated with owner occupation. Our research points up a need for a greater recognition and a clearer understanding of the problems of being an owner occupier. As the tenure is opened up to more and more people, consideration needs to be given to the sorts of policy initiatives that might be introduced in order to support and sustain owner occupation in an efficient and equitable fashion.

Conclusion

In this final section there are a number of points to be made arising from the paper's central theme of the importance of housing in use. First, we have argued that maintenance by home owners has been largely ignored by both technical and social science researchers, but that the notion of the home owner as housing manager opens up a new perspective, and highlights the need to look at maintenance management in the owner occupied sector. A whole new research agenda is established by this approach, in which some fundamental questions about home owners' decision-making processes are posed:

1. To what extent can owners recognise and diagnose disrepair and defects?
2. How do they prioritise and schedule repair, maintenance and improvement work? To what extent do they have a coherent plan?
3. Who does what and why?
   a) How dependent are owners on their own skills and labour?
   b) To what extent do they use the informal economy?
   c) When and how do owners choose to use builders and specialist contractors?
4. How much do owners spend?
   a) Do they know how much they spend each year?
   b) How do they decide to pay for work done?
5. To what extent are owners satisfied with the work that is done and is their satisfaction justified?

These and other questions require to be asked about maintenance management strategies at different levels in the housing market, and of different types of household. It may be found that resources and labour inputs mesh in different ways in different contexts, and it may be unwise to assume that increases in financial resources can compensate for decreases in other resources, and vice versa.

It seems to us that new insights into wider questions of housing policy can be gained by seeing owners as proprietors who have the authority and responsibility for making management decisions relating to the maintenance and improvement of their houses. There is a need for future research to clarify how such decisions are made and how they are constrained by a lack of financial and non-financial domestic resources.

Lastly, although this paper has concentrated on issues related to the individual's predicament as a manager of a complex commodity, it should be recognised that the wider community also has an interest in the efficiency of the decisions made in the owner occupied housing sector. In other words housing as a commodity is further complicated by the fact that it has associated with it non-proprietory as well as proprietory interests. In all sorts of ways a house can be regarded as a social good and a community asset. Society as a whole has an interest in how private houses are maintained because poor maintenance has a 'neighbourhood effect' on the value of adjacent properties. Also the next generation of householders has an interest in how the present stock is looked after. These non-proprietory interests tend to be long-term and area based, and if they predominated, they would tend to lead to a maintenance strategy which is different (possibly very different) from that which is determined by the shorter-term and more narrowly viewed interests of the owner occupiers.

References

1. The DoE (1981) English House Condition Survey. HMSO, London, estimated that expenditure by all households on maintenance and improvement during 1981 was around £6.1 billion. A later study BSA (1886) "Home Improvements". BSA Bulletin No. 48, suggested that expenditure by all households in 1985 was about £10 billion. As the majority of expenditure is made by owner occupiers rather than tenants we estimate that current expenditure by owner occupiers alone must be about £9 billion annually.
2. Ibid.
3. Bristol City Council (1984) Housing Condition Survey: Final Report
4. Holmes, R., Droop, C., and Mellor, P., (1985) A Coding System for Building Maintenance. CIOB Technical Services Paper No. 47.
5. Cmnd 9513 (1985) Home Improvement: A New Approach. HMSO, London, para 9.
6. Ibid. Part 1, Report of the Physical Condition Survey, Table 21, p 22.
7. Ibid. p 3.
8. Karn, V., Kemeny, J., and Williams, P. (1985) Home Ownership in the Inner City: Salvation or Despair? Gower, Aldershot.

9. The research is part of a larger project being undertaken within the Department of Surveying, Bristol Polytechnic, under the broad title of the Management of Property. The work is supported by funds from The National Advisory Body for Public Sector Higher Education.

PROFITS AND MAINTENANCE DECISIONS OF OWNERS WHO RENT FOR INCOME

J. A. J. MOOHAN
Department of Surveying, Trent Polytechnic

Abstract
The economic theory of property maintenance is riddled with ad hoc
and naive assumptions concerning both human behaviour and physical
deterioration. Key questions are posed concerning the economic
analysis of property maintenance, maintenance policy and practice
of owners who rent for income. A literature review includes the
analysis of maintenance technology in filtering models, the
economic life of a building, optimal control theory applied to the
landlord's investment decision, the analysis of controlled rental
markets for residential property, the extent of landlord control
over the quality of the building unit, models of the behaviour of
landlords where depreciation occurs and maintenance is possible,
and contemporary valuation practice. The focus of the paper is a
critique of the economic theory of property maintenance and in
particular the dominance of the neoclassical perfectly competitive
paradigm. In essence it challenges the assumptions of the rational
economic man, the utility maximisation hypothesis and the
reluctance to elaborate the mode of abstraction.
Key Words: Filtering, Economic life of a building, Optimal control
theory, Rent control, Economic models, Valuation practice, Utility
maximisation, Mode of abstraction.

1. Introduction

Recently it has become fashionable for academics to analyse the
economics of property maintenance, maintenance policy and
maintenance practice of owners who rent for income. However,
beneath the surface little has changed, and just as the literature
regarding issues such as residential location has been dominated by
the neoclassical perfectly competitive paradigm, it appears that
the literature on property maintenance is explicitly or implicitly
so dependent.   This is hardly surprising, but the purpose of the
paper is to argue that technique is no substitute for philosophy
and that the predictions of the academic literature are crucially
dependent on the mode of abstraction, which all too often is taken
for granted. Section 2 provides a review of the literature with a
particular focus on the behavioural and physical assumptions while

Section 3 presents a critique of the literature and its implications for maintenance policy and practice.

Historically property maintenance has been both an unfashionable element of the building industry and of peripheral interest to academics analysing the property market. However, maintenance expenditure is often considerable and Noble (1980) estimates that maintenance generally accounts for 5 to 10 per cent of annual occupancy costs, or 1 to 3 per cent of the total building replacements costs per annum for commercial and industrial organisations. It should, however, be appreciated that the annual expenditure on fuel and power would in many cases be comparable to that on maintenance. Noble (1980) comments that maintenance seems to be a relatively insignificant part of the owner's or tenant's activities and some people conclude from this that it does not need much skill to run a maintenance service and the most elementary control techniques will be adequate.

As if to rebut the implication of Noble's contention more sophisticated monitoring and control techniques have emerged. Holmes and Mellor (1985) have investigated the incidence and characteristics of maintenance expenditure on local authority housing and schools. They have extended their maintenance coding approach to all types of building in an effort to provide any local authority with a sound basis on which to allocate limited resources effectively. Whilst it is important to record and indeed applaud such developments at the practical end of the spectrum, the economic theory of property maintenance is curiously riddled with ad hoc and naive assumptions.

2. Literature Review

It is not the purpose of this review to produce a comprehensive bibliography. Rather an attempt is made to reveal the fundamental tenets of the literature. The literature on filtering (Ratcliff 1949, Lowry 1960 and Grigsby 1963) represents some of the earliest attempts to analyse the effects of age on dwellings. Filtering generally means a change in either quality of the housing service provided by a structure or the relative socioeconomic position of the occupants. Such models require the assertion that maintenance does not fully offset the effects of time. However, the analysis of maintenance technology is superficial and possible influences on landlord behaviour such as prices are denied any role in determining depreciation rates. Margolis (1981) notes how Sweeney (1974) departs from previous models of filtering by explicit reference to the effect of relative prices on the supply of and the demand for housing by quality category. Consumers maximise their own utilities through choice among categories. A supplier will maintain a structure within a given category so long as the marginal cost of doing so, plus the return to the structure when in a lower category is less than the rent in the present category. A price increase in any category will increase the amount of time for which maintenance of the unit within the category is profitable. Sweeney continues to assume that maintenance does not fully offset the effect of ageing and produces the result that in equilibrium there is filtering from higher to lower level categories.

Hall (1968) showed how time may affect the valuation of the flow of services from capital goods through wear and tear, obsolescence and the quality of the capital good as originally constructed. He maintains that the distinction between wear and tear and obsolescence is of little economic significance. Evans (1973) highlights the fact that the maintenance costs of a building rise over time, whilst rental income falls. Net rent falls more rapidly than gross rent as the age of the building increases. Beyond the point where the net rent is equal to the opportunity cost of the land, the profit maximising landlord will demolish the building and redevelop the site. Refurbishment may extend the economic life of the building but only for a finite period. There comes a time at which the building will be demolished because there is no economic or financial gain in continuing with the present use. The model is based in comparative static equilibrium analysis under the usual profit and utility maximising hypothesis.

Dildine and Massey (1974) apply optimal control theory to the landlord's investment decision. Following Lowry (1960) maintenance expenditure is divided into "normal maintenance" which just preserves the present structure quality of the unit and "under maintenance" which leads to a reduction in structure quality. This can logically be extended to the suggestion that "over maintenance" exists which improves the structure quality of the unit. Accordingly at this point the ability of the landlord's maintenance manager and the ability of the landlord and the maintenance manager to select the optimal investment becomes significant. Failure to maintain the building adequately can have several significant effects. First, the structure of the quality of the building unit can decline which will in turn affect the future potential revenue, and in the long run reduce the landlord's profits. Secondly, following Davis and Whinston (1961) if the lack of maintenance is carried out by a number of landlords acting independently but owning property in the same area, neighbourhood quality can deteriorate. Thirdly both the economic and structural life of the building unit will decline.

Frankena (1975) states that in a typical text book treatment, the effect of rent control on the price and quality of housing is analysed assuming that rent control imposes a ceiling on the rent of a dwelling unit and that the level of housing services yielded by a given dwelling unit is not variable. The latter assumption is unrealistic and such analysis is deficient because the prediction that effective rent control imposes losses on landlords and leads to excess demand for housing could be incorrect and because the analysis of the effect of rent control is not based on an explicit model of the housing market. Frankena presents a geometric model of the housing market which can be used to analyse quality adjustments and demonstrates that under effective rent control landlords could earn profits and quality adjustments could

367

eliminate excess demand. He distinguishes between the effect of rent control that imposes a ceiling on the rent per unit of a housing service and rent control which imposes a ceiling on the rent of a dwelling unit. Under both forms it is predicted that there will be a reduction in the quantity of housing services if rent control is imposed below the initial equilibrium level on previously uncontrolled housing. However the predictions regarding price per unit of housing service, excess demand, the quality of the stock, the profitability of the landlord's investment and the attainment of equilibrium are quite different and dependent on the form of rent control. Frankena's model, with quality variable, exhibits the major conceptual difference of homogeneous housing services yielded by dwelling units rather than the housing services of homogeneous dwelling units, being traded in a perfectly competitive rental market. Maclennan (1982) provides a useful summary of the model.

Ingram and Oron (1977) suggest that building services are dependent on the quality of structure services provided by the building unit, the neighbourhood quality of the unit and the accessibility of the unit. Of these only the quality of the structural services is controlled by the landlord but in certain cases, for example privately owned estates, the landlord may have a certain degree of control over neighbourhood quality. If, however, only the structure quality can be varied by the landlord, the maintenance decisions made by the landlord in each operating period will affect the stock of quality capital in the unit in the subsequent operating period. Generally the landlord's objective will be to select the level and form of maintenance expenditure which maximises his future net revenue from the dwelling unit. However, landlords do not have perfect market knowledge and will be predicting the form of maintenance which will lead to the greatest return in subsequent periods. Such maintenance decisions are made in a dynamic market.

Margolis (1981) examines the quasi-fixed factors embodied in a structure which will be allowed to diminish by a profit maximising landlord in an environment where prices are unchanging. He notes that in much of the urban literature ad hoc assumptions are made regarding ageing of structures and that there is little agreement among researchers on this subject. Margolis presents a model of landlord behaviour in which depreciation occurs but maintenance is possible. If the underlying rate of depreciation is constant and installation of replacement capital occurs with increasing marginal cost, then the optimal maintenance path converges on some positive and constant quantity of capital. Such a result conflicts with the notion of filtering of housing, which requires that houses are allowed to decline in quality with the passage of time. Contrarywise filtering is possible if there are either increasing returns to scale in the maintenance activity (marginal cost diminishes) or the underlying rate of depreciation is an increasing function of time. The maintenance issue is an economic one, not simply technological. A building left unmaintained will lose value while a structure could be maintained in original condition

368

indefinitely with sufficient expenditure. Neither extreme need be
profit maximising and so it is necessary to determine and describe
efficient behaviour.

Britton, Davies and Johnson (1981) note the common practice for
the landlord to seek to impose the duty of meeting various
expenditures on property on the tenant by means of the full
repairing and insuring lease for non residential property let to a
single tenant and through service charges for dwellings in multiple
occupation. Clearly the level of outgoings has an effect on
property dealings. The condition of repair of a property has a
significant effect on capital value while the cost of repairs
affects rental value.   The age, nature and construction of
buildings will affect the allowance to be made for repairs. They
identify traditional valuation practice in respect of immediate
repairs, annual repairs allowance, conditions of tenancy, the
possibility of extensive works of repair, maintenance or even
rebuilding and the use of a sinking fund for the reinstatement of
buildings at the end of their useful life.

A sustained period of inflation followed by deep recession in
which the demand for space has slumped has made property owners
aware of the facts that buildings do gradually wear out and
depreciate in value (Bowie 1983). The full repairing and insuring
lease may not protect the owner against depreciation, a problem
compounded by changes in economic activity in districts and in
whole regions. Physical and functional obsolescence may be
arrested or slowed down by expenditure but some depreciation is
incurable, notably the insidious process of ageing. Chartered
valuation surveyors need to be made aware of the weaknesses and
strengths of the original construction in terms of the consequences
for maintenance and avoid the simple application of x per cent as
the capitalisation rate for a building. Bowie provides a framework
in which the component parts of any building will have different
lives, some being replaced with ease, while others are more
troublesome and expensive.   The precise point in the age of a
building at which remedial action should be taken cannot be
determined in advance as no exact pre-planning is possible. Given
the lack of perfect information and foresight, to predict the lives
of buildings and to nominate terms of years for leases is not a
very practicable proposition. In this respect it is interesting to
note the greater realism amongst practising economists (valuers)
than amongst contemporary academic economists.

3. A Critique of the Economic Theory of Property Maintenance

The economic literature on property maintenance is dominated by the
neoclassifical perfectly competitive paradigm and ad hoc
assumptions regarding physical deterioration.   In essence the
theory is being considered as a blueprint of reality and the basic
premises of theory are rarely brought into question. An
understanding and evaluation of the validity and explanatory power
of economic theory should be incorporated into a general analysis

of economic methodology and ideological content (Dehesh 1984).

The assumption of rational economic man implies a decision maker who has a single profit goal, omniscient powers of perception, reasoning and computation and is blessed with perfect predictive abilities (Wolpert 1964). Allowances must be made for man's finite abilities to perceive and store information, to compute optimal solutions and to predict the outcome of future events, even if profit were his only goal. More likely his goals are multidimensional and optimisation is not a relevant criterion. The point is that rationality is a relative not an absolute term. It fluctuates around available information and value judgement. More simply real man does not behave in the same way as economic man.

The theory is based on utility maximisation subject to constraints. A long standing criticism of the utility concept is that utility is not measurable except by a crude ranking of preferences. Marginal utility can only be expressed in terms of a diminishing marginal rate of substitution (Hicks 1939). Preferences are assumed to be expressed adequately in market outcomes, but since utility is not measurable it cannot be empirically tested and does not conform to accepted positive models of scientific explanation.

Further it must not be assumed that the internal consistency of a theory is a reason for its approximation to the reality which it is supposed to represent. Internal consistency is not synonymous with realism. Using different conceptual apparatus, the same phenomena can be interpreted in different ways. The main problem lies in the process of abstraction because it has the potentiality of concealing reality by simplifying it to an extent that the cause effect relations may be misunderstood or misinterpreted. Theorists of property maintenance have been more involved in providing elegant and coherent models than in elaborating the mode of abstraction. Obtaining testable results should not be an end in itself. The question is how much they contribute to our understanding of the real world. Models are only tools of analysis, not tools of interpretation. Factual evidence cannot be used to prove a theory.

Urban property markets are characterised by different groups of people and changes in land use or the exchanges in the function of the building's services derive from the way in which these diverse groups obtain and secure that interest. There is a link between economic behaviour and social interaction in the urban scene. For example, neoclassical models fail to give adequate consideration to the structural, institutional and historical factors governing housing supply.

The filtering models imply the existence of a well defined urban social structure but maintain that the structure is spatial and manifested through the competitive workings of the housing and land markets. However there is no real attempt to articulate and conceptualise the underlying supply and demand conditions (though see Sweeney 1974). The behavioural relationships are oversimplified, as is the nature of maintenance technology.

It has been left to land economists to conceptualise market

370

conditions. Generally the approach is highly deductive, the
analysis being based on the assumption that all supply and demand
side changes or transactions are achieved instantaneously. The
urban system is always in equilibrium and no adjustment problems
are experienced. In reality there are information constraints on
property market behaviour which are assumed away as non existent.
Property markets may be segmented and subject to varying degrees of
disequilibrium. The crucial issue is whether or not equilibrium is
achievable in principle.

Maclennan (1982) notes that the theoretical analysis of rent
control is framed in the context of either perfectly competitive
markets with representative firms (landlords) or in relation to
well behaved markets with theoretically deducible demand and supply
curves. The deductive identification of the firm and industry
supply curve assumes that the market is in competitive equilibrium.
But the competitiveness and structure of the market cannot be
assumed. Maclennan argues that despite these qualifications the
private rented sector is sufficiently decentralised for actors to
compete with each other and to identify the supply curve. However,
given the possibility of complex firm objectives, a less precise
relationship may pertain and the supply curve may be both unstable
and only deducible ex post.

Frankena (1975) notes certain weaknesses in his own model, in
particular the time it takes for a firm to adjust to a new short
run equilibrium position, tenant expenditure to increase the flow
of housing services, indivisibilities in the supply of housing
service and non-price controls. He does show how different sets of
assumptions lead to different predictions concerning rent control.
Similarly Margolis (1981) shows how different assumptions regarding
the rate of depreciation and replacement capital cost conditions
affect the possibility of filtering. He also notes the
significance of the assumptions that landlords adopt maximising
behaviour and that capital is divisible and replaceable in small
bits at any time. Bowie (1983) has identified clearly the naivety
of the latter assumption in practice.

4. Conclusion

The purpose of this paper has been to consider the general
direction of the economic theory of property maintenance. It is
critical of economists' reluctance to consider the mode of
abstraction. The literature is dominated by the neoclassical
perfectly competitive paradigm and ad hoc assumptions regarding
physical deterioration. It is traditional to argue that the
unreality of assumptions is irrelevant and in particular that as
resources are limited non-maximising behaviour will be penalised,
cannot stay for long and that eventually only approximate
maximisers will survive. Some would argue that the unreality of
the assumptions is trivial and that what matters is whether the

implications of the theory can be subject to scientific test
because in the absence of a testable theory, there is simply no
objective measure of the power of argument. But scientific testing
is not an end in itself and the acid test is how much theory
contributes to our understanding of the real world.

References

Bowie, N. (1983) The depreciation of buildings. J. of Valuation, 2,
    1, 5-13.
Britton, W., Davies K. and Johnson, T. (1980) Modern Methods of
    Valuation, Estates Gazette, London, 58-61.
Davis, D.A. and Whinston, A.B. (1961) The economics of urban
    renewal, Law and Contemporary Problems, 26.
Dehesh, A. (1984) Technique is not a substitute for philosophy,
    staff seminar paper, Department of Urban and Regional Studies,
    Sheffield City Polytechnic.
Dildine, L.L., and Massey, F.A. (1974) Dynamic model of private
    incentives to housing maintenance, Southern Economic Journal,
    40, 631-39.
Evans, A.W. (1973) The Economics of Residential Location,
    Macmillan, London, 97-114.
Frankena, M. (1975) Alternative models of rent control, Urban
    Studies, 12, 303-308.
Grigsby, W.G. (1963) Housing Markets and Public Policy, University
    Pennsylvania Press, Philadelphia.
Hall, R.E. (1968) Technical change and capital from the point of
    view of the dual, Review of Economic Studies, 35, 35-46.
Hicks, J.R. (1939) Value and Capital, The Clarendon Press, Oxford.
Holmes, R. and Mellor, P. (1985) Maintenance coding and monitoring:
    two case studies, Technical Information Service, The Chartered
    Institute of Building.
Ingram, G.K., and Oron, Y. (1977) The production of housing
    services from existing dwelling units, in, Residential Location
    and Housing Markets (ed. Ingram G.K.) Ballinger and National
    Bureau of Economic Research, Cambridge, Mass.
Lowry, I. (1960) Land Economics, 35, 362-370.
Maclennan, D. (1982) Housing Economics: An Applied Approach,
    Longman, London and New York, 204-237.
Margolis, S. (1981) Depreciation and maintenance of houses, Land
    Economics, 57, 1, 91-105.
Noble, V. (1980) The value of building maintenance, The Chartered
    Institute of Building Maintenance Information Service
Ratcliff, R.V. (1949) Urban Land Economics, McGraw Hill Book Co.,
    New York.
Sweeney, J.L. (1974a), Quality, commodity hierarchies and housing
    markets, Econometrica, 42, 147-167.
Sweeney, J.L. (1974b), A commodity hierarchy model of the rental
    housing market, Journal of Urban Economics 2, 288-323.
Wolpert, J. (1964) The decision process in spatial context, Annals
    of the Association of American Geographers, 54, 4, 537-558.

THE ECONOMIC SIGNIFICANCE OF BUILDING MAINTENANCE

LINDSAY PULLEN
Building Maintenance Cost Information Service

In 1972 the DOE published a report reviewing the problems involved in maintenance of buildings, made recommendations, identified priorities for research and development and made proposals for future studies.

A notable feature of the 1972 report was the assessment of the economic significance of Building Maintenance. One particular feature of this chapter was the estimate of annual expenditure on repair and maintenance as the proportion of the gross replacement cost of the building stock. The committee observed that the level of R + M expenditure was in all probability insufficient to prevent a gradual deterioration in the quality of the building stock. BMCIS has, as far as possible used the same calculation methods to calculate the level of repair and maintenance in the last decade.

Buildings and Building Maintenance in the Economy

Where BMCIS has updated figures from the original DOE report, then the text of the paragraphs follows that of the original report.

Buildings and other construction work forms over two-thirds of the nation's capital stock valued in terms of current gross replacement costs. The committee noted "They provide living and working facilities and are a major factor of production". Viewed in these terms it is difficult to understand why there is still a reluctance to recognise the importance of maintenance.

In our update of the economic significance, BMCIS has chosen 1980 figures because they are the most recent where all input figures can be derived. The output of the construction industry in 1980, including that of directly employed labour in the public sector was £22052 million of which some £8997 million (41%) was for repair, maintenance and minor improvement work, and in 1985 R + M was £12,930m, (or 46%). This compares with 28% identified by the 1972 committee. Figures for unrecorded maintenance and associated work using their own direct labour (est. £1368 million) and by house occupants providing their own labour free (£1591 million) has been estimated to bring the total cost of maintenance to £11956 million at 1980 prices. This represents an annual expenditure of only about 1.6% - down on the 1.8% identified for 1969 by the committee and represented the highest level for the years 1974 - 84. In 1977 it slumped to a low of 1.2% (Table 1).

Table 1

	1980	1981	1982	1983	1984
CONSTRUCTION OUTPUT (1980 prices) £ million (1)	22052	19947	20260	21101	21842
REPAIR AND MAINTENANCE OUTPUT (1980 prices £ million (1)	8997	8189	8069	8413	8693
D.I.Y. EXPENDITURE ON REPAIR AND MAINTENANCE (1980 prices) (2)	1591	1604	1604	1662	1775
D.L.O. PRIVATE SECTOR (Guestimate) (3)	1368	1246	1227	1280	1322
TOTAL R & M £ million (1980 prices)	11956	11039	10900	11355	11790
TOTAL REPLACEMENT VALUE OF BUILDING STOCK (1980 prices) £ billion (4)	763.1	777.3	792.9	809.3	827.0
REPAIR AND MAINTENANCE AS A PERCENTAGE OF BUILDING STOCK	1.6%	1.4%	1.4%	1.4%	1.4%

Notes   1. Housing and Construction Statistics, Department of the
            Environment.
         2. Family Expenditure Survey 1984, Department of Employment
         3. Estimate Based on Building Maintenance Statistics,
            R & D Paper 1970 (Directorate General of Research &
            Development).
         4. National Income and Expenditure. HMSO.
         5. Excludes cleaning.

Estimated expenditure in 1980 on the maintenance of civil engineering works in roads, railways and other public utilities was about £1514 million and this has been excluded from this review. The cleaning of buildings was however regarded by the committee as within the scope of their terms of reference. BMCIS has derived the estimated cost of cleaning from its own data as £2468 million at 1980 prices. Thus the total cost of the maintenance and cleaning of buildings, including minor improvements but excluding energy and other operating costs can be estimated as running at an annual rate at 1980 prices in excess of £14,400 million.

This scale of expenditure, the committee noted, is, "the result of a great number of individual decisions and it is not known whether it represents an effective use of resources. Certainly maintenance expenditure can, often too easily, be postponed without immediate loss or harm, but it can also prevent unnecessary deterioration and/or depreciation. Expenditure on maintenance to standards beyond those dictated by relevant technical and economic considerations may be wasteful, though high standards can have a general beneficial influence on attitudes and may also prolong the lives of some buildings on environmental grounds".

"It is clearly important that a correct balance for the individual unit and the economy in general is struck between expenditure on new works and that on maintenance, and that decisions are based on the appropriate economic and other relevant criteria. It seems likely that in many cases this correct balance is not struck and that inadequately based decisions are made".

The committee saw the problem at three levels. Strategic decisions as between investment in new buildings or in renovation and maintenance have to be made taking into account the condition of the stock. Decisions at the design and construction stages of building also affect the scale and range of maintenance expenditure. Thirdly, the economy and effectiveness with which maintenance operations are performed affects the benefits for the economy. How these three levels of decision can be better informed is discussed later.

The Building Stock

The Committee went on to say,

"Maintenance expenditure should reflect the physical condition and composition of the building stock. The different proportions of maintenance expenditure on dwellings in the private and public sectors as against the stock value may indicate that the former are maintained to a higher standard than the latter, and/or that maintenance in the public sector is more efficient because of economies of scale or because of different characteristics of the stock". Figure 2 reveals some of the pattern of maintenance in 1980.

375

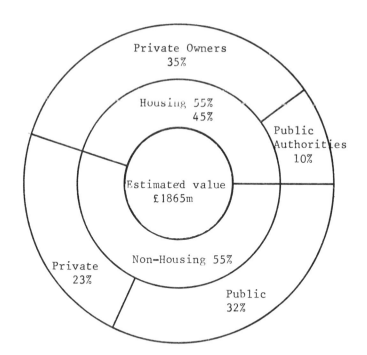

The pattern of maintenance 1969

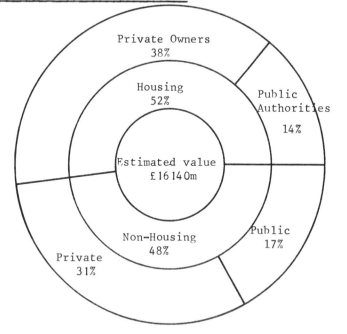

The pattern of maintenance 1984

Figure 2

Unfortunately information about the size, composition and physical condition of the building stock is still as limited as it was in 1969. More information is available about the housing element of the stock and Figure 3 summarises some of the results of the English House Condition Survey. Of the total housing stock of 18.1 million dwellings at that time in England 11.1% were in need of expenditure of over £7000 and 24% were in need of expenditure of over £2500. One in ten dwellings was classified as unfit for use (one in nine in 1967) and of the remainder about one in twenty lack one or more of the basic amenities - internal W.C., fixed bath, sink, washbasin and hot and cold water at three points (compared with 1 in 4 in 1967). The results of two surveys by the Association of Metropolitan Authorities (AMA) and the DOE show the backlog of rehabilitation, improvement and repair of the public sector stock in 1985 to £19 billion. The backlog to both private and public sectors is estimated by the AMA to be £46.5 billion. Housing repair and maintenance arrears are therefore about 7 times the volume of work actually carried out in 1985. (Compared to 8-9 times in a survey by the National Institute of Economic and Social Research carried out in the sixties). These estimates presumably reflect the age distribution of the nation's housing stock; nearly one in three were built before 1919 and one in two before 1945.

The Committee were concerned at the arrears of maintenance in other sectors other than housing despite its probable lower age. A survey of the non-housing stock would possibly reveal more of a maintenance problem even more perhaps than worried the Committee in 1972. The Committee coinsidered "simple surveys of the number, age, condition and estimated maintenance and repair costs of specific building types, such as factories and offices, would better inform the Government and industry of the scale and significance of the maintenance and replacement requirements".

NEDO in their report into investment in the public sector infrastructure studied six main categories

- Roads and bridges
- Water supplies and sewerage
- Public sector housing
- School buildings
- Health service properties
- Central government's civil estate (PSA)

NEDO concluded that in many areas the present criteria, systems and levels of resource allocation had led "to backlogs of maintenance, repair and renewal because they do not allow spending decisions to be based on value for money". They note that the government estimated backlog for maintenance in hospitals was £2 billion, that maintenance expenditure in schools fell short by as much as 40%, that public sector housing defects backlog estimated by the AMA was £5 billion (now revised to £19 billion), they also note that "the consequences of delaying required maintenance work can be well illustrated by roads", delayed surface dressing can lead to structural deficiencies and resurfacing at a cost of ten times the delayed dressing.

The condition of the housing stock

England and Wales

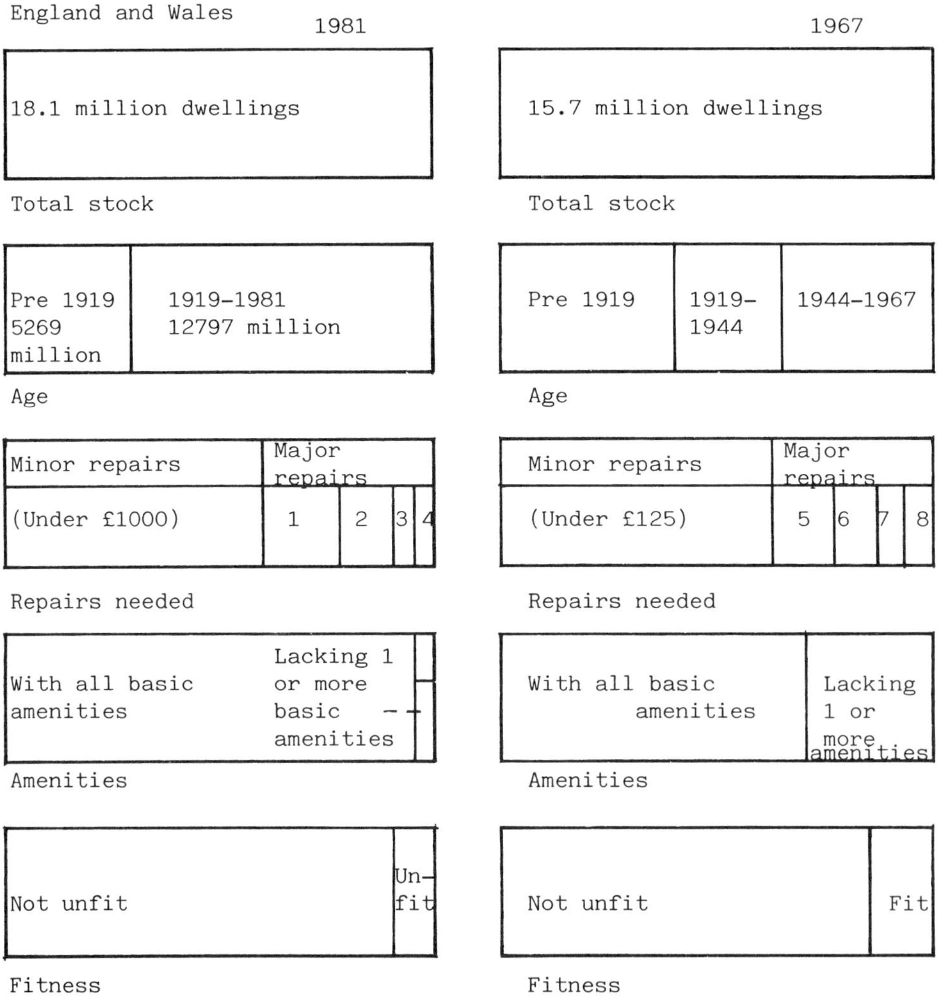

1981	1967
18.1 million dwellings	15.7 million dwellings

Total stock   Total stock

Pre 1919 5269 million	1919–1981 12797 million

Age

Pre 1919	1919–1944	1944–1967

Age

Minor repairs (Under £1000)	Major repairs 1	2	3	4

Repairs needed

Minor repairs (Under £125)	Major repairs 5	6	7	8

Repairs needed

With all basic amenities	Lacking 1 or more basic amenities

Amenities

With all basic amenities	Lacking 1 or more amenities

Amenities

Not unfit	Un-fit

Fitness

Not unfit	Fit

Fitness

Figure 3

1.	1000–2499	5.	£125–£249
2.	2500–4499	6.	£250–£499
3.	1500–6999	7.	£500–£999
4.	Over 7000	8.	£1000 and over.

It must be accepted that more rather than less maintenance work is necessary if the value and amenity of the nation's building stock is to be kept at present levels.

The 1972 report pointed to legal and institutional factors which might affect the flow of resources into maintenance work. For example lack of investment in the maintenance of some elements of private housing for rent is often attributed to the effect of rent control legislation. The incidence of taxation is alleged further to discourage necessary expenditure on maintenance, and improvements in property attract increases in rateable value and rate payments. In addition different systems of tenure may influence standards of building maintenance. These factors are examined later in this Report.

The Maintenance Industry

Firms which carry out maintenance work are only part of the construction industry, many of them carrying out new work. In addition maintenance work carried out by direct labour of firms and organisations in other industries, and by householders themselves, is not formally included or recorded as part of the construction. The following paragraphs relate to the recorded statistics of the construction industry.

Over recent years about 40% of contractors' output has consistently been attributed to repairs and maintenance compared with one-fifth in the 1972 report. The committee found maintenance makes special demands on firms with specialist skills, which are responsible for about half of maintenance work but only about a quarter of new work.

Repair and maintenance expenditure has risen by 34% in real terms in the decade 1975 - 1985 but although the overall construction workload remained fairly constant - in 1985 output was £22,120 million compared with £22,054 million in 1975 at constant 1980 prices - there has been a significant shift in the construction market sectors. The increase in repair and maintenance has been counterbalanced by the decline by 15% of new work, notably public construction which has dropped by one-fifth. By far the hardest hit sector is public housing, down by 72%, private sector housing has remained much the same but overall repair and maintenance for all types of housing has risen by 46%.

This shift in emphasis has also affected the structure of the industry with larger firms shedding staff and increasing productivity. Between 1975 and 1984 the number of firms with between one and seven employees has rocketed by 128% but all other firms have decreased in number.

The increase in repair and maintenance works in favour of the smaller sized firm. Despite the workload being constant in monetary terms the workforce has dropped from 1.27 million in June 1975 to 0.95 million in June 1985. 379

Number of private contractors
(Source: DoE census)

Size of firm	1975	1984	% change	% market share 75	% market share 84
1	28,131	71,386	+154	1	6
2-7	39,079	81,614	+109	8	19
8-24	14,183	12,163	-14	13	16
25-59	4,108	3,133	-24	12	13
60-114	1,283	890	-31	9	8
115-299	801	555	-31	13	11
300-599	234	134	-38	11	7
600-1,199	127	74	-42	11	7
1,200 & over	82	40	-51	22	13

The Committee predicted that an increase in demand for maintenance might affect the operations of the specialist trades and smaller firms. Quite correctly the committee suggested that an increase in maintenance work would lead to small firms predominating because of the ease with which one-man firms and small businesses can enter the industry.

Maintenance and the Building Owner

The Committee noted with regret that many building owners, notably in industry and commerce were unaware of the cost of maintaining their properties. Although some progress has been made since 1972, the lack of information given by subscribers to BMCIS would indicate that this is still true. What little information exists is still kept by building owners and that if the information is ad-hoc rather than systematic. The 1972 committee observed that on industrial or commercial firm's maintenance, policies ought to be determined in relation to programmes for new building. Their ideal of a building owner having a co-ordinated building strategy to co-ordinate and integrate long term programmes for both new work and maintenance remains largely unrealised.

The committee advocated that careful consideration should be given to the potential maintenance cost of a building being designed, purchased or rented. The RICS has continued to endorse this view and published in October 1986 "A Guide To Life Cycle Costing for Construction" as a follow-on to the report "Life Cycle Costing for Construction" published in 1983.

The endorsements of the R.I.C.S. for Life Cycle Costing will encourage the supply of information on operating and maintenance costs of buildings and building types but BMCIS' view is that there is still too little data. Further backing is available from the new B.S. 8210 which aims to provide guidance on a "systematic approach to the management of building maintenance in the U.K. which can be applied to all types of building". It:

o   Stresses the many advantages, including economy, which can result from a programme of regular and planned maintenance of a building and its services.

o   Provides a checklist of types of construction, materials and components commonly encountered.

o   Considers how external and internal environments together with the type and intensity of use, will have a bearing on the frequency of inspection and maintenance needed.

o   Shows the importance of up to date building fabric and engineering services records, and makes recommendations as to their content, preparation and use.

o   Considers the advantages of maintenance guides for individual buildings.

o   Makes recommendations for the frequency of types of inspection, reports, planning the necessary maintenance work and making arrangements to carry out the work.

o   Discussed health and safety requirements applicable to inspection and maintenance work, including the provision of safe access facilities.

Do Buildings Need To Last?

The notion that buildings would be constructed for a pre-determined life span and the concept of maintenance free short life buildings were considered by the committee. They concluded that, although a series of short life buildings may be cheaper than an equivalent long life building for the same total life span and that short life buildings have the advantage of frequently revised design briefs, the technique would only be possibly suitable for certain industrial buildings. Rapidly changing technological needs may indicate that the committee's view is now dated and the idea of short life-span buildings may be usefully re-examined.

381

Conclusions

The 1972 committee's enquiries showed building maintenance to be consuming a very substantial part of the output of the economy which was well justified. Nevertheless they felt there was evidence that neglect of the building stock had left the nation with a pressing need for remedial measures. The numerous recent reports from the Audit Commission, the Association of Metropolitan Authorities, the House Condition Surveys, NEDO's "Ways to Better Housing", the National Federation of Housing Associations and the Church of England have shown an increasing concern about the state of maintenance in the U.K. and particularly with regard to housing.

Recommended also was that the building owner should make a serious review of the current state of his building stock and his level of expenditure. Condition appraisals and maintenance audits have to become a little more common, but a great deal or work remains to be done.

The lack of cleaning statistics was identified and that more appropriate information should be made available. BMCIS has made some progress through its Property Occupancy Costs and its Average Occupancy Costs data supplied by subscribers.

MANAGEMENT OF BUILT ASSETS - VALUE FOR MONEY

V. SAHAI
Regional Architect, South Western Regional Health Authority,
Bristol (U.K.)

Abstract
In order to obtain 'Value for Money', maintenance must be seen in
the overall context of Estate Management. It must relate not only
to the condition of a property but almost more importantly to its
function, occupancy, location and several other factors. There
cannot be absolute standards for maintenance; these are decided
upon by users. For this reason owners of large property holdings,
especially public authorities, need to involve users in property
management. The National Health Service has developed multi-
disciplinary training modules titled "Mereworth", with a view to
making the best use of its estate resources. In order to achieve
this, the information collected must be manageable and capable of
manipulation in a creative manner.
Key words: Property Appraisal, Condition Survey, Estate Data,
'Mereworth', Training, Notional Rent.

This paper attempts to put into context the management of maintenance of built assets. Maintenance is a subject with many facets as
is obvious from the vast range of papers at this conference. It is
therefore necessary to focus on the prime issue - which I would
submit is 'Value for money'. A lot has been said about data bases
for managing maintenance. However, as soon as one poses the
question of value for money, one cannot help asking as to how one
might set about establishing whether an investment in maintenance
represents good value. What are data bases for? Or questions such
as the depth to which condition surveys should be undertaken, and
a great many others.
   Here I should make the qualification that I am posing these
questions with reference to organisations with large property holdings. An individual owning a building or two, or even a handful of
properties, can make ad hoc decisions; he doesn't need a sophisticated methodology to assist him in decision making. However, it does
no harm to put oneself in his position and see how he might reach
decisions in the context of a small property holding. His decisions
are likely to be based upon:

(1) What is the property used for; is it the house he lives in or is it one that he lets out to students? i.e. function.

(2) Is the property used all the year round (or at all times) or only for a part of the time? for example, it may be his holiday home, i.e. utilisation/occupancy.

(3) Where is the property located; is it in a posh neighbourhood or in a run down area? i.e. location.

(4) Is the property safe or does it constitute a hazard? i.e. condition/safety.

(5) (a) Does the investment in maintenance represent an economic pay back period? e.g. re-painting timber windows or letting them rot away.

   (b) Would the property after investment be worth more than its present value plus the money spent? i.e. economics.

These criteria are not isolated or compartmentalised considerations, but interact one with the other and therefore must be viewed as a whole e.g. economic considerations may be sacrificed to location if the owner doesn't want to move, because his children are still at school. Furthermore, condition is not something with merely physical attributes; it must be related to people - the use to which a building or part thereof is put (e.g. is the space in question a director's suite, or a cleaner's room). For this reason there are no absolute standards for maintenance, because it is people who determine standards. It is therefore necessary to integrate information about condition with information about the use.

One method which has been used in the National Health Service (Training document - "Mereworth III" published by Department of Health and Social Security in association with the NHS and Leicester Polytechnic) for integrating the various types of information about a building before deciding how much, if any, money should be spent on maintenance, is shown in the Table I titled Property Appraisal Summary. It displays in a very simple and easily intelligible format the factors to which reference has been made earlier, as listed below:

Property Appraisal Factors (data bases for management of properties):

(a) function
(b) percentage utilisation
(c) suitability for purpose
(d) location
(e) condition
(f) energy efficiency
(g) fire/safety risk

384

Table I. Property Appraisal Summary chart

Title of property ....

Location ....

Block Ref. No.		Facility (function)		
Area (m²)	Utilisation (percentage)	Energy	Fire/Safety	Condition

Comments

Average Remaining Life	Total to upgrade to Condition 'B' £000s ....

Totals

Functional suitability:
A Ideal, 'user' satisfied
B Acceptable without structural change
C Tolerable with minor change
D Tolerable only with major change
X(suffix) Replacement is only option, impossible to improve

Utilisation:
1 Empty or grossly underused
2 Underused
3 Adequate
4 Overcrowded/overused

Energy:
A Ideal
B Adequate
C Does not meet Building Regulations
D Major change required
X(suffix) ˋReplacement is only option, impossible to improve

Fire/Safety:
A Meets current Building Regulations
B Local Brigade standards
C Minor changes required
D Dangerous high risk

Condition:
A   As new
B   Adequate
C   Minor change required
D   Major change required
X(suffix)   Replacement is only option, impossible to improve.

In order to minimise subjective judgements with regard to the
condition of the Estate, due allowance has to be made for the
differential lifespans of the elements that make up a building.
This is illustrated in Table II titled Condition Survey/Costs to
Repair.

Table II.   Condition Survey/Costs

Hospital ....   Total Cost to bring
                              to Condition B   £...........

Site plan ref:			Portion	

Gross volume (M^3)
Care group reference
Construction/roof type
Building age
No. of storeys

Condition Survey	1 Condition	2 Cost to Repair	3 Remaining Life	4 Cost to Upgrade
Structure				
External fabric				
Roof				
Internal fabric				
Internal fixtures & fittings				
Fire precautions standards				
Electric installation				
Heating system				
Steam system				
Ventilation system & air conditioning				
Hot & cold and mains water				
Communications systems				
Piped medical gases				
Lifts				
Boiler/calorifier plant				
Drainage				
Thermal performance				
External works and grounds				
Totals				

1 Condition defined above
2 Cost to repair = cost in £'000s for urgent work to ensure
   remaining life (col. 3)
3 Remaining life (after repair) before upgrading (col. 4)
4 Cost to bring to condition B

Condition category:
A As new
B Minor deterioration
C Major improvement required
D Unusable/unsafe

Remaining life:
Bldg   Eng
60+   20+   a
20-60   6-20   b
3-20   1-6   c
0-3   0-1   d

   One factor which cannot be covered in simple forms such as those
illustrated is the economic factor which is fundamental to the
concept of Value for Money.   This is the consideration whether a
property is worth upgrading at all. A property may not be worth
maintaining; it may be worth letting it run down because of the
developmental potential of the site. This is after all what often
causes the problem of run down inner city areas. That is a vast and
complex subject in its own right and I do not propose to dwell upon
it, but mention it in passing because it has a bearing upon decisions
relating to maintenance.   The land upon which a property stands may
be worth a great deal more because of its location than the property
after upgrading. These considerations are part and parcel of the
concept of Value for Money. The answers to these questions in turn
raise social considerations which determine land values. A manager
of maintenance must be mindful of these factors and cannot afford to
take the narrow view of condition and safety only.
   The issue of the value of property is further complicated by the
fact that the sale value of a property may be different from its
replacement value. This is of particular importance for properties
in public ownership. For historical reasons, it is often the case
that a fair proportion of publicly owned building stock is situated
in wrong places. This is because of movements in populations,
changes in patterns of industry and commercial practices, and many
other factors which result in properties being mislocated in terms
of populations that they serve or are a service to. In those
instances it would be better to move out of certain districts and
explore the differential in land values between one part of town and
another.
   In public bodies there is also the conflict between the standards
of maintenance which the users expect and that which the owning
authority can afford. As an instance, a school head or librarian
may expect better standards for the buildings they use than that
which the local authority can afford. In such situations, the

concept of 'Notional Rent' may be found to be a useful one. Basically this means that there will be a sum included in the school or library budget as an Estates budget. The Head or the Librarian would pay a rent for the building. Under these circumstances, if the properties are not maintained to a previously agreed standard, the Head or the Librarian would no doubt negotiate a reduction. It gives the user a choice in standards and removes a lot of hassle and dissatisfaction. Under such arrangements, one would be paying only for what each one is getting.

From what I have said, maintenance will have been seen to be a subject of much wider interest than for just the technical professions and builders. The user plays an important role and may need certain appreciation of technical factors. In the National Health Service, training modules titled "Mereworth" have been developed. These involve not only the technical professionals, but also doctors, nurses, accountants, administrators and others. Jointly, they look at ways in which best value for money may be obtained from the National Health Service Estate. In so doing the Estate Data referred to earlier is seen in the context of the opportunity costs of a property holding in relation to the future needs of the Health Service. The total picture required for planning purposes is grouped under the following headings:

1. Estate Catalogue (title deeds, ownership rights etc.)
2. Estate Data Bases (condition, suitability etc.)
3. Estate Operational Costs (running costs, outstanding maintenance costs etc.)
4. District Strategic Plan (ways of meeting the future needs of population to be served)
5. Stock Valuation and Sale Potential (replacement costs, identifying surplus or mislocated stock)

Information collection so often becomes an end in its own right and all too frequently one finds oneself in the position of saying:

"the information we have we do not want
 the information we want we do not need
 the information we need we do not have".

For this reason the Mereworth course lays special emphasis on the following criteria:

(a) all the information will have been analysed and summarised in ways which pick out and highlight key issues, not just a mass of raw data;
(b) although comprehensive, it is not so bulky nor expensive to produce that it is restricted to a favoured few;
(c) data can be easily manipulated and updated.

Management of the Maintenance of Built Assets will thus have been seen in the context of:

(a)   the users
(b)   the function, and
(c)   the location

It is the integration of these factors with the Condition Survey
which will provide the owner with Value for Money.

PRESERVING THE ASSETS

BRIAN WHITEHOUSE
Department of Education & Science
Architects & Buildings Branch

Abstract
Maintenance expenditure in educational building is rising per capita in real terms. The factors at play are falling rolls in schools and an underlying need for greater resources per unit area. School rolls will reach a low point in the early 1990's after which a slow rise will occur. The need for greater resources per unit area is due to the bulge in educational building activity in the 1970's, the buildings in question now reaching their first period of major cyclical renewal. Actual resources devoted to maintenance and renewal have been rising significantly for a number of years but the rising trend must continue in order to eliminate a backlog of work and to allow the demand bulge to pass through. The providers of resources will need to be convinced that an unecessary surplus of buildings is not being maintained and that the management of maintenance programmes is efficient and well planned. Practitioners need also to understand the very different chacteristics of different elements, to consider energy conservation at the same time and to develop sound methods of economic appraisal for decisions and priorities.

Introduction

This account is about the educational building stock, excluding universities. It begins by describing the character of this stock, how much it costs to maintain, its current condition and how demographic trends and the needs of the education service affect the amount of buildings needed.

It goes on to describe the advice the DES has issued on the management of the assets required for the future and ends with technical considerations of different elements,the link between building maintenance and energy conservation and the use of techniques to arrive at good economic decisions.

Most of the data quoted is public knowledge but since this is scattered amongst different sources,it is felt valuable to bring it all together into the context of this topic.

Some information given is the author's broad assessment, given to illustrate the size and nature of particular issues. This information and the views expressed must be regarded as personal and not the official view of the DES or of its ministers.
Key words: Peak population, Surplus, Resourcing, Adequacy, Characteristics, Management, Energy, Economics.

Size and age of building stock

The peak population in maintained primary schools was 4. 9 million pupils in 1973 and 3. 9 million in secondary schools, reached in 1978, making nearly 9 millions in all. School provision was made to meet these numbers and since the population in 1985 was about 7 millions, it can be seen that unless something were done, about 2 million surplus places would exist today costing many millions to maintain.

Programmes were mounted to reduce this surplus and to date almost one million places have been removed, either by closure or alternative use. But secondary school rolls will continue to fall until about 1991 and more surplus needs to be removed.

The building stock existing in 1985 totalled about 54 million square metres of schools and 12 million square metres of further and higher education establishments. Replacement value of this built provision would be about £25 billions, excluding land, fees, furniture and equipment. The costs of repairs and maintenance to these buildings, based upon 1984/1985 actual expenditure, was about £425 millions at current prices plus about £70 millions in capital expenditure on major repairs making £500 millions in all.

The above estimates of the size of the building stock are based upon the amount existing at the dates when peak pupil numbers applied. The Study of School Building 1977 measured the extent at that time with a 10% sample survey.These data, and other derived data, are probably the lowest estimates. More recent data from various samples of areas per pupil currently existing suggest this and an estimate of the upper bound can be taken as 20% higher.

ESTIMATES OF SIZE, VALUE & RESOURCE COSTS
SCHOOLS, FURTHER EDUCATION, 1985

	Lower bound	Upper bound	Best estimate
Floor areas ($m^2 x 10^6$)	66	79	73
Replacement value($£ x 10^9$)	25	30	28
Repairs & maintenance, resource input (recurrent & capital) 84 / 85 ($£ x 10^6$)	475	525	500
Resource input of replacement value (%)	1.6	2.1	1.8
Resource input per unit floor area ($£ x m^{-2}$)	6.0	8.0	6.8

Adequacy of current resourcing

How adequate is the current level of resourcing ? Data from the annual reports of the Society of Chief Architects in Local Government (SCALA) sets out the following data on the relationship between the committed funding and the assessed needs.

FIGURE 1

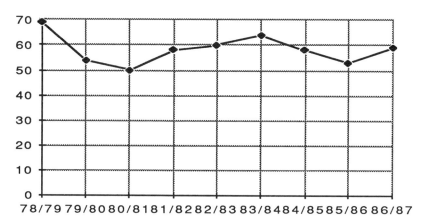

% Actual spend of assessed need

The answer seems to be that it is not and this analysis is supported by the assessments of Her Majesty's Inspectorate that comments on the conditions in which education is practised and of course by the population at large that sees and experiences the particular conditions from an individual viewpoint.

A deeper understanding of the shortfall of investment in maintenance and repair is however necessary before any view can be taken of its consequences and in establishing the best management policies to be operated within available resources.

Characteristics of current resourcing

Day-to-day maintenance, that is work of an emergency or unpredictable nature, (reactive therefore) currently accounts for c.47% of current spending. This level has varied over the years from between 43% and 54% and is obviously conditioned by the adequacy of the budgets of the time. Increasing the level of spending to the desirable level would not affect the amount of day-to day work except for plannable items which might have degraded into day -to -day due to financial pressures.

An analysis of priorities reveals that 18% or so of committed spend is for items which can be deferred without effect on either health and safety, keeping schools in operation or on the cost effectiveness of carrying out work at the right time. Therefore only a third of current spending relates to work which is both planned and of a priority to require prompt action. The shortfall below desirable levels, shown in figure 1 above, will be noted as relatively constant over the 9 years of data. Over the same period actual expenditure has risen in real terms;

FIGURE 2

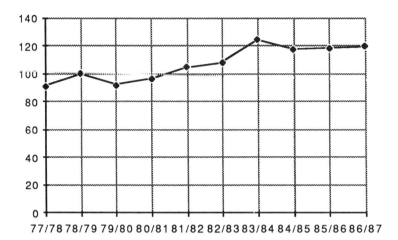

Actual expenditure, real terms (78/79 =100)

Arguably, therefore, the following conclusions might be drawn,

Spending in real terms has increased significantly.
Planned work has risen accordingly.
Shortfall below perceived requirements has remained relatively constant.
Overall condition of stock, although not satisfactory, is probably not
progressively deteriorating
Further increases in real spending required merely to maintain overall condition.
Additional resources required to attain acceptable condition.

More resources ?

Why have greater resources been required, why must further real increases be made
and when will some equilibrium be reached ?
   It has been indicated that peak pupil rolls occured in the 1970's and consequently
the provision of buildings was at the highest levels just before. This high volume
reaches its period of maximum maintenance need at 20 years or so. Changes in
specification have also occured implying shorter renewal cycles.

Roofs
Flat roof construction using built-up felt on a variety of substrates was the
dominant feature in the 1960's and 1970's. Some of these roofs failed very
quickly, due either to unsuitable substrates or to poor workmanship, and the
remainder have required or will require renewal before their expected life. The
present substantial proportion of planned spending will continue probably well into
the 1990's when a combination of dealing with the remainder from this period and
the greater durability of present finishes should show some fall from present levels.

Walls, Windows

The use of poor quality timber combined with some poor design detailing has led to similar trends as roofs but because remedial action is a little less imperative progress has been slower. Much of the backlog of plannable work is probably of this category.

Services

Heating systems using fan assisted air distribution were in vogue in the same period. This has resulted not only in high maintenance costs but also in high running costs. Many of these systems require replacement but under current constraints are being repaired at high cost. Boilers, although of shorter life are cheaper in real terms. Electrical wiring is more durable than its predecessor.

Floor finishes

Floor finishes in post-1950 schools have become less long-lived. Little replacement is presently being undertaken except on health and safety grounds.

Towards a policy

Summarising the broad analysis of the present situation and its dynamic features described above leads to the following main policy requirements.....

The amount of building stock maintained must be no more than that reasonably required to provide an education service suited to current and planned needs. (It is important to note that not only are resources for maintenance involved but the costs of cleaning, heating, lighting, rates etc.)

The management of the maintenance of the required stock should be well planned and efficient.

These two axioms are critical in convincing society that additional resources really are necessary and that existing resources are not being wasted.

Management issues

Design Note 40, Needs and Priorities, published by DES, makes the following principal recommendations relating to management practices.....
Systematic, uniform and objective methods should be adopted for assessing maintenance needs and determining priorities, related to the ascertained condition of an authority's buildings and their individual elements.
Efficient maintenance management requires the preparation and upkeep of accurate property records and related information. These data should be centrally held and readily accessible - requirements which clearly point to computerisation. (A&B Paper 10 deals with property information in greater detail).

A rolling programme approach to planned maintenance operations based on early identification of needs is desirable. Wherever possible the planned element of maintenance budgets should be protected. The aim should be for something like two-thirds of the total budget to be devoted to properly programmed work.

The condition of all properties should be inspected on a regular basis (at least annually). In addition a fuller inspection should be undertaken at longer intervals (eg five yearly) to identify any less obvious but potentially serious faults affecting structural elements.

Standardised systems of assessment should be introduced incorporating grades of condition for each element; these should be carefully defined to ensure consistency of marking and preferably numerically based for ease of storage and manipulation on a computer. Systems may be started in a comparatively basic form; enhancement can follow gradually with the accumulation of information and experience.

Priorities for planned maintenance are best determined as a second stage operation, following the assessment of property condition. It is recommended that a standardised definition of priority gradings should be .... Data from the centrally held information base should be drawn upon to support and confirm final priority decisions.

Further research is needed into the life cycle chacteristics and associated maintenance and repair costs of major building elements and equipment. Useful management information may be derived from the analysis of past maintenance expenditure and costed lists of full needs. Such analyses should become part of a comprehensive property information base.

Maintenance staffing levels should be related to the building stock and its needs, rather than to the level of the budget. The increasing use of computer aids will enable manpower resources to be re-deployed more productively throughout the maintenance operation.

The inclusion of costed lists of full needs in reports to committees responsible for budgeting for building maintenance serves to draw attention to the consequences of significant and repeated under-funding.

Energy conservation

There is obviously a strong link between energy conservation work in existing buildings and maintenance and repair, needed to put many of these buildings into an acceptable state. According to " A Study of School Building " 51% of primary and 72% of secondary capacity was built after 1946. With the removal of nearly a million places up to 1986 and continued new provision to meet new needs, these percentages have undoubtedly increased by now.

The dominant roof form of the period was flat. Coincidentally, the replacement of many of these forms comprises a large measure of current investment in priority work. The trend should continue for some time. These roof forms are difficult to upgrade to contemporary standards of insulation for either physical or economic reasons. The same considerations apply to external walling and cladding systems. The need to renew such major elements provides the opportunity to deal with energy aspects also, both contributing to saving premises costs.

The replacement of services installations - boiler plant and electrical systems - also provides the opportunity to install new equipment more sensitive to the demands and use of buildings.

These choices do however depend upon the choice of the option making good economic sense.

Economics

Design Note 46 - Flat Roofs - gives two examples of upgrading flat roofs, one example where the finish and substrate must be replaced in any event, and the other which does not require renewal, but which would benefit from the additional protection of an overlay. Both show acceptable rates of return on the investment.

Example A (D.N.46)

Cost saving from the energy saved from 38 mm cork insulation in lieu of 25 mm = 0.47 litres of oil @ 18.5p = £0.087
Cost difference between 38 and 25 mm of cork insulation = £1.04 per square metre

Internal rate of return (simplified) = (0.087 ÷ 1.040) x 100 = 8.37%

The same Design Note considers more generally decisions to repair or renew existing systems . The advice is that such judgements should be based upon careful technical interpretation of the type of fault affecting the roof and the diagnosis of system factors as being crucial in coming to a decision. The elements of good practice are set out as being regular inspection, correct diagnosis, correct remedial action and avoidance of delay.The penalties of getting this wrong are illustrated in an example which shows the effect of correct diagnosis in time.

Specification:	3-Layer felt roof on 50 mm woodwool substrate fixed to steel beams, no deliberate ventilation of the void below, plasterboard ceiling.
Sensitivity:	Moisture and thermal movement.
Renewal cost	No problems to date, overlay possible. .£13 m^{-2}
	Defects over a wide area, increasing rate, degradation of deck partial deck replacement required, total refelting................... .£15 m^{-2}
	Serious degradation of deck, complete replacement needed...................................... .£33 m^{-2}

The time scale suggested over which this type of roof passes from the one condition to the other is between three and six years. The cost of increasingly frequent and extensive patching, consequential damage to ceilings, electrical installations and room finishes and the inconvenience to the occupier are not taken into account.

It might appear to the purseholders that the investment of scarce resources in an apparently sound roof is madness. These arguments must be countered by showing what has happened to other apparently sound roofs. The evidence is there but it needs collection into a property information system to point up the sort of reasoning that a layman would understand.

References

" A Study of School Building": H.M.S.O., 1977

Design Note 40: Maintenance and Renewal in Educational Buildings, Needs and
                Priorities
Design Note 46: Maintenance and Renewal in Educational Buildings, Flat Roofs,
                Criteria and methods of assessment, repair and replacement
A&B Paper 10: Property Information Systems and the Educational Building
                Stock ,Towards a Common Framework

                Publications Despatch Centre
                Department of Education & Science
                Government Buildings
                Honeypot Lane
                Stanmore
                Middlesex
                HA7 1AZ

398

A NEW FINANCING SYSTEM FOR DUTCH SCHOOL-BUILDINGS (PRIMARY SCHOOLS & SCHOOLS FOR SPECIAL EDUCATION)

Ir. P.L. Wentzel
bouwcentrum bv

Introduction

At the end of the sixties the municipalities' budget deficits for primary education were substantial.

The municipalities argued that the contribution from the central government was too low, but in the opinion of the central government the budget deficits were due to excessive expenditure by the municipalities.

As a result in 1974 the Minister of Education set up an independent committee whose task it was to investigate discrepancies between the contribution from the central government and expenditure on a local level for public schools run by the municipality and private schools.

The main conclusions of the committe were:

- The deficiencies of the former financing system for primary education were so large that there was only one solution left, namely developing a totally new financing system;
- The new financing system should be based on standard costs; and
- The individual circumstances of each school should be taken into consideration and the contribution from the central government should be 100% in principle.

This investigation started in 1974. The final report for primary schools was ready in February 1985. The system is in operation since 1-8-1985. A similar system for special education is being worked out now.

The philosophy of the new financing system

In Holland the central government pays 100% of the personnel costs and in principle 100% of the cost of building a new school and of the operating costs. The new financing system for primary education concerns the cost of building and the operating costs. The following conditions for a new financing system were formulated by the committee:

- The costs should be based on standard costs. This is a great improvement in comparison with the former financing system because in the new system costs are based on the necessary (standard/actual) costs and not on the occasional historic costs.
- The costs should be calculated for all the sizes of school-buildings, for the different periods of building and for the quality of school-buildings (permanent and temporary).
- The contribution from the central government should be 100% in principle.
- All kinds of educational and technical developments (for instance intro-duction of the computer) should be allowed to be introduced.
- Cost-consciousness should be stimulated. The costs should be based on what is necessary and every inefficiency should be excluded.
- The costs should be corrected yearly for the actual costs, the effects of inflation etc.
- All the component elements of the contribution from the central govern-ment should be published in so-called special programs of requirements, with indexed prices. The programs of requirements should be evaluated periodically.
- The contribution from the central government should serve as a guide-line; in this way the municipalities (public schools) and school-boards of private schools should retain their complete freedom to realise their priorities on a local level.

The new financing system has been built on the basis of these starting points. The general lines for all the investigations and the structure of the new financing system are presented in figure 1. The new financing system relates to the existing stock of school-buildings and to school-buildings which are to be built in the near future (i.e. after the year 1985).

Figure 1

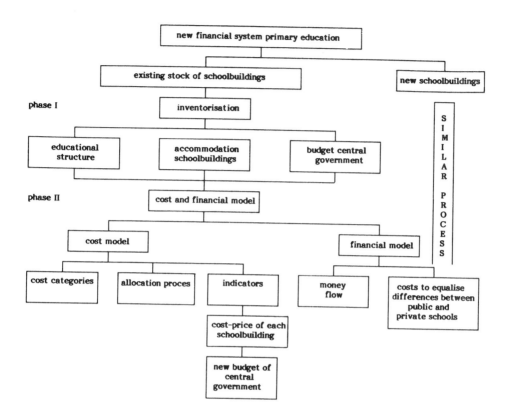

Existing stock of school-buildings

In general two phases can be distinguished, namely:

Phase I   : –   Educational structure.

              – The accommodation situation of the existing stock, the budget and the information about the former financing system.

              – Central government budget.

Phase II   : –   The development of the model of costs and financing model (i.e. the new financing system).

The ingredients

In general it can be said that in industrial firms a physical product is made and the production process can be planned and controlled because the technical process is predetermined. That is why extremely reliable technical standards for products and cost-prices can be developed for such processes.

In education, however, such a production process is lacking.

That is why a similar process has to be constructed for developing adequate standards and for fixing the performance prices.

The next phases can be distinguished in the cost model:

A. **Definition of costs**

In the new system only the necessary costs are quantified. Accordingly influence of inefficiency does not play a rol in the system.

B. **Cost-categories**

The central government has to decide which cost-categories are taken into account in fixing the contribution such as the costs of heating, cleaning and taxes.

C. **Allocation process**

The standards for each cost-category are developed in the allocation process. To fix the performance price the goods and money flows have to be reconstructed. This is realised by making special models (input-output models) per cost-category in which the causality between the cost cause and the costs is defined. The standards developed can be distinguished in so-called special programs of requirements and the price which has to be paid for these performances. A special program of requirements is developed per cost-category. In this program of requirements the level of all the necessary activities is defined by the central government.

On the basis of the defined activities in these programs of requirements the performance is priced which enables the costs to be quantified per cost-category.

D. Cost variability

In the new system special attention has been paid to cost variability. The costs can be divided into fixed costs, semi-fixed costs and variable costs. The variation in costs is investigated on the basis of the insight into the cost structure per program of requirements. For instance are the costs fixed per school i.e. independent of the number of pupils, or classrooms or are the costs variable per pupil or square metre?

E. Life cycling costs

In the new system the costs can be divided into annually recurring costs such as heating, cleaning, taxes and the costs which are not yearly. The non-yearly costs concern the cost-categories of maintenance, teaching equipment and furniture.

The costs of these cost-categories are periodic such as the costs of replacement in the fifteenth year for heating installations.

This means for cost-category maintenance that the average technical depreciation is the main factor for quantifying the yearly depreciation.

In order to quantify the costs of the educational equipment the depreciation is based on the economic depreciation, i.e. the technical depreciation is corrected by 20% for educational renewal.

The depreciation costs for furniture are based on technical depreciation.

The new system also takes a special moment into account, namely a general renovation of the school-building in the fortieth year.

F. Indicators

In the allocation process the causal connection between the costs' cause and the costs' variability is investigated. The relations which result from this allocation process are the basis for fixing the indicators. Moreover, these indicators are the basis for fixing the amount of the contribution from the central government for each school (-building).

The indicators for the contribution from the central government are:

- The building year of the school (building).
- The quality of the building (permanent or temporary).
- The number of square metres of the schoolyard (A).
- The number of square metres of the school-building (A).
- The total area of the envelope of the building (A_o).
- The netvolume (V) in cubic metres of the school-building.
- The number of teachers (c).
- The number of pupils (a).

With these limited indicators the contribution from the central government can be fixed for the individual circumstances of each school-building. In this way the cost-price is fixed for each school-building.

Tension between the number of indicators and the simplicity of the new system

If the central government is prepared to pay a 100% contribution for each cost-category you need a large number of indicators. The risk of too many indicators is that this information has to be inventorised in an information system and then maintained.
This costs a lot of money and working hours. Moreover, the chance of fraud is increased (you have to control this information) and for the school-boards the insight into the system diminishes because of the complexity of the system.
Thus the committee has tried to reach a compromise between the number of indicators and the simplicity of the system.
If the school-boards and municipalities have grown accustomed to the new system within a few years and budget deficits are due to the choice of this limited number of indicators in the near future, the central government may consider increasing the number of indicators. The results of all the investigations are still available for this decision.

The new financing system

I. Provisions of accommodation

1. **New school-building**

   In this program of requirements the costs of a new building or the costs of replacement are quantified for both permanent and temporary school-buildings.

2. **Educational equipment and furniture**

   In this program the costs of investments are fixed for new school-buildings and for expansion of the existing stock of school-buildings.

3. **Enlargement**

   If an existing school-building is enlarged the costs of this expansion and interior modification are quantified in this program.

4. **General renovation**

   When a school-building is forty years old, a face-lift takes place for technical or educational reasons.

5. **Partial modification**

   If the Minister of Education wants to take special measures such as an energy program, the Minister can do this on the basis of ad hoc policy.

6. **Radical maintenance**

   The maintenance activities concern the technical life time period of forty and sixty years.

   NB The general renovation and the radical maintenance have to be combined for a declaration (on standard basis) through the central government.

II Other provisions

1. **Technical maintenance**

   The maintenance activities concern the period from 10-40 years.

2. **Technical and functional modifications**

   In this program a lump sum is fixed for small educational modifications.

3. **Replacement and modification.furniture**

   The costs of investment for the replacing of the furniture are fixed in this program.

4. **Insurance**

   The risks of fire, burglary etc. are taken into account in this program.

5. **Estate taxes**

   The costs of the estate taxes of the local authorities are calculated in this program.

6. **Other provisions**

   No special program has to be developed for this cost-category to date if necessary.

III Provisions for the operating costs

1. **Preventive maintenance**

   The maintenance activities concern the activities in the period 0-10 years.

2. **Maintenance of the garden**

3. **Use of electricity**

4. **Use of heating.**

5. **Use of water.**

6. **Cleaning.**

7. **Taxes:**

   7.1 Costs of purification.

   7.2 Costs of the body of the surveyors of the dikes.

   7.3 Costs of sewerage.

   7.4 Costs of cleaning department.

8. **Costs of participation.**

9. **Maintenance, replacement, renewal of teaching equipment and maintenance of furniture.**

   The costs concern the annually recurring costs such as the costs of paper, pencils and the costs of depreciation of the educational equipment. The economic life time for the teaching equipment is 8 years (including 20% educational renewal).

10. **Costs of the school-board and accounting.**
11. **Insurance of persons.**
12. **Other provisions:**
    12.1 Cultural education.
    12.2 Other expenditures.

The system as a management tool

In the former system the central government was the only source of finance of primary education. Using a couple of general indicators lump sum amounts were fixed. The choice of these indicators in the former system was insufficient in the context of the cost structure.

Because of the general character of the former system no answer could be given to the allocation of the costs and the component elements of the contribution from the central government.

Thus all kinds of very thoroughly performed investigations were needed to establish all the details.

The details of these investigations are represented in the so-called programs of requirements. Such a complex philosophy is translated into a few limited indicators.

Central government

The advantages of the new system for the central government are:

- Better allocation of the central government budget to the individual school-boards.
- The new system is based on standards which stimulate cost consciousness.
- A better instrument for fixing the yearly budget and the budgets for the coming 5 to 10 years.
- The central government is not only the financier of primary education. The central government now has an instrument to control the quality of education by controlling the fixed levels in the special programs of requirements and the prices of these performances.

- The new financing model is a decision and communication model for the central government with the municipalities and the school-boards of private schools.
- If new deficits occur in the budgets of the municipalities and the school-boards of the private schools, the central government has an instrument to determine whether these deficits are due to the policy of the central government or to the policy of the municipalities and the school-boards of private schools at local levels.

Local authorities and school-boards of private schools

The special programs of requirements have to be published. Thus the municipalities and the school-boards of the private schools have a clear insight into the composing elements of the contribution from the central government.

Moreover, the local decision makers get all the information through the special programs of requirements of how to control their expenditures. In this way the local decision makers have the opportunity to influence their level of expenditure in accordance with the fixed level of the contribution from the central government.

If the Minister of Education is forced to raise or lower the central budget he has to motivate this and moreover he has to translate this decision into the level of the programs of requirement and the prices of these performances.

Follow up

The Ministry of Education will organize in spring 1988 a congress to discuss their management system for school-buildings. For the congress we want to have also information from other systems. When there is interest to make a paper please send us an outline of your subject to Ir. P.L. Wentzel, Bouwcentrum, PO Box 299, 3000 AG Rotterdam.

Index